D1599109

An Introduction to Machinery Analysis and Monitoring

An Introduction to

MACHINERY ANALYSIS AND MONITORING

John S. Mitchell

PennWell Publishing Company
Tulsa, Oklahoma

Copyright © 1981 by
PennWell Publishing Company
1421 South Sheridan Road/P. O. Box 1260
Tulsa, Oklahoma 74101

Library of Congress Cataloging in Publication Data
Mitchell, John Stewart.
  An introduction to machinery analysis and monitoring.

  Includes index.
  1. Machinery—Testing. I. Title.
TJ148.M55   621.8′028′7   80-20939
ISBN 0-87814-145-6

Printed in the United States of America

1   2   3   4   5   85   84   83   82   81

CONTENTS

REMARKS

THIS BOOK is dedicated to the countless and for the most part unheralded machinery engineers and technicians who, through observation, dedication, and insight, have evolved and developed the knowledge and methods described within. It is also dedicated to those who will follow, in the hope they won't have to learn quite so much through hard experience.

Although working with and around machinery can be frustrating, it can also be extremely rewarding. I will never forget the experience and pleasure derived during countless days and long nights in pursuit of an elusive answer to a difficult problem.

An Introduction to Machinery Analysis and Monitoring was written as a guide for people who will be using machinery analysis. It is not intended for a theoretician or a machinery designer, but for the person who, on a cold, wet night, must pack his instrumentation and trudge out to decide if some warm piece of metal will last 'til dawn. For these people, the book will introduce the fundamentals that must be mastered as well as provide a measure of direction in problem solving.

Most of the information presented is opinion; however, much of machinery analysis is opinion. Since your judgment will count on your machinery, I hope this text will provide beneficial facts, insight, and guidance.

Special appreciation is extended to those who assisted in the preparation of this book. John Dufour and the people at Amoco, Texas City, for providing the initial incentive; John Cummings of Exxon USA; Thomas Purackal of Kuwait Oil Company; Randy Fox of IRD; Brian Turner of Imperial Oil; Charles Jackson of Monsanto; and Vince Beiter, Marty Krueger, Tim Kincaid, and all the others at Veco Turbo Services who contributed their many excellent comments. Finally, deepest gratitude to Pat Mitchell who cheerfully typed thousands of words without a clear understanding of anything that was said, and Kathryne Pile who had to edit, punctuate, and correct an engineer's ponderous prose.

John Mitchell
October 1980

1

Introduction

Far from being anything new or unusual, the fundamentals of machinery analysis should be familiar to anyone living in a mechanized society. The sound of a refrigerator and the vibration of an automobile are just two examples of information transmitted to our human senses which we unconsciously relate to the condition or health of some mechanical marvel. One does not have to be familiar with the mechanism itself or how it works to use this type information. If, for example, the sound or vibration emitted by a household appliance changes or intensifies, a housewife, who may have no idea how the machine works, will generally conclude that larger trouble is imminent. Fearing the worst (an outright failure late some Friday night), she will probably call a repairman. The repairman might discover her fears were justifed and a failure was close at hand, or he might discover something simple like a loose fitting or a foreign object which had fallen against the appliance and changed its characteristics.

The analogy holds true in the analysis of industrial rotating machinery. Almost anyone will recognize the existence of a problem sooner or later, but the objective is to recognize it as soon as possible, hopefully before any damage has occurred. Next, the nature and cause of a problem, as well as its severity, must be assessed so that the risk and consequences of a failure can be weighed against the financial impact of an unscheduled shutdown and lost production. At this stage a great deal of knowledge is required, for only when presented with knowledge and facts will a production-minded operations manager consent to removing a critical machine from service. Thus, the success of machinery analysis is determined by the ability to accomplish the following tasks successfully:

- Acquire a characteristic which is related to and defines mechanical condition.
- Identify and recognize an out-of-limit condition or a change or deviation from a norm.
- Analyze and localize to determine the cause and nature of the problem.
- Assess severity or the time to failure.
- Recommend and implement cost-effective corrective action.

Machinery analysis can take two forms: predictive analysis, in which the characteristics of mechanical conditions are recorded periodically and analyzed for early identification of potentially damaging trends; and diagnostic analysis, directed toward understanding and localizing the cause of identified problems as well as determining the specific components affected. Predictive analysis is preventive, or before the fact; diagnostic analysis is corrective, or after the fact. Most, if not all, of the methods used in one type of analysis are the same as in the other. Thus, although there are two types of analysis designed to meet different objectives, the two are actually complementary. In fact, most organizations are led into programs of regular predictive analysis by the success of diagnostic analysis and the realization that discovering a problem early, even though it may not be averted, will often lessen its financial impact.

COMMONLY MEASURED OPERATING VARIABLES

Although machinery analysis has been with us since the first machines, the accelerating trend toward smaller design margins at higher power levels and speeds, along with reduced manning and the spiraling costs of lost production and repairs, has hastened the implementation of formal programs using modern electronic technology. Vibration, position, bearing temperature, pressures, and lubricating oil condition are some of the accessible parameters which can be measured at varying intervals, normalized, and compared to limits to reach an accurate assessment of machinery health. Taking these quantities in order, vibration is probably the best operating parameter to judge dynamic conditions such as balance, bearing stability, and the dynamic stress applied to components, e.g., blading and gear teeth. In addition, other common machinery anomalies (misaligned couplings and improper clearances) are often manifested as vibration characteristics.

By measuring a rotating shaft's position relative to stationary components, clearances are measured to guard against changes which would result in catastrophic contact.

Temperature measurement can be used for two purposes. It can be measured to assess mechanical condition or the load applied to a specific component such as a thrust bearing. Temperature is also measured as an operating variable to ensure that auxiliary systems (coolers, for example) are functioning properly and to determine thermodynamic performance and efficiency. In this discussion temperature will be limited to its role as an indicator of mechanical condition.

Pressure is nearly always measured as an operating variable; however, it can also be a valuable diagnostic aid, for a changing pressure is often a symptom of problems such as fouling or a change in internal clearances which affect thrust load.

Monitoring oil condition warns of an increase in foreign substances such as water which can degrade the lubricating properties of the oil and cause bearing failures. It also detects the presence of metallic particles which are carried into the oil stream as wetted surfaces wear.

ESTABLISHING NORMS AND LIMITS

If one were not aware of a normal value, these measurements would not be particularly valuable. Thus, criteria must be established to compare them. In some cases—pressure, temperature, and position, for example—establishing a range of normal values is not particularly difficult, for most are direct measurements which are closely related to a physical constraint. On the other hand, vibration is more empirical in nature, requiring experience and judgment.

There are two different types of limits: those representing absolute values, outside of which failure is a virtual certainty, and the more qualitative limits normally associated with vibration, particularly casing vibration.

First there are manufacturers' design limits such as pressure, temperature, and speed. To be more specific, most instruction manuals will list the maximum bearing temperatures, inlet, stage, and differential pressures as well as speed at which a machine may be safely operated. Although generally not stated directly, clearances can be easily transformed into position limits. Some of these limits, such as clearances, are absolute limits which cannot be exceeded without damage.

Next there are more empirical limits such as those imposed on vibration. Vibration limits can be obtained from a number of sources: manufacturers' data, guidelines published by instrument manufacturers, and the experience of others operating identical or similar machinery. It is safe to say, however, that vibration limits are generally made to be broken, for it seems that a tolerable level of vibration, at least in the eyes of those who are operating the machinery, is always slightly above whatever its current level happens to be.

One thing to be aware of when establishing vibration limits is that machinery manufacturers' limits may be too high if the primary objective is uninterrupted, reliable operation for two to three years. Conversely, the limits supplied with vibration instruments may be too low for certain types of equipment which normally vibrate at levels which other equipment might find intolerable.

Assuming that one knows which measurements to make, where and how to make them, and what limits to set, how can this information help judge condition? To make a judgment one must know what is out of limits or has changed, by how much, if changes are occurring rapidly or slowly, and if there are any other changes which either confirm or contradict initial observations. To cite an example, a changing thrust position should be accompanied by a changing thrust bearing temperature. How fast they change will provide a good measure of how much time is available to take action. To determine the cause for the change, investigate the thrust balance across the machine and the couplings to see if the force is generated within the machine or applied externally.

It would be presumptuous to assume that a text of any reasonable size could make the reader an expert in machinery analysis. What a text can do, however, is acquaint a reader who will be directly involved in machinery analysis with the fundamental principles, methods, and instruments he will need to master. With this basis as a beginning, analytical skills will develop rapidly with a minimum of lost time spent sorting out instrument problems and figuring out how to obtain and display the proper information.

2

Fundamentals of Vibration

A course on machinery analysis must begin with the fundamentals of vibration and the relationship between the different measures of vibration, for it is here that so many vital criteria have their beginning.

SIMPLE PERIODIC MOTION–RELATIONSHIP
BETWEEN DISPLACEMENT, VELOCITY, AND ACCELERATION

If one observes the path or displacement traced by a rotating vector or, more correctly, a phasor on a time axis (figure 2-1), it will describe a sine wave defined by the equation:

$$X = A \sin \omega t \qquad (2.1)$$

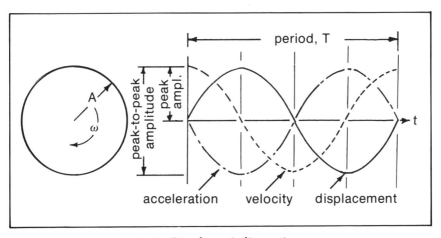

2–1—Simple periodic motion.

where:

X = instantaneous displacement amplitude from a zero or neutral axis

A = length of the rotating vector or its peak value

ω = its rotating speed, radians/sec

t = time, sec

In addition to these properties which generated the sine wave, there are some familiar terms. The distance between any two consecutive repetitive points on the waveform is its period, T. Since the period is the reciprocal of the frequency, one only has to measure and invert the period to determine the frequency of an unknown periodic waveform. For example, in figure 2-1, if each horizontal division along the time base represented 5 milliseconds (5×10^{-3} seconds), the period of the waveform would be 20 milliseconds (4 divisions times 5 milliseconds). Taking the reciprocal of the period or $1/20 \times 10^{-3}$ a frequency of 50 cycles per second or more commonly 50 Hertz (Hz) is obtained. Of course, this can quickly be converted to cycles per minute by multiplying by 60. The foregoing is a commonly used measurement in machinery analysis. From a vibration waveform displayed on an oscilloscope, one counts the divisions from peak to peak on the graticule and multiplies the number of divisions by the time base setting on the oscilloscope to obtain the period.

Amplitude measurement

Digressing slightly for a moment, there are different ways of measuring amplitude. Zero to peak or simply peak amplitude (A in figure 2-2) is used conventionally in the United States as a measure of velocity and acceleration. Double or peak-to-peak amplitude (2A in figure 2-2) is used for virtually all displacement measurements. A third quantity, RMS (root mean square) amplitude, is commonly used in Europe to measure velocity and acceleration amplitude where RMS is considered by many as the quantity most representative of condition. The RMS value of a sine wave is 0.707 times its peak value; however, this relationship holds true for sine waves only. In a complex waveform consisting of fast rise time/short duration spikes, the true RMS value will be considerably less than 0.707 times the peak value.

Expressing the amplitude of an AC signal in terms of its average value is a fourth method in common, but often unrecognized, use. Although most AC voltmeters display RMS amplitude, it is not a true RMS but an average amplitude calibrated to read RMS with a sine wave

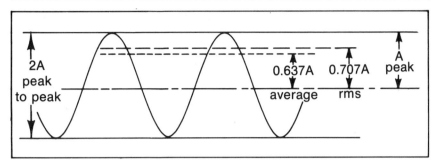

2–2—Relationship between the various methods of expressing the amplitude of a sine wave.

input. For nonsinusoidal inputs, the value read on an average detecting AC voltmeter will not be the true RMS of the input signal but some other, perhaps misleading, value which will likely be less than the true RMS amplitude.

Table 2.1 lists the conversions between peak to peak, peak, RMS, and average amplitudes for a sine wave. Since most instruments and systems used in machinery analysis are calibrated with sine waves, one must know what a particular instrument displays, how it obtains that display, and how to convert from one method of expressing a sine wave amplitude to another. One must also be aware of the differences that will occur when the input signal deviates from a sine wave. To illustrate some of these points, take two inputs with identical peak-to-peak

TABLE 2.1

Amplitude Conversion Multipliers—Sine Wave Only

Multiply	By	To Obtain
Peak to peak	0.5	Peak
	0.354	RMS
	0.318	Average
Peak	2	Peak to peak
	0.707	RMS
	0.637	Average
RMS	2.828	Peak to peak
	1.414	Peak
	0.901	Average
Average	3.14	Peak to peak
	1.57	Peak
	1.11	RMS

amplitudes as observed on an oscilloscope—one a sine wave and the other a short-duration pulse as obtained from a noncontact phase reference pick-up—and connect each to the input of various instruments used in machinery analysis. On a shaft displacement monitor with true peak-to-peak detection, observe the same amplitude from both inputs. Read on an AC voltmeter and most vibration analyzers used with casing pickups, the amplitude displayed with the sine wave input will be considerably larger than the amplitude displayed with the pulse input even though both have the same peak-to-peak value. The value displayed on the AC voltmeter with the pulse input is not 0.707 times the peak value as it is with the sine wave input.

The phaser has two other distinct properties, velocity and acceleration, in addition to its instantaneous displacement. Velocity, the first derivative of displacement as a function of time, is a vector representing the rate of change in displacement. Thus, velocity is a maximum as displacement passes through zero and zero when displacement is at the limits of its motion. Expressed mathematically, velocity as the first derivative of displacement is:

$$\text{velocity} = \dot{X} = A\omega \cos \omega t \qquad (2.2)$$

In the phase relationship between velocity and displacement in figure 2-1, velocity leads displacement by 90°.

Next, differentiate the expression for velocity with respect to time and obtain acceleration, the rate of change of velocity. Expressed mathematically, acceleration is:

$$\text{acceleration} = \ddot{X} = -A\omega^2 \sin \omega t \qquad (2.3)$$

The negative sign indicates that acceleration is 180° out of phase from displacement, illustrated graphically in figure 2-1.

Thus, periodic motion has three measurable characteristics: displacement, or motion; velocity, or the rate at which the displacement occurs; and acceleration, or the rate of change in velocity. Although they are related mathematically, they are three different characteristics—not three names for the same quantity.

Looking at a simplified case of damped forced vibration, a model closer to rotating machinery, displacement, velocity, and acceleration—when multiplied by stiffness, damping, and mass, respectively—combine to describe force as a function of time:

$$F(t) = KX + C\dot{X} + M\ddot{X} \qquad (2.4)$$

where:

 K = stiffness or resistance to a change in length, lb/in.
 C = damping or resistance to motion through a fluid, lb-sec/in.
 M = mass (amount of material present), lb-sec ^{2}/in.

In cancelling units, both sides of the equation are expressed in pounds.

Variation of force with frequency

Next, it is important to examine the significance of ω. Recognizing that $\omega = 2\pi f$ (where f = frequency) and substituting this value in the three terms for displacement, velocity, and acceleration, the amplitude of the displacement term (A sin ω t) is independent of frequency. On the other hand, velocity amplitude, (Aω cos ω t) will increase in direct proportion to frequency even though peak displacement A remains constant. Likewise, acceleration amplitude ($-$Aω^2 sin ω t) will increase as the square of the frequency at a constant amplitude of displacement.

This variation in the values of velocity and acceleration with frequency is extremely important, for it forms the basis for vibration severity criteria, provides guidelines for selecting the variable which will be most representative for a particular purpose, and explains how failures can occur without warning if the wrong variable is monitored.

Perhaps this principle can best be explained with two extreme examples. First, calculate the velocity and acceleration for 10 mils (254 μm) peak-to-peak displacement at 10 Hz. Since only peak velocity is desired, set cos ωt = 1 as its maximum value. With this accomplished and $2\pi f$ substituted for ω, the equation relating displacement and velocity then becomes:

$$\dot{X} = \text{velocity} = 2\pi f A \qquad\qquad (2.5)$$

where A is zero-to-peak amplitude

Calculating:

$$V = 2\pi \times 10 \times \frac{10 \times 10^{-3}}{2} = 0.314 \text{ in./sec}$$

$$\times \frac{254 \times 10^{-3}}{2} = 7.98 \text{ mm/sec}$$

Next, the equation relating acceleration to displacement may be manipulated in the same fashion. Setting sin ω t = 1, its maximum value—neglecting its sign which really indicates phase—and substituting $2\pi f$ for ω:

$$\ddot{X} = \text{acceleration} = (2\pi f)^2 \ A \qquad (2.6)$$

At this point, additional manipulation must be made to obtain acceleration in the conventional G units instead of in./sec². Since $1\,G = 386$ in./sec² (9.807 m/sec²), divide both sides by 386 then simplify to obtain:

$$\ddot{X} = \text{acceleration (Gs)} = 0.0511f^2DA \text{ (in.)} \qquad (2.7)$$
$$= 2.011f^2DA \text{ (m)}$$

The equation was also divided by 2 so that DA, peak-to-peak amplitude conventionally used as a measure of displacement, would appear in place of A:

$$\text{Acceleration} = 0.0511(10)^2 \times 10 \ \ \times 10^{-3} = 0.051 \text{ G}$$
$$= 2.011 \ (10)^2 \times 254 \times 10^{-6} = 0.051 \text{ G}$$

In this example, a displacement amplitude of 10 mils has been used, which would be of concern on a 10-Hz, 600-rpm machine such as a fan. Likewise, the calculated velocity value of 0.314 in./sec (7.98 mm/sec) would be of concern, yet no one would worry about an acceleration of 0.051 Gs.

Now for a look at the opposite extreme, an acceleration level of 30 Gs at 10 kHz—a level which would certainly cause concern at a typical blade passing frequency. The corresponding values of velocity and displacement are as follows:

Velocity	0.1843 in./sec peak	4.68 mm/sec
Displacement	0.0058 mils, peak to peak	0.149 micrometer, peak to peak

Here again is a velocity level which would be of concern, yet displacement at approximately 0.006 mil (0.149μm) would be extremely difficult to measure and certainly of no concern.

The preceding examples and figure 2-3 demonstrated how the contribution to total dynamic force shifts from displacement to acceleration as frequency increases. At low frequencies displacement × stiffness is the dominant factor; at high frequencies, mass × acceleration dominates. Also note that the velocity value appears to be a valid indicator of

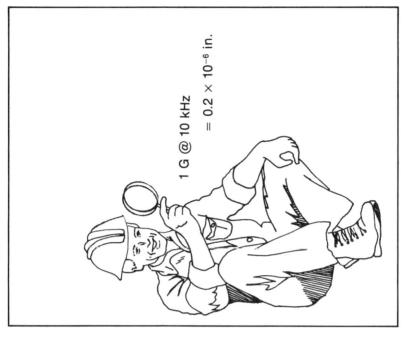

1 G @ 10 kHz
= 0.2 × 10⁻⁶ in.

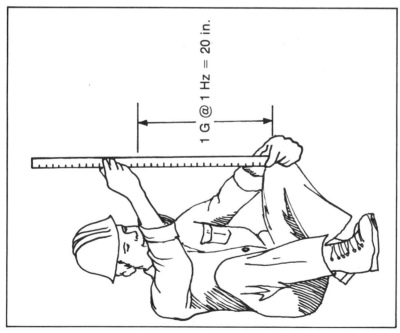

1 G @ 1 Hz = 20 in.

2–3—Relationship of acceleration and displacement.

condition across the entire range of frequencies. That, in fact, is exactly what occurs, leading many to propose a constant velocity criterion as the prime indication of mechanical condition. Velocity has an advantage; it is weighted by frequency and therefore is much more representative of force than the more commonly used displacement which must always be evaluated, considering the frequency at which it occurs. Thus, the equation of force as a function of time forms the basis for severity criteria and explains why tolerable amplitudes, expressed in terms of displacement, must always decrease with frequency.

The relationship between displacement, velocity, and acceleration also provides the best indication of which parameter should be measured to assess condition. For example, if one is examining the low frequencies around or below the running speed of most machinery, displacement or velocity measurements are likely to produce the best quality signal. On the other hand, phenomena such as gear mesh and blade passing at 5–10 kHz and above are best measured in terms of acceleration. Of course, there are often other factors which enter into the measurement, such as making seismic or absolute measurements at very low frequencies. In special cases such as these it may be necessary to compromise and make a measurement, which may be something less than ideal, and then use signal conditioning techniques such as integration and filtering to synthesize the appropriate variable. Figure 2-4 attempts to tie all this together by plotting displacement and acceleration versus frequency at a constant velocity amplitude of 0.3 in./sec (7.5 mm/sec).

The illustration clearly shows the dominance of acceleration at high frequencies due to frequency squared as well as its rapid attenuation at low frequencies for the same reason. The advantages of a displacement measurement at low frequencies as well as its disadvantage at high frequencies are likewise readily apparent.

RESONANCE–NATURAL FREQUENCIES

Nearly everyone is familiar with a tuning fork (figure 2-5). When the fork is struck, it produces an audible tone at a frequency which is determined by its physical dimensions. Every structure and component has a similar fundamental natural frequency as well as higher natural frequencies determined by its physical qualities.

If the fork is excited with a single-frequency sound wave and the amplitude is measured as an indication of its response with a noncontact displacement transducer and a plot is made of response vs. exciting frequency, the curve in figure 2-6 will be obtained. At frequencies well below the tuning fork's natural frequency, the response will be essen-

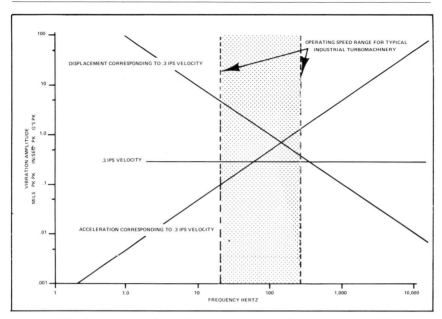

2–4—Displacement and acceleration corresponding to 0.3 IPS velocity.

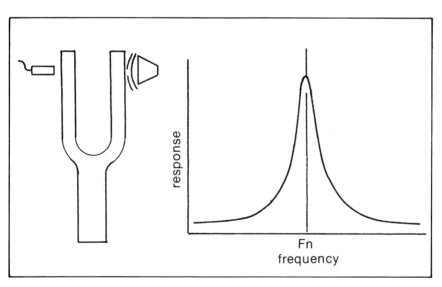

2–5—Tuning fork.   2–6—Resonant response.

tially independent of frequency with the major variation due to variations of the incident energy. As the natural frequency is approached, however, response or amplification increases sharply with no increase in the incident energy level. At a natural frequency the response peaks, then begins to fall off as frequency is increased still further. Finally, at frequencies well above the natural frequency the condition returns where response is essentially independent of frequency.

The ratio of the peak amplitude at reasonance to the amplitude away from resonance is the amplification factor, Q. Q is a measure of the system's damping. A large Q indicates a small value of damping and, in the case of a machine rotor, can warn of a tendency toward instability.

What are the effects of changing mass and stiffness on the location of a natural frequency? Increasing mass lowers the natural frequency while increasing stiffness increases the natural frequency (figure 2-7). A rotor bearing system has a natural frequency or critical which depends on a number of characteristics. If weight is added to the rotor by adding an impeller, the natural frequency or critical will decrease. Conversely, adding stiffness by increasing the shaft diameter will generally raise the critical even though the added diameter also adds material.

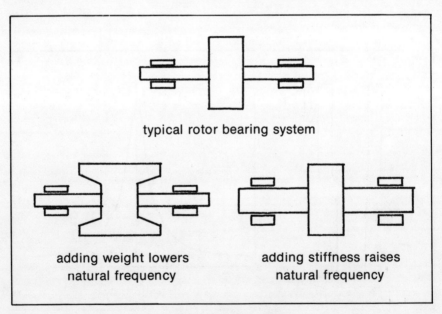

2–7—Rotor bearing system.

Calculating natural frequencies

In the simplified case of a single disc rotor model supported on rigid supports, the critical speed can be approximated with the expression:

$$\omega_n = \sqrt{\frac{K}{M}} \qquad (2.8)$$

where:

K = stiffness or spring constant of the shaft
M = mass

In this simplified case, the shaft is assumed to be massless with all the system's mass lumped in the center. Stiffness or spring constant is defined as pounds/inch deflection and is determined by dividing the weight producing a deflection into the resulting deflection. A shaft's deflection at the center produced by a weight also at the center is calculated from the following:

$$Y = \frac{WL^3}{48EI} \qquad (2.9)$$

where:

Y = deflection, in.
W = applied weight
L = length of the shaft between supports
E = modulus of elasticity of the shaft, about 30×10^6 psi for steel
I = shaft's inertia, $\pi d^4/64$

As stated, K is simply the applied weight divided by the deflection or:

$$\frac{W}{Y} \qquad (2.10)$$

Simplifying:

$$K = \frac{48EI}{L^3} \text{ or } \frac{48E\pi d^4}{64L^3} \qquad (2.11)$$

Next, substitute the expression for K in the critical speed equation and separate the constants:

$$\omega n = \sqrt{\frac{48E\pi}{64} \times \frac{d^4}{ML^3}} = \sqrt{70.65 \times 10^6 \times \frac{d^4}{ML^3}} \qquad (2.12)$$

Thus, in the greatly simplified model, the natural frequency or critical will vary directly as the shaft diameter squared (increasing shaft diameter increases the critical by the square of the change) and inversely with the square root of the mass and length to the 3/2 power. The use of this approximation can be illustrated by working an example developed from a test rotor having the following characteristics:

Length of rotor-bearing center to bearing center   21 in.
Weight with a single center-mounted mass   21.91 lbs
Average shaft diameter   0.94 in.

Substituting eq. 2.12:

$$\omega n = \sqrt{70.65 \times 10^6 \times \frac{(0.94)^4}{\dfrac{21.91}{386}} \times (21)^3}$$

ωn = 324 radians/sec or 3,095 rpm

Amplitude and phase response

Figure 2-8 is a plot of amplitude and phase response versus speed obtained as the rotor in the previous example was run up to and coasted down from full operating speed. The amplitude peak and 90° phase shift show the critical speed occurred at about 3,700 rpm. Thus, the calculation provided a reasonably close approximation of the critical speed observed on this very simple rotor.

Another property of a dynamic system, damping, affects the response of a body or component at its natural frequency. Damping, the resistance to motion through a fluid, has a slight effect on the location of the natural frequency; however, its major effect is on the amplification and phase response at resonance.

Recall that as the tuning fork was brought into resonance, its response peaked then fell off again as the excitation progressed above the natural frequency. If one could measure a phase angle phi between excitation and response, there would be a 180° shift as the exciting frequency increases through resonance. The two responses are shown graphically in figure 2-9.

As damping is added to the system, perhaps by inverting the tuning fork and dipping it into very viscous liquid, the peak response de-

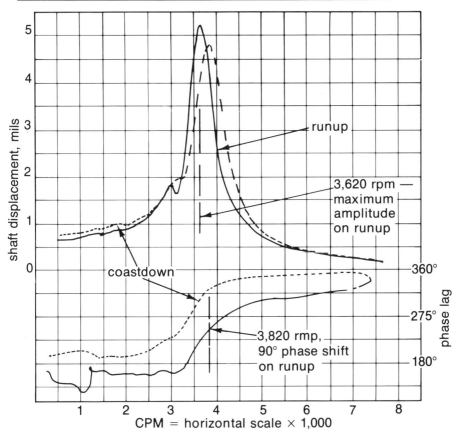

2–8—Amplitude and phase response of test rotor.

creases and the phase shift spreads out (figure 2-9). When amplitude no longer increases at resonance, the system is critically damped. The effect of critical damping on the phase shift is readily apparent; the phase shift takes place over a larger frequency range at a slower rate as damping is increased.

As implied by figure 2-9, damping is the only factor acting at resonance to limit amplitude. Without damping, the amplitude at resonance would be infinite, thereby restricting operations to something less than a system's natural frequency. Of course, this is not true; damping makes it possible to traverse critical speeds. There have, however, been cases where damping was lost or suddenly reduced on a rotor system at its critical speed with catastrophic results.

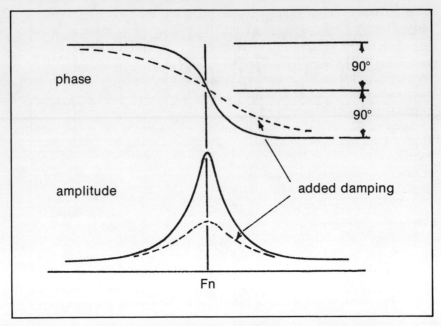

2–9—Amplitude and phase response at resonance.

Resonant damping

The resonant damper (figure 2-10) consists of a weight whose position can be varied along the length of a rod which is rigidly attached to a vibrating surface. The resonant damper is an energy absorber. In operation, it is tuned to the frequency of the excitation by moving the weight along the shaft until its excursion or displacement is maximized. At that point the damper is in resonance just like the tuned reed of a reed-type tachometer. As long as the excitation remains at a constant frequency, the damper, excited into resonance, will absorb a significant amount of energy and actually decrease the amplitude of the excitation. This type of device can often be used to quiet structures and piping, although its vibration can be objectionable.

MECHANICAL IMPEDANCE

Mechanical impedance is a transfer function defined as the input force divided by the system's response to that force. In rotating machinery there are several areas where the concept of mechanical impedance is very helpful in understanding a system-measured response to an applied force.

Take, for instance, the mechanical impedance of a simple resonant system with a response similar to figure 2-6. At resonance the system's impedance will be quite low compared to its impedance away from resonance. Therefore, the actual value of mechanical impedance may vary significantly with frequency, depending on the location of natural frequencies and Q or damping.

A typical plot of mechanical impedance versus frequency is shown in figure 2-11. In this case log values are used on the ordinate to illustrate the wide variance in impedance which may exist at various frequencies. Also note that, although impedance is used for illustrative purposes, there may be advantages in using mobility, the reciprocal of impedance, to create a similar plot.

Why is mechanical impedance important in machinery analysis? The concept is important because its effects are present in many measurements, and without a clear understanding of what is occurring one can quickly draw a false or misleading conclusion.

To illustrate with a couple of practical examples, the vibration measured on a machine casing must traverse a path with some impedance between the location at which the force is applied and the spot where the transducer is attached. The losses in the path or its impedance will determine the attenuation of the signal between its origin and the transducer. It is easy to see how the type and stiffness of a machine's casing and support structure, as well as differences in bear-

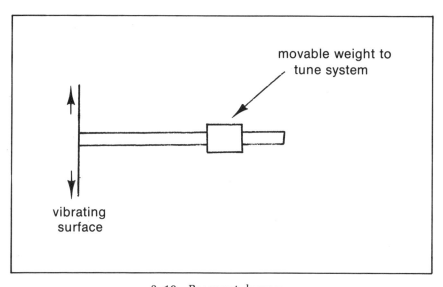

2–10—Resonant damper.

ing types, will affect the impedance of the transmission path and hence the amplitude of vibration measured at an external point.

As a second but less obvious example, consider a variable-speed machine producing a high-frequency excitation at a gear mesh or blade passing frequency. In this situation a minor variation in speed of 100 rpm will produce a magnified shift in the high-frequency excitation which could be 100 Hz or more. This change could move the excitation through a significant change in impedance and thereby produce a variation in amplitude measured at the transducer without any change in excitation or applied force. Thus, an observer might conclude there had been a force variation with frequency, when in reality his observation applied only to the transmission path and had nothing to do with the force applied.

ROTOR DYNAMICS

A subject as complex as rotor dynamics cannot be covered effectively in a few pages; however, there are some principles which should

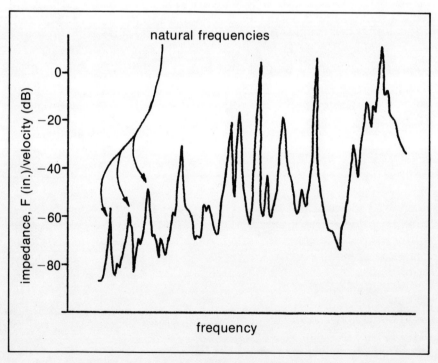

2–11—*Typical plot of mechanical impedance.*

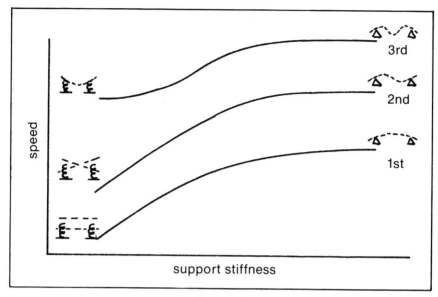

2–12—*Lateral critical speed map.*

be recognized and understood in machinery analysis. A rotor system has natural frequencies or criticals which are determined by the mass and stiffness of the rotor as well as the support structure. There are several widely used calculational routines which, for a given set of rotor and support parameters, will produce a lateral critical speed map (figure 2-12).

Lateral critical speed maps

The critical speed map plots the lateral critical speed, generally for three or more criticals, versus support stiffness ranging from a freely supported rotor at the left side of the plot to a rotor clamped between infinite stiffness bearings on the right. When a curve of actual support stiffness versus speed is superimposed on the critical speed map, the points at which the curves intersect define the location of the system's critical speeds.

At the left side of the critical speed map, the support structure is very flexible compared to the rotor itself. The rotor will thus assume the rigid body modes as the first and second criticals are traversed. At the right side of the map, the support structure is infinitely rigid, forcing the rotor into its bending modes. A critical speed map applies to one specific physical configuration and should be recalculated if changes are made. There are, however, some generalities derived for a simplified case in eq. 2.12 to indicate the effects of certain changes. Increasing stiffness by decreasing span or increasing shaft diameter will move the curves up, causing the criticals to occur at higher speeds. Adding weight, decreasing shaft diameter, or increasing span will move the curves down, causing the criticals to occur at lower speeds.

The curve of support stiffness versus speed generally increases with speed (figure 2-13); however, it may first increase then decrease or assume other shapes, depending on the dynamics of the actual system.

Because the location of a critical nearly always varies slightly with speed, there may be a several-hundred rpm difference between the critical observed as the machine is passing through compared to the critical excited at speed. In cases of resonant whirl instability, the shift in critical speed may appear to be an inconsistency and may confuse the diagnosis.

Support stiffness may also vary significantly between the horizontal and vertical planes and produce two separate and distinct criticals, depending on which plane the response is viewed. Normally under these circumstances there will be some cross coupling between planes which will produce the two-peaked critical response shown in figure 2-14. The first, lower peak occurs as the off-plane response passes

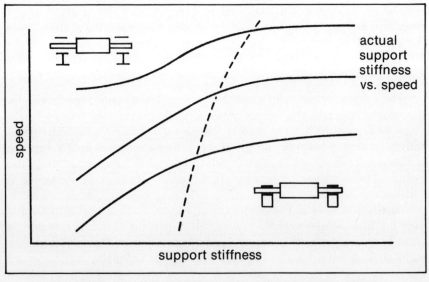

2–13—*Lateral critical speed map with actual support stiffness.*

through its critical with the second, higher peak, occurring at the critical in the plane of measurement.

Differences in stiffness and/or bearing load from one end to the other of a machine can likewise produce variations in critical speeds. On one occasion a highly asymmetric rotor having most of its weight concentrated at one end had measured critical speeds which differed by 800 rpm from one end to the other.

A single-value critical speed for any given machine is probably unrealistic. It is much better to think of the critical speed of a machine as a speed range which encloses the criticals measured in all planes at both ends of a machine.

While on the subject of criticals and mode shapes, it is important to have some idea of the latter and their variation with imbalance so that measurement points can be chosen which will accurately reflect total shaft deflection. Enough about rotor imbalance response must be known to ensure shaft transducers are not located at nodal points where shaft deflection crosses the 0 or quiescent axis.

Before leaving rotor response, note that there are numerous guidelines specifying the location of critical speeds. Although a well-damped rotor can operate indefinitely on a critical speed without any adverse effects, this is generally inadvisable. The American Petroleum Institute (API) specifies that first lateral criticals on flexible-shaft machines (machines operating above their first critical) shall be a

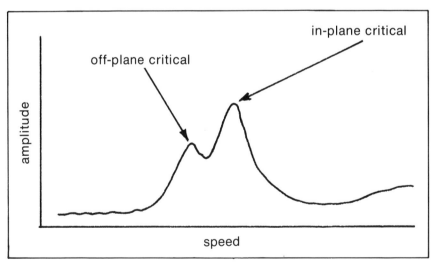

2–14—*Critical response with differing stiffness between planes.*

minimum of 15% below the lowest operating speed. First critical speeds on stiff-shaft machines (machines operating below their first critical) and the second criticals on flexible-shaft machinery have been specified by the API to be at least 20% above the maximum continuous speed. Due to the potential for self-excited instability, critical speed should be between approximately 40% and 55% of an operating speed. With variable-speed machines which must operate over a wide speed range, meeting this criteria is often difficult. If a compromise is necessary, it is generally best to require the highest critical that can be obtained. Thus, a critical located at 55% of an operating speed would be better than one located at 40% of the same speed.

Although discussion has been restricted to lateral responses and critical speeds, torsional natural frequencies also exist and must be accounted for in the design of large machine strings, especially those with gears. A torsional is quite different from a lateral critical speed in at least three areas. First, a torsional is a system natural frequency which depends mostly on the torsional stiffness of couplings and gears and their interaction with the system's inertia. On the other hand, lateral critical speeds are defined for each machine and don't vary appreciably with the machines coupled. Second, the excitation of a torsional natural frequency can produce stresses in excess of limits, leading to a catastrophic failure without any easily recognizable external symptoms. Finally, the lack of external symptoms requires much more care in making torsional measurements than lateral measurements. One must have some knowledge of the torsional mode to ensure measurements are made in the proper location.

3

Vibration Transducers

As the device responsible for converting mechanical motion into an electrical signal which can be conveniently amplified, recorded, displayed, and analyzed, the transducer must be correct for the task, properly mounted, and thoroughly understood. The previous chapter showed how the force necessary to produce a given response varied significantly with frequency. Force also places real limitations on the measurements that can be made by a given transducer.

As an example, 100 Gs acceleration at 10 kHz, an unreasonably high amplitude at a typical blade-passing frequency, represents only 0.02 mils (0.5 micrometers) displacement. In this case an intolerable force level produces a displacement which is, for all practical purposes, immeasurable even though it is within the frequency response specified for most displacement measuring systems.

Acceleration measuring systems experience a similar problem in reverse. As frequency decreases, force limitations continually reduce the signal-to-noise ratio until even moderate levels of motion are difficult to measure in terms of acceleration.

Limitations associated with the sensor itself include whether it measures seismic or relative motion, its size and weight, the location of natural frequencies, and its susceptibility to outside influences, such as those generated by surface imperfections and electrical and magnetic fields. While many of these considerations are specific to a given application, there are general guidelines:

- Force considerations and noise from shaft imperfections usually limit displacement measurement to a maximum frequency of approximately 1,000 to 1,500 Hz.

- Construction limits measurement with velocity pickups to a range of from approximately 10 Hz to 1,500 Hz.
- Acceleration measurements may be made from below 1 Hz to well above 20 kHz, although not necessarily with the same transducer.

Transducers are like windows through which portions of the frequency spectrum may be observed. The type of machine, measurement location, and characteristics to be evaluated as well as the characteristics, advantages, and limitations of transducers must all be well understood and considered if the basic data represent actual condition. Adding sophisticated analytical equipment may decrease analysis time and enhance accuracy, but it cannot improve limitations inherent in the data.

NONCONTACT DISPLACEMENT TRANSDUCERS

Noncontact displacement transducers, generally operating on eddy-current principles, have achieved general acceptance for industrial machinery protection and condition monitoring. In reality, the noncontact displacement transducer is a system comprised of the transducer or a probe, a length of extension cable, and an oscillator demodulator.

Construction and operation

The probe consists of a coil of wire mounted in a nonconductive plastic or ceramic material which is housed in a threaded body (figure 3-1). In operation the probe is excited at a radio frequency of approximately 1.5 mHz generated by the oscillator demodulator and transmitted through the extension cable. This excitation produces a magnetic field radiating from the tip of the displacement probe.

Within the demodulator section of the oscillator demodulator, the radio frequency excitation to the probe is converted to a DC output proportional to its amplitude (figure 3-2). When the probe tip is brought close to a conductive material, eddy currents are induced at the surface of the material, extracting energy from the probe's excitation and decreasing its amplitude. Thus, as the distance from the probe tip to a conductive material is varied, a corresponding DC voltage is produced at the output of the oscillator demodulator which varies in proportion to the distance between the probe tip and the conducting material.

A typical calibration curve for an eddy current displacement measuring system is shown in figure 3-3. The curve may be divided into three regions, beginning with the probe contacting the conductive

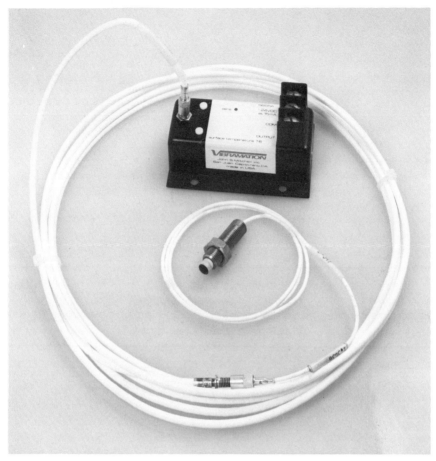

3–1—Typical noncontact eddy-current probe, extension cable, and oscillator demodulator.

surface and a zero DC output from the oscillator demodulator. In most systems the probe may be withdrawn a short distance before the output voltage will begin to change. At some point as the probe is withdrawn, the output voltage will suddenly increase then transition to the second or linear region where any change in distance (gap) produces a corresponding proportional change in the DC output from the oscillator demodulator.

Within the linear range, which typically may extend from 10-90 mils gap, (250-2,250 μm), current standards require either a 100 mv/mil

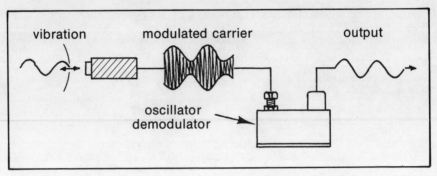

3–2—Eddy current displacement measuring system schematic.

(4 mv/μm) or 200 mv/mil (8mv/μm) proportionality between gap and voltage. Thus, a 10-mil (250 μm) change in gap should produce a voltage change of 1 volt at 100 mv/mil (4 mv/μm) or 2 volts at 200 mv/mil (8 mv/μm).

To digress slightly, the probe, extension cable, and oscillator demodulator make up a tuned resonant circuit. In order to establish and maintain a constant ratio between gap and voltage, the probe, oscillator

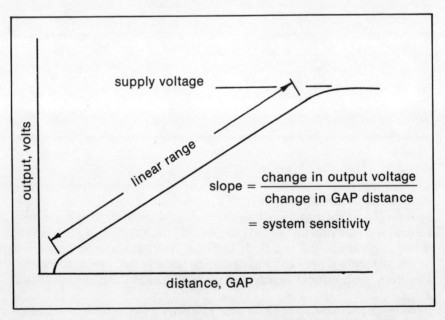

3–3—Typical eddy current displacement probe sensitivity calibration curve.

demodulator, and extension cable must be properly matched and calibrated. Most manufacturers will specify the type of probe, generally tip diameter, and the total electrical length of the extension and probe cables which must be used with each oscillator demodulator. As long as these instructions are followed, manufacturing tolerances will maintain acceptable measurement accuracy without recalibration as components are replaced.

As the probe is withdrawn further, the system loses its linear relationship between output voltage and gap as the output from the oscillator demodulator approaches its supply voltage. Thus, whenever accuracy is desired, the probe must be set so that it is operating within its linear range.

The slope of the curve, the linear range, and the DC output corresponding to a given gap will vary with changes in a target's conductivity and permeability. If a probe and oscillator demodulator calibrated for 4140 steel are used without recalibration on a material such as stainless steel or Inconel, the curve shifts to the left, producing a higher-output voltage for a given gap. In addition, the slope of the curve will change corresponding to a change in sensitivity. Due to this shift and potential inaccuracies, a noncontact probe system calibrated for one material should not be used with another without recalibration.

Temperature may also affect the range limits of a noncontact probe and the DC output at a given gap; however, the shift is generally small across the temperature range experienced within a bearing housing.

Elevated pressures may also affect the sensitivity of a noncontact probe. If the probe is installed in an area of high or fluctuating pressure, its response should be tested in the actual environment to determine what changes in sensitivity or output will occur.

With everything else equal, the maximum linear range obtainable with a noncontact displacement measurement system will increase with increasing probe tip diameter and, as implied from figure 3-3, will likewise increase with an increasing supply voltage At a sensitivity of 200 mv/mil (mv/μm), linear range of typical noncontact measuring systems observing 4140 steel will vary from approximately 60 mils (1,525 μm) with a 0.190-in. (5-mm) tip diameter and -18 VDC supply to 85 mils (2,160μm) with a 0.300-in. (8-mm) tip diameter and -24 VDC supply.

Thus far only slowly moving measurements have been discussed; however, the oscillator demodulator system can produce output variations proportional to a change in gap to frequencies over 10,000 Hz. As a result the system can be used to measure the vibration of a conductive surface placed within its measuring range as well as its relative position. The term relative is very important to understand, for measurements taken with displacement probes—unlike those taken with velocity or acceleration transducers—are measurements of the relative position or movement between probe and observed surface and may not reflect the true or spatial movement of either.

Limitations

When the target is a moving surface such as the periphery of a shaft, the displacement measuring system cannot distinguish between shaft motion or vibration and defects such as scratches, dents, and variations in conductivity or permeability. As a result, the output, rather than being pure vibration, is the sum of vibration and all surface variations passing beneath the probe. Since the magnetic field of the probe penetrates the surface of the observed material, any repair which results in an interface between two materials (when the shaft is plated or metal sprayed) will introduce distortion in the output signal measured by an eddy current displacement transducer.

Figures 3-4 and 3-5 illustrate two types of distortion which must be avoided when using eddy current transducers. In figure 3-4 a large scratch is readily visible in the waveform, resulting in a distorted orbit and a doubling of the amplitude which would be read on a meter. If the scratch shifted 180° relative to what appears to be shaft motion, the vibration amplitude would be more than double. There are real dangers in a situation such as this other than the difficulty in drawing a meaningful conclusion from the displayed data. For example, depending on its phase, an increase in actual vibration may not produce any change

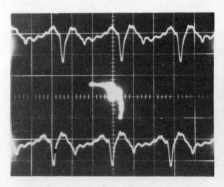

3–4—Shaft with large scratch.

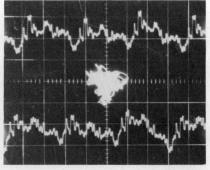

3–5—Shaft with small scratches.

at all in the amplitude read on a meter or, even worse, may produce a decrease in amplitude.

Figure 3-5 illustrates a second example of a defective surface, except this time the defect is a series of small scratches rather than a single large scratch.

In either case, total runout, or the deviation measured with a noncontact displacement transducer from actual shaft motion, must be held to a minimum. As a goal, total runout measured with a noncontact sensor should be less than 10% of the operating shaft displacement. Since it is very difficult to reduce total runout below 0.2 mils (5 μm), a practical value of 0.25 mils (6 μm) is generally accepted as the maximum permissible runout on high-speed machines.

The primary problem with excessive runout is that it obscures shaft vibration and may seriously compromise the ability to analyze and monitor condition. It is especially important to recognize that runout is a vector quantity and thus cannot be subtracted as an absolute value only. Furthermore, runout usually alters the shape of a vibration waveform as well as the response curve obtained by plotting amplitude versus speed during a runup or coastdown.

Eliminating excessive runout is often a very difficult task. The first and obvious step is during manufacture when every effort must be taken to ensure the surface which will be observed by the shaft probe is concentric with the journal, has a smooth finish, and is protected from damage during handling and assembly. If, despite all these efforts, excessive runout persists, it may be electromagnetic in nature. Produced when the shaft is machined, ground (forbidden by API Standards for this specific reason), or degaussed incompletely following a magnetic particle inspection, electromagnetic runout can generally be eliminated by degaussing the shaft surface observed by the probe. If, after degaussing, runout persists despite a smooth and concentric shaft surface, it is likely due to a changing permeability or conductivity around the circumference of the shaft. Often a problem with high-alloy, precipitation-hardened shafts, this type of runout has been successfully reduced by burnishing the area—running it on balancing machine rollers or producing a similar effect in a lathe with a special roller tool.

Should all these steps fail or be impossible to implement for one reason or another, runout can be eliminated electronically with a runout subtractor. The runout subtractor digitally memorizes a phase-referenced shaft motion at slow roll when all motion is assumed to be runout then automatically subtracts the slow-roll waveform from the raw waveform observed by the probe to produce a corrected waveform representative of actual shaft motion.

Mounting

As with all transducers, attention must be given to probe mounting to ensure it is rigid, reasonably protected from windage, and secured so it won't work loose. Where possible, it is highly desirable to mount displacement probes in adapters which can be removed and replaced without disassembling the machine (figure 3-6). Of the numerous methods used to mount probes internally, one of the most successful is shown in figure 3-7.

In this configuration a block, usually cut from ½ or ⅜-in.-thick steel or aluminum, is threaded to mate with a probe and held to the outboard end of the bearing cap with two socket-head cap screws. Slotting the block lets one of the two screws hold the block to the bearing cap while the probe's gap is set. When this has been completed, the other screw is tightened to lock the probe securely in place.

Along with precautions to ensure the probe mounting is rigid, one must be certain the tip is clear and not shaded (figure 3-8). Any conductive interference within the probe's magnetic field will greatly alter its response to movement. For maximum safety there should be nothing conductive within a 45° cone originating at the separation between tip and threaded body and ending on the observed surface. This same rule applies when mounting a probe on a flat surface such as a bearing housing; the probe must be mounted far enough away so the cone and surface do not intersect.

Probes are often mounted through small clearance holes (figure 3-9).

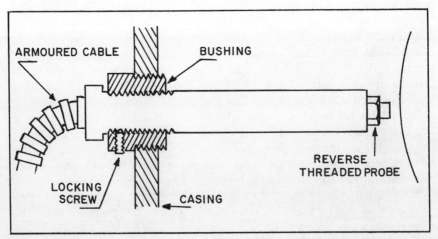

3–6—Adapter to permit probe replacement without interrupting operation.

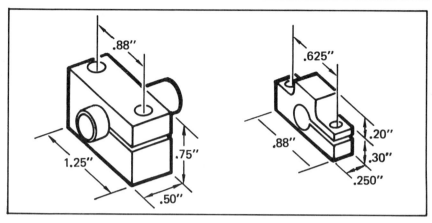

3–7—Typical internal probe mounts (courtesy Spectral Dynamics).

When gapping a probe in this situation, the gap voltage will decrease as the probe enters the hole, often dropping below the desired value. When this occurs, one must resist the temptation to lock the probe in position, for its output at this point is determined by its proximity to the hole. As the probe is inserted further and clears the hole, the gap voltage will increase then decrease as the shaft is approached. It is at this second decrease that the probe should be locked in position. As an aid to determine an approximate position, a depth gauge can be used to

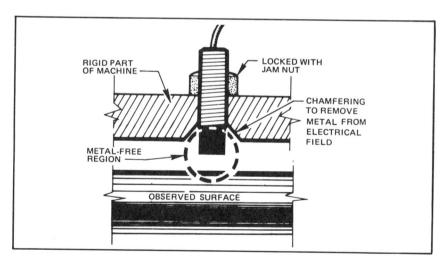

3–8—Noncontact probe tips must not be shaded by adjacent material (courtesy Spectral Dynamics.

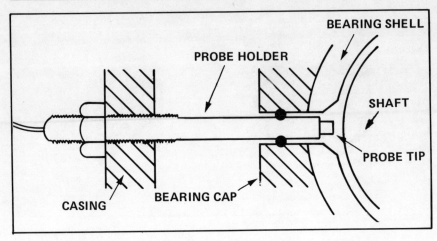

3–9—Probe mounted through small clearance hole.

measure the distance from the probe mount to the shaft and marked on the mount for visual indication of the probe's distance to the shaft. Most displacement probes are not designed for shaft contact; doing so quickly destroys the tip and is somewhat embarrassing to the person making the adjustment.

Routing cables from noncontact probes is another key area to ensure long-term reliability. Although most prefer to have connectors located outside the machine, it is generally easier to achieve an oil-tight seal if the extension cable is permanently sealed at its penetration through the machine casing and the connection to the probe pigtail made inside the machine. In either case, the wire from a displacement probe must be tied down to prevent movement due to the windage which exists within a typical bearing housing. Preferably, the probe wire should exit the casing without having to cross an area of strong windage, such as will occur at a coupling hub. If this is impossible, the wire must be securely tied down or otherwise protected in this area. Cable exits should have beveled or rounded edges to prevent chafing and eventual cable damage.

From their exit from the machine to the enclosure housing the oscillator demodulators, cables from displacement probes should be protected in conduit. Generally, a run of rigid conduit to a point on the machine then a short length of flexible conduit to the exit fitting is the best arrangement to ensure protection while providing easy disassembly and assembly.

VELOCITY PICKUPS

Construction

A typical velocity pickup is shown schematically in figure 3-10. Within the pickup a cylindrical coil attached to the case surrounds a permanent magnet suspended on springs. The spring suspension system is designed to have a very low natural frequency so that the magnet remains stationary in space at frequencies above 8-10 Hz. A damping medium, typically a synthetic oil, is generally added to damp the natural frequency of the spring mass system critically and roll off its response below approximately 10 Hz.

Operation

When the velocity pickup is attached to a vibrating surface, relative motion between the stationary magnet and the vibrating coil causes the magnetic lines of flux from the magnet to cut through the coil, inducing in it a voltage proportional to the velocity of vibration. Thus a velocity pickup is a self-generating device which produces a low impedance signal that can be used directly with analysis or monitoring equipment without any additional signal conditioning.

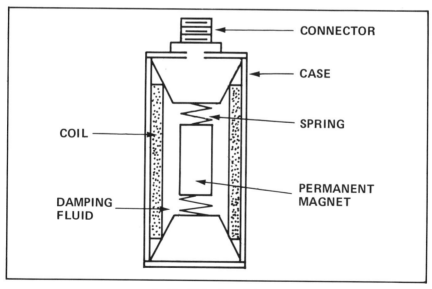

3–10—Velocity pickup.

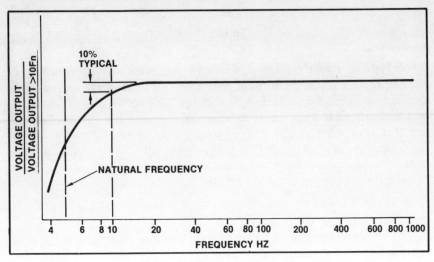

3–11—Typical velocity pickup sensitivity.

The sensitivity vs. frequency response curve of a velocity pickup is limited at low frequencies by the critically damped first natural frequency; at high frequencies its response is limited by the amount of motion necessary to overcome the inertia of the system as well as by the presence of higher order natural frequencies. For practical purposes, a typical velocity pickup is limited to frequencies between approximately 10 and 1,500 Hz. Of course some will operate accurately at lower frequencies and some will operate accurately at higher frequencies; however, the basic limitations remain.

Because of the damping fluid, a velocity pickup may be limited to operation within a relatively narrow temperature band. There are, however, special units available capable of operating at temperatures in excess of 500° F.

Some velocity pickups may obtain a portion or all of their damping electrically. This type of pickup must be loaded with a specific value of resistance in order to meet its design characteristics. A velocity pickup utilizing electrical damping will always have its response characteristics, sensitivity and frequency range, specified into some value of resistance. If one contemplates using this type of pickup with an instrument, such as oscilloscope, other than the one for which it was designed, check its output characteristics on a shaker to determine the effect of changing input impedance. In the event a large change is observed, a shunt resistor can be used to provide the necessary damping.

Limitations

Although a velocity pickup can produce a high-level, low-impedance signal at the frequencies around the running speed of typical industrial machinery, it is an electromechanical device with moving parts that can stick or fail. As a result the velocity pickup has gradually fallen from favor in applications where ruggedness in a hostile environment is paramount. The velocity pickup has, however, retained a favored position with portable analysis and monitoring equipment, for it is more forgiving in areas such as mounting, does not require special cable or sophisticated signal conditioning, and is easily integrated electronically to provide a displacement readout.

ACCELEROMETERS

Construction

Of the transducers which measure acceleration, the piezoelectric are by far the most common in machinery applications. A typical piezoelectric acceleration transducer (figure 3-12) contains one or more piezoelectric crystal elements which may be either natural, such as

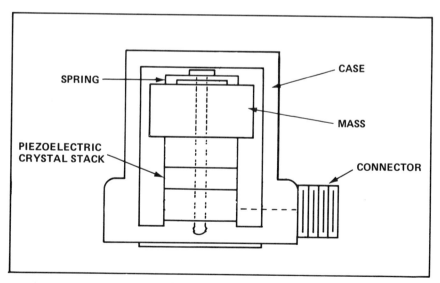

3-12—Accelerometer, compression type.

quartz, or man-made. The crystal element is preloaded by a mass of some type and the entire assembly is enclosed in a rugged protective housing.

Operation

The piezoelectric crystal produces an electrical output when it is physically stressed. In operation, the crystal is stressed by the inertia of the mass as the accelerometer and its crystal are vibrated by the component to which they are attached. The variable force exerted by the mass on the crystal produces an electrical output proportional to acceleration.

Unlike the velocity pickup, an accelerometer operates below its first natural frequency (figure 3-13). The rapid rise in sensitivity approaching resonance is characteristic of an accelerometer, which is an undamped single-degree-of-freedom spring mass system. Generally speaking, the sensitivity of an accelerometer and the ratio between its electrical output and the input acceleration is acceptably constant to approximately 1/5 to 1/3 of its natural frequency. Note that in the general curve shown in figure 3-13, the frequency axis is normalized and represented as the ratio of operating frequency to resonant frequency.

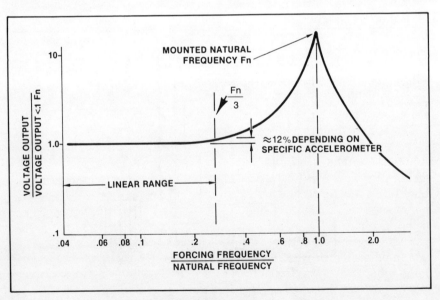

3–13—Typical accelerometer sensitivity.

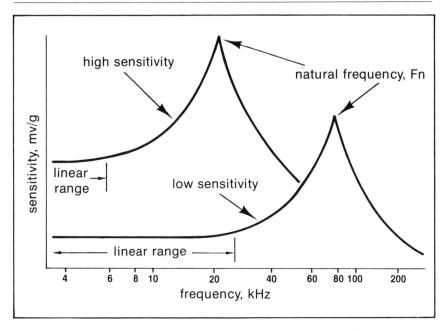

3–14—*Relationship of accelerometer sensitivity to natural frequency.*

For a given piezoelectric material, the sensitivity of an accelerometer is a direct function of the mass. Increased sensitivity usually means larger size and weight with a corresponding reduction in resonant frequency (figure 3-14). Conversely, very high frequency accelerometers are small and light and have low sensitivities. Although an accelerometer typically has a very large dynamic range of 90 dB or more, best results are obtained when the accelerometer has the highest sensitivity available for the highest frequency of interest.

Although the piezoelectric accelerometer is a self-generating device, its output is at a very high impedance and is therefore unsuited for direct use with most display, analysis, or monitoring equipment. Thus, electronics must be utilized to convert the high impedance crystal output to a low impedance. The impedance conversion electronics may be located within the accelerometer, outside of but near the accelerometer, or in the monitoring or analysis device itself (figure 3-15).

Accelerometers with internal electronics are convenient and can use inexpensive conventional plugs and cable, but they are limited to temperatures of approximately 250° F (125° C) (figure 3-15a). Locating the electronics in a cool location away from the accelerometer allows the transducer to tolerate higher temperatures, to 1,400° F (760° C) on

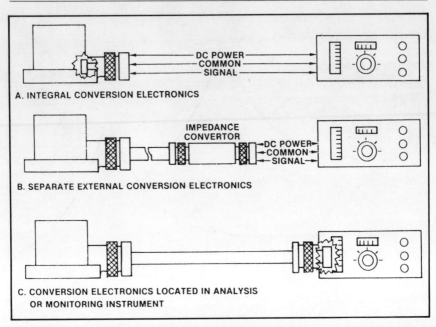

A. INTEGRAL CONVERSION ELECTRONICS

B. SEPARATE EXTERNAL CONVERSION ELECTRONICS

C. CONVERSION ELECTRONICS LOCATED IN ANALYSIS
OR MONITORING INSTRUMENT

3–15—Three methods for converting a high-impedance accelerometer output to a low-impedance signal suitable for use in recording and analysis equipment.

some special units; however, transmitting the high impedance signal from the accelerometer to the conversion electronics requires special expensive low-noise plugs and cable, and the cable must be securely tied down to minimize noise pickup (figure 3-15b). Placing the conversion electronics in the display or measuring device is often convenient and less expensive than separate electronics; however, a long length of low-noise transmission cable is required which, if damaged, must be replaced in its entirety (figure 3-15c). In machinery applications, housing the electronics within the accelerometer case is generally best unless it is precluded by temperature.

Conversion electronics may be of two types: charge or voltage. A charge conversion system is generally more complex and therefore more expensive than a voltage conversion system; however, the sensitivity of the charge system is independent of the length of cable between the accelerometer and the charge converter. When voltage conversion systems are used with accelerometers with low internal capacitance, changes in cable length may represent a significant change in overall capacitance and hence produce corresponding changes in sensitivity. Since cable length is not a factor when the conversion electronics are installed within the accelerometer and voltage conversion electronics are small and easier to implement, most accelerometers with integral electronics have voltage conversion electronics. The voltage system used in most accelerometers with integral electronics produces high sensitivity with low noise, can be operated over inexpensive two-conductor cable, and provides a low impedance output suitable for direct operation with most measuring and analysis equipment.

Limitations

Due to their sensitivity and wide dynamic range, accelerometers may be quite sensitive to environmental input. Incident thermal radiation can create a large, low-frequency output. Base strain, caused by distortion of the accelerometer base by mounting it on an irregular surface, can significantly alter sensitivity. Both of these difficulties can be minimized in the design of an accelerometer. In general, a shear type where the mass imposes a shear force on the crystal in response to vibration (figure 3-16) is less affected by thermal radiation and base strain than a compression device (figure 3-12).

Due to the combination of high impedance and low signal strengths, ground loops may be a problem when using accelerometers. Generated when current flows between two grounds at different poten-

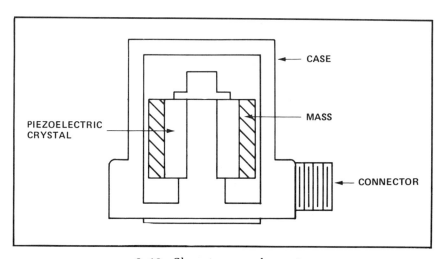

3–16—Shear-type accelerometer.

tials, ground loop problems can be eliminated by ensuring the system is grounded at one point only. Since accelerometers sometimes have one side of the crystal stack connected to their casing, it may be necessary to employ an insulated mounting to isolate the accelerometer. When this step becomes necessary, one must be aware that an insulated mounting can lower this mounted resonant frequency of the accelerometer.

As a final word of caution, remember that one of an accelerometer's major strengths is its ability to examine a much wider frequency range than any of the other transducers discussed in this chapter. As a result, the signal from an accelerometer may contain numerous components which are not present at all in the signals obtained from other transducers. Signal conditioning may be used to alter, modify, or limit the signal in some way; however, be prepared for some differences in the same variable as measured by two different transducers. For example, the output from an accelerometer may be electronically integrated to velocity. If the integrated acceleration signal is compared to a velocity signal obtained directly from a velocity pickup mounted at the exact same spot, the two signals will be essentially identical from approximately 1,000 Hz to 10 Hz. Below that point the integrated acceleration signal will probably contain much more low-frequency activity, for its sensitivity is still linear while that of the velocity pickup is dropping off. The characteristic linearity of an accelerometer to very low frequencies can be particularly bothersome if the signal is integrated a second time to displacement. Under these conditions, the very large gain necessary to maintain the frequency squared relationship between acceleration and displacement at low frequencies amplifies characteristics not associated with machinery condition such as structural motion and duct rumble which must then be eliminated by filtering.

COMBINATION TRANSDUCERS

In some applications it may be desirable to measure shaft absolute motion. This can be accomplished in two different ways.

First, and perhaps the least complicated, is to attach a seismic sensor such as an accelerometer or velocity pickup to a spring-loaded plunger fitted with a nonmetallic tip capable of contacting the shaft and following its motion for extended periods. With this design the output of the seismic pickup is proportional to the shaft's absolute spatial motion and independent of bearing or casing motion.

A shaft-riding pickup must be able to follow shaft motion exactly and must be free of any natural frequencies which might affect or distort the motion it is sensing. The tip should be spring loaded with enough force to hold it in contact with the shaft up to a level of at least 5 Gs peak acceleration (25 mils, 0.7 mm peak-to-peak displacement at 3,600 rpm) and must be lubricated to minimize wear and chatter. A shaft-riding pickup assembly must be fitted with some type of positive mechanical stop to prevent the metallic rider assembly from contacting the shaft as the tip wears. A visible wear indicator is usually provided to ensure the shaft rider is within the limits of its spring travel and not against the mechanical stop.

The shaft surface on which the shaft rider tip rides must be smooth with mechanical runout less than about 10% of the allowable shaft amplitude.

The maximum shaft speeds at which a shaft rider can function depend on tip design, surface speed, lubrication, and the spring loading force of the tip against the shaft. In general, shaft riders can be used up to surface speeds of approximately 20,000 ft/min (6,000 m/min) when the shaft has a surface finish of 20 μin. (0.05 μm) rms.

A second method of making the same measurement electronically subtracts bearing motion, obtained from a seismic transducer and integrated to displacement, from shaft motion relative to the bearing housing obtained from a noncontact displacement transducer. This method eliminates the mechanical shaft rider and is not limited by shaft surface speed at the expense of added electronic complexity.

4

Signal Conditioning

Signal conditioning electronic instruments such as filters, integrators, and amplifiers find wide use in machinery vibration analysis, and the analyst should understand their function, characteristics, use, and limitations.

DECIBEL UNITS

One common term which must be defined is decibel, commonly abbreviated as dB. The dB scale is nothing more than a logarithmic scale relative to some reference. In sound measurement the dB scale is referenced to a specific sound pressure level; however, in machinery analysis the dB scale is used to express the ratio between two voltages—an output to an input, for example.

Mathematically and again in terms of voltage, a dB is a 20-log voltage ratio where the voltage ratio is the output divided by the input. When the output equals the input, 20 log 1 = 0 or 0 dB. Thus, the zero point or reference on the dB voltage scale occurs when input and output are equal. It follows that perfect reproduction of an input signal could be stated by specifying a 0 dB permissible tolerance or deviation. In practice, however, this is impossible to achieve with anything other than an unbroken length of wire, so it is customary to specify the output of an instrument as a tolerance, ± 3 dB for example, over a given frequency range as a measure of the instrument's deviation in voltage output compared to the voltage input. The smaller the dB value, the closer the output voltage will follow the input.

If the output is one tenth the input (ten-to-one attentuation across the instrument) 20 log 1/0.1 = 20 log 10 = 20. Similarly, a 100-to-1 attentuation corresponds to 40 dB and 1,000-to-1 = 60 dB.

The dB scale can be used equally well for gain or an increase in voltage. Using the previous examples, a gain of 20 dB equals an increase in voltage by a factor of 10, 40 dB equals an increase by a factor of 100, etc.

The dB scale is nothing more than a method to express the ratio between two quantities. Of course there is still the problem of converting a ratio other than a multiple of 10 to a dB value or vice versa. Although the conversion between dB and voltage ratio is relatively easy to calculate if one has access to log tables or a calculator with a log function, a reasonably accurate estimate can be made if 4 or 5 key values from the following table are memorized.

TABLE 4.1
db Voltage Radio Conversion

dB	Voltage ratio	dB	Voltage ratio
1	1.12	13	4.46
2	1.26	14	5.01
3	1.41	15	5.63
4	1.58	16	6.30
5	1.78	17	7.08
6	1.99	18	7.95
7	2.24	19	8.92
8	2.50	20	10
9	2.82	40	100
10	3.16	60	1,000
11	3.55	80	10,000
12	3.98	100	100,000

Although the table may look somewhat complicated at first glance, remembering the dB equivalents for voltage ratios of 2, 3, 5, 10 and multiples of 10 will allow one to make a quick, reasonably accurate mental conversion from one unit to the other. As pointed out earlier, 20 dB represents a voltage ratio of 10 with multiples of 20 dB equal to powers of 10. Next, 6 dB represents a voltage ratio of approximately 2:1, while 10 dB approximates 3:1, and 14 dB, 5:1. As a voltage ratio, 50 dB = 40 dB + 10 dB. Since adding logarithms is equivalent to multiplying numbers, 50 dB equals a voltage ratio of 100 (40 dB) × 3 (10 dB), or 300. Normally a conversion from dB to voltage ratio is the most often made and, as in the example, it is done by subtracting the nearest multiple of 20 then multiplying the voltage ratio of the multiple by the voltage ratio of the remainder to obtain the overall voltage ratio.

FILTERS

Filters are probably the most widely used of all vibration analysis equipment. Simply stated, a filter limits a vibration signal in some predictable fashion such that a single frequency or group of frequencies may be isolated for measurement or study. Filters can be classified in at least four different ways:

Frequencies passed or passband

High pass, low pass, bandpass, and band reject describe the frequencies which will be passed unchanged through a filter.

Method of tuning

Fixed, manual, or automatic/tracking.

Type components used

Active, using operational amplifiers, or passive, using inductive capacitive resistive circuits.

Electronic characteristics

Initial rolloff, final rolloff or slope of the filter skirts, maximum sweep rate, and phase shift are a few of the principal characteristics which should be understood.

As an illustration of the use of these different filters in machinery analysis, nearly everyone should be familiar with tunable bandpass filters used in vibration analyzers. Low-pass filtering is often used with shaft displacement signals to eliminate high frequencies generated by shaft scratches. High-pass filters are generally required whenever the signals from accelerometers are double integrated to displacement. Finally, notch or band reject filters are provided on some analyzers to permit a rapid assessment of the total vibration energy present, exclusive of a specific frequency.

Two types of bandpass filters are commonly used in tunable analyzers. First is the constant bandwidth filter which, as the name implies, will pass a constant frequency band regardless of where the filter center frequency is positioned. This type of filter provides uniform resolution across the frequency scale but requires more time to scan across a given frequency range when compared to a constant percentage bandwidth filter. In the second type, a constant percentage bandwidth filter, the frequencies passed are some fixed percentage of the filter center frequency such that as the filter is tuned to higher frequencies, the bandwidth becomes larger with a corresponding reduction in resolution.

Passband

The first and possibly most basic descriptions of a filter are the frequencies which will be passed with less than some specified deviation, usually 3 dB. As the names imply, a high-pass filter passes all frequencies above some specified frequency. Conversely, a low-pass filter passes frequencies below a specified frequency. A bandpass filter passes a band of frequencies while eliminating frequencies both above and below the desired passband. A notch or band reject filter is the reverse of a bandpass filter, eliminating all frequencies within a specified band while allowing all others both above and below to pass. Although this simplified description implies a sharp cut-off of unwanted frequencies, the sharpness by which unwanted frequencies are cut off is a filter characteristic.

Tunable filters, in which the cut-off point(s) can be continuously varied across the frequency spectrum, provide the analyst with the ability to isolate specific frequencies. Although the tunable bandpass filter is more common in machinery analysis, tunable high and low-pass filters often save time in searching for specific frequencies and may clear a cluttered signal. Quite often, particularly with shaft displacement signals, the clearest picture of machinery condition may be obtained by limiting an oscilloscope display to running frequency plus 4 or 5 harmonics and eliminating the higher frequencies which may be caused by shaft scratches (figure 4-1). The tunable low-pass filter allows this simple modification in the signal while preserving the low-order harmonics which would have been lost had a bandpass filter been used.

The automatic or tracking filter is nothing more than a tunable filter where the tuning signal is generated by and synchronized with the shaft under study. In this fashion the automatic or tracking filter can be locked to a specific component, normally rotating frequency. It can, however, track any synchronous multiple of running frequency if the proper multiplication/division networks are included or available as an accessory. The automatic or tracking filter is widely used in balancing applications and for tracking phase and amplitude response during a startup or coastdown.

Method of tuning

Classifying filters by their method of tuning is reasonably obvious. Fixed filters have no tuning capability short of changing components and are commonly used in monitoring or analysis applications where a known or predictable frequency spectrum is limited or divided for a specific purpose. As stated earlier, fixed high and low-pass filters are often used in various types of equipment, including analyzers, to eliminate unwanted frequencies. Fixed high-pass filters can be created when two electronic instruments are connected together or when a coupling capacitor is used to eliminate a DC offset or bias voltage.

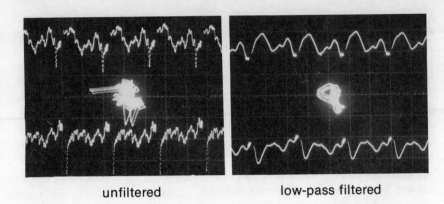

unfiltered   low-pass filtered

4–1—Unfiltered and low-pass filter limited shaft displacement signals.

Conversely, the speed of an FM tape recorder has a direct relationship to the highest frequency passed and therefore acts like a low-pass filter. Regardless of whether a filter is designed into the system for a specific purpose or is the result of connecting or operating instruments in a particular configuration, the analyst must be aware of any limitations or restrictions placed on the incoming data.

Components

Filters can also be classified by the type components used in their construction. Active filters using operational amplifiers are the most common in machinery analysis because (in general) they are physically smaller, more stable over a broad range of connected impedance, and provide a voltage gain compared to an equivalent passive filter. Passive filters using inductive capacitive or resistance capacitive networks may be sharper than an active filter at a penalty in size and weight. As a point of interest, all electronic measuring devices and instruments have input and output resistance and capacitance; thus, the analyst must be aware that, when two instruments are connected together, the combination may produce a passive filter which can alter the signal characteristics in some fashion not immediately apparent from the instrument specifications.

In order to describe a filter one must know its transfer characteristics. Before developing this subject, however, octave must be defined. An octave is another relative term signifying a doubled or halved frequency, depending on whether the frequency is being increased or decreased. For example, one octave above 100 Hz (6,000 cpm) would be 200 Hz (12,000 cpm), while one octave below 100 Hz would be 50 Hz (3,000 cpm). Thus, while the dB was a convenient method to express amplitude ratio, the octave is a convenient way to express a frequency ratio.

Rolloff characteristics

The rolloff of a filter is commonly expressed as dB per octave. Simply stated, this means that if the frequency is doubled or halved, depending on the filter, the ratio between output and input will vary by the specified value. If a 20-dB/octave bandpass filter were centered at 100 Hz (6,000 cpm) and a variable frequency of 1-volt input were applied, the filter output would be 0.1 volt at 50 Hz (one octave below the filter center frequency), 1.0 volt at 100 Hz, and 0.1 volt at 200 Hz (one octave above the filter center frequency). With the same inputs and a 40-dB/octave filter centered at 100 Hz, one would have a 0.01-volt output at 50 Hz, a 1.0-volt output at 100 Hz, and a 0.01-volt output at 200 Hz. Rather than an immediate cutoff of all frequencies outside the passband, a filter attenuates frequencies on a sloped line defined in dB per octave.

While this explanation holds true in the second octave and beyond, it may not be absolutely correct in the first octave. As shown in figure 4-2, there is a transition between the unity gain or bandpass portion of the filter and the attenuation or skirt of the filter. Although ideally the transition should be a sharp corner, in reality it is a curve with an increasing slope. To get the filter started down as quickly as possible, its rolloff generally begins inside the desired bandpass which is then specified as 3% or 3 dB points. This designation simply means that at the edge of the bandpass the output from the filter is either 3% below or 0.707 (1/1.41) times the input, respectively (figure 4-3).

Filters may be named to describe a particular initial rolloff characteristic. Of the filters shown in figure 4-2, a Butterworth filter has the flattest response within the passband. But to achieve this characteristic it has a slow initial rolloff. The Bessell filter has the most linear phase shift across the filter, while the Chebyshev has the sharpest initial rolloff, at a penalty of some ripple within the passband. Thus, the characteristics of a filter can be optimized for a specific task at some compromise in other areas. Of concern to the analyst, the first octave attenuation may be slightly different than the filter specifications would indicate.

Filters must be understood if they are to be used effectively. As an example, most filters used in machinery analysis are fairly broad, and one may have difficulty distinguishing between closely spaced frequencies such as the second harmonic of a low-speed gear shaft and the high-speed shaft when the ratio is close to 2:1. Additionally, since a filter attenuates frequencies on a sloped line, the output of a filter can include contributions from components outside the specified 3 dB or 3% passband. If these components are large enough and close enough, the amplitude can be significantly altered.

As mentioned earlier, each filter will produce a phase shift as it is tuned through its cutoff point. This characteristic can greatly affect the location of a phase mark on a filtered waveform or orbit displayed on an oscilloscope. In balancing, the phase shift is generally not a problem, for in order to freeze the shaft with a strobe light the filter must be tuned to the exact rotational speed of the shaft.

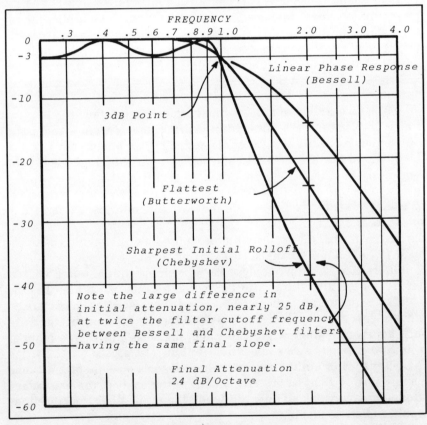

4–2—Filter response.

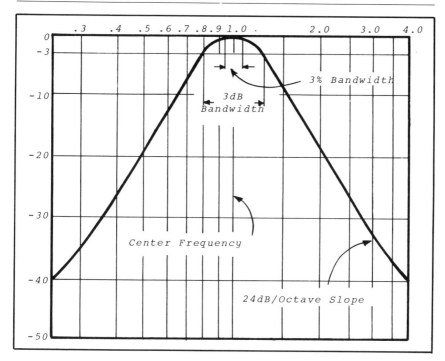

4–3—Bandpass filter shape and terminology.

Another term often used with filters is the number of poles. Poles are a part of the mathematical description of a filter's transfer function and represent the slope of the filter's rolloff. Used with single-skirt filters (high or low pass), one pole is equivalent to a 6-dB/octave slope. In the case of a bandpass filter with two skirts, one pole equals a slope of 3 dB/octave. In machinery analysis instruments, 6, 12, 18, 24, or possibly even 48-pole filters are seen.

Sweep limitations

A discussion of filter characteristics would not be complete without mentioning the time necessary for the filter output to approximate a suddenly applied input. While this may appear academic, it dictates the maximum rate at which a filter can be swept across a given band of frequencies or a tracking filter can follow a speed change. In this regard the time (in seconds) required for the output of a filter to approach its final value is on the order of 1/B where B is the filter bandwidth. Said another way, in order to perform a measurement with a filter of bandwidth B, a minimum measurement time of 1/B is required.

As the time necessary to make a given measurement through a filter varies, the maximum rate at which the filter can be swept will also vary in some inverse proportion. The approximate maximum rate a filter may be swept is B^2Hz/sec. For this reason, a portable vibration analyzer with a selectable bandwidth filter must be tuned more slowly in the sharp or narrowband position than in the broad position to achieve the same accuracy.

To cite a specific example, examine the time necessary to make a measurement and the maximum sweep rate for two filters with 1 and 10 Hz bandwidths (60 and 600 cpm, respectively):

	1 Hz	10 Hz
Minimum time to make a measurement 1/B	1 sec	0.1 sec
Maximum sweep rate	1 Hz/sec	100 Hz/sec

Although these are only approximations, they show one compromise that must be made with filters: the higher the resolution (narrower the bandpass), the longer the time required to sweep a given frequency range. Taking the previous example one step further, to analyze a 1,000-Hz frequency range with 1-Hz resolution would require approximately 1,000 seconds (17 minutes), whereas analyzing the same 1,000-Hz range with a 10-Hz filter can be accomplished in 100 seconds, or a little over 1.5 minutes.

Use in machinery analysis

In machinery analysis, a filter permits identifying the presence or even perhaps absence of specific frequencies, for it is in this information that a problem is defined. In use, a filter is normally tuned first to the running frequency of a machine and the amplitude is noted. If the filter is then removed by switching the analyzer to its filter-out position and the amplitude remains unchanged, all the measured amplitude is at the running frequency. If amplitude increases in the filter-out position, then other components either above or below running frequency must be contributing to the signal. The filter is then tuned until an amplitude increase signifies the presence of a second component and its frequency and amplitude are noted. In this way, often a very slow tedious process, the components in a vibration signal can be located and their amplitudes recorded for analysis. The real time analyzer performs the same process rapidly enough that the result can be presented as an amplitude versus frequency spectrum on an oscilloscope.

The potential for problems due to the inadvertent assembling of a passive filter network is always worthwhile to emphasize, for it is a phenomenon which may not always be recognized by an instrument user and can have a large and misleading effect on the data. When inserting a filter by the manner in which an instrument is operated, the analyst must be aware that tape recorder mode and operating speed and whether an amplifier is AC or DC coupled can affect frequency response. For example, if an FM tape recorder is operated too slowly, it may not have the frequency response to reproduce a sharp pulsed signal such as might be generated by a phase reference (figure 4-4).

This type of distortion can occur even though the fundamental frequency of the incoming signal is well below the upper frequency limit of the recorder for that particular speed because the recorder is acting as a low-pass filter and eliminating many of the high frequencies contained in the pulse which are necessary to reproduce its shape accurately. The same problem occurs in reverse on a tape recorder in the direct mode. In this instance the recorder acts like a high-pass filter, greatly attenuating frequencies below approximately 50 Hz.

The AC coupling capacitor provided in most instrumentation amplifiers to reject a DC bias is nothing more than a high-pass filter set

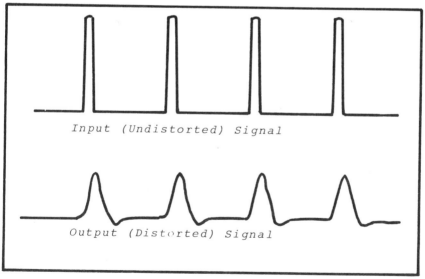

Input (Undistorted) Signal

Output (Distorted) Signal

4–4—Distortion caused by inadequate high-frequency response.

at a very low frequency. Thus, when an amplifier is switched from DC coupled to AC coupled, there will be some loss in low-frequency response. Just how much loss is determined by the input impedance of the amplifier and the value of the coupling capacitor. If the capacitor is too small, the loss of low-frequency information can be significant.

A loss of low-frequency information can occur if one attempts to connect a high-impedance output to a low-impedance input. In this situation the resulting high-pass filter has its 3-dB point at a frequency defined by:

$$f_{3dB} = \frac{1}{2\pi RC}$$

where:

R = the input resistance of the instrument
C = the applied capacitance

To cite a specific example of the foregoing, see what happens when a high impedance accelerometer is connected directly to an oscilloscope. Although an oscilloscope with about 1 megohm (1×10^6 ohms) input resistance is normally considered a high input impedance device, it is low relative to an accelerometer which may have a resistance of well over 10^9 ohms and a capacitance approaching 2,000 pico farads (2×10^{-9} farads). In this example:

$$f_{3dB} = \frac{1}{2\pi \, (10^6) \, (2 \times 10^{-9})} = 79.6 \text{ Hz}$$

Thus, in this simplified example, connecting a high-impedance accelerometer to an oscilloscope will produce a high-pass filter which will be 3 dB down at approximately 80 Hz.

Like so many other problems, the ability of a resistance capacitance network to produce high or low-pass filtering can often be used to advantage. For example, the high frequencies generated by shaft scratches can be eliminated from a shaft displacement signal by installing a simple resistive capacitive passive filter between the output of the displacement transducer and the input to the oscilloscope. Shown schematically in figure 4-5, this simple passive filter can be easily constructed on a banana plug adapter which fits the input of most oscilloscopes. To find the component values, use the same expression as in the previous example (except the frequency, a known value) and find the component values which will produce the desired 3-dB point. In this example, set the 3-dB point at 1,000 Hz (60,000 cpm) and use a 10-K ohm resistor (10×10^3 ohms). Solving:

$$f_{3dB} = 1,000 = \frac{1}{2\pi\,(10 \times 10^3)\,C}$$

therefore:

$$C = \frac{1}{2\pi\,(10 \times 10^3)\,1,000} = 0.159 \times 10^{-6} \text{ farads}$$

Thus, a capacitor with a value of approximately 0.16 microfarad is required with a 10-K ohm resistor to achieve the desired low-pass filtering.

INTEGRATION

Within electronic instrumentation, the process of single and double integration can be accomplished with a low-pass active filter to establish the required attenuation. In this way the mathematical process of dividing each spectral component by frequency or frequency squared to attain a single or double integration is easily achieved. To demonstrate how this occurs, go back to equations 2.5 and 2.6 and construct the following table for a constant zero to peak acceleration of 1 G:

TABLE 4.2

Frequency, Hz	Velocity, ips	Ratio	Displacement, mils	Ratio
12.5	4.92	—	125	—
25	2.45	2.0	31.3	4.0
50	1.23	2.0	7.8	4.0
61.4	1.0	—	5.2	—
100	0.6	2.0	1.96	4.0
140	0.44	—	1.0	—
200	0.31	2.0	0.49	4.0
400	0.15	2.0	0.12	4.0

Although this information is generally shown in a graphical form, the tabular presentation illustrates several points much better than a graph. First, observe that as the frequency doubles or increases in octave steps, the ratio between the decrease in velocity and displacement remains two and four, respectively. Going back to the discussion on the decibel, recall that these two ratios correspond to 6 and 12 dB. Thus, single and double integrators are equivalent to low-pass filters with skirts of 6 and 12 dB/octave, respectively.

The tabulation also shows the zero gain or crossover points in the English system where 1 G equals 1 ips velocity (61.4 Hz) and where 1 G equals 1 mil displacement (140 Hz). Metric acceleration-to-velocity and acceleration-to-displacement crossover points are 1,560 Hz (mm/sec) and 705 Hz (μm), respectively.

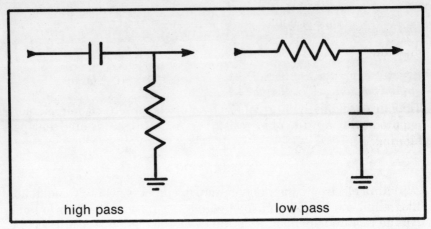

high pass   low pass

4–5—Simple passive filters.

Also observe the rapid increase in displacement at 1 G acceleration as frequency decreases. This is due to the frequency squared relationship between acceleration and displacement and can present problems when double integrating to very low frequencies. To explain this in more detail, decrease frequency two more octaves to 3.125 Hz. At this point the displacement equivalent to 1 G acceleration is approximately 2.0 in. or 2,000 mils (51 mm). Double integration from acceleration to displacement requires a large amount of amplification at very low frequencies. As one would suspect, the integration process cannot continue to zero frequency, for it would require infinite amplification. Because of the amplification at low frequencies, an integrator includes a high-pass filter to attenuate frequencies below some predetermined point. As the requirements for double integration go to lower frequencies in machinery applications using acceleration transducers, the high-pass filter must be progressively sharper to reject the very low frequencies which are generated by structural and seismic motion and picked up by the transducer, yet which may not indicate machinery condition.

To illustrate this point, examine a vibration measurement on the order of 10 mils (254 μm) at 10 Hz (600 rpm) on a machine such as a fan that has structural motion of approximately 100 mils (2,540 μm) at 5 Hz. In order to make the desired measurement yet reject the noise, the incoming signal must be attenuated by a factor of 100 in the octave between 10 and 5 Hz if the noise is to be reduced to less than 10% of the component measured. This attenuation will require a 40-dB/octave filter, which is quite steep and difficult to attain. Normally, conditions won't be as severe as those described; however, one must be aware of the potential for problems when double integrating to very low frequencies.

In view of these problems, why integrate at all? First, and despite all the arguments for the use of velocity, many people express vibration amplitude in terms of displacement. Second, if low-frequency (below approximately 8–10 Hz) absolute or seismic motion is examined in terms of displacement, there is little choice but to double integrate the signal from an acceleration transducer and accept some complex signal conditioning to eliminate interference from unwanted low frequencies. Third, since integration attenuates the high frequencies on a fixed 6-dB/octave slope, it can reduce the dynamic range required to record a wideband signal. Finally, many people believe that a constant velocity criterion over a broad frequency range is the best measure of machinery condition. For wideband response one almost has to utilize an acceleration sensor then integrate its output to velocity.

AC-TO-DC CONVERTERS

Any instrument which displays the amplitude of a vibration signal as a meter reading will have an AC-to-DC converter. Although the electronic process of converting an AC signal to a proportional DC value is relatively straightforward, there are different methods of implementation which can produce significant differences in the output for a given input signal.

There are three basic methods of converting an AC input to a DC output proportional to the average, RMS, or peak value of the incoming signal. As long as the input is a sine wave, an average detector can be easily calibrated to read peak or peak-to-peak by multiplying its output by 1.57 or 3.14, respectively. Thus, as long as the input is a sine wave, the output from any of the converters will be or can be easily made equal to the output from any other (figure 4-6a). The problem arises when the input deviates from a sine wave.

To take an extreme example, visualize an input of a high-amplitude, short-duration pulse such as might be generated by an impact or a scratch or phase reference mark passing a noncontact displacement probe (figure 4-6b). In this case, the peak value measured with a peak detector would be much higher than the amplitude obtained by multiplying the output from an average or RMS detector by 1.57 or 1.41, respectively. This occurs because the average and RMS values are integrated over a half cycle with the result that high amplitude but short duration pulses can have very high peak values but very low average and RMS values.

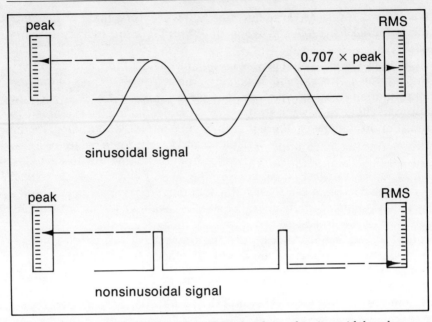

4–6—*Comparison of peak and RMS values of a sinusoidal and nonsinusoidal signal.*

This may all be quite interesting, but how does it affect machinery vibration analysis? Just as differences in bandwidth between analyzers and monitors can influence the measured amplitude, so can the method of detection. Thus, one must be careful when comparing measurements taken with different types of instruments or equipment that the method of detection is equivalent. If it isn't, differences can be expected depending on the input waveform. In general, a peak detector will always produce an output which is equal to or greater than an average or RMS detector calibrated to read peak.* Of course, this in itself could be a valuable indicator of machinery condition, for it is a measure of the number of impulses contained in a signal. In fact, the ratio between peak and RMS, crest factor, has been used to measure rolling element bearing condition. What could be a potential problem can be used to advantage so long as its behavior is understood.

One additional point which should be recognized by a machinery analyst is the response time or delay which must be built into AC-to-DC converters, particularly peak detectors designed to operate at very low

---

*Many feel that RMS amplitude is much more representative of the force applied. It is commonly used in Europe in place of peak values, which are generally used in the U.S.

frequencies. When an AC-to-DC converter detects a signal, it must wait an entire cycle for that signal to repeat. Going back to the example of a peak detector operating with an input of a high-amplitude but short-duration pulse, for most of the time during the cycle the input to the detector is zero. If the detector is to hold the peak value within some reasonable accuracy during the part of the cycle when the input is zero, it must have a large time constant controling the rate of decay. Thus, the output responds slowly and, if the signal is suddenly removed, will not drop immediately to zero but will slowly decay at a rate determined by the time constant of the detector. Although other factors such as meter damping may have an even larger effect in a typical analyzer, a meter will generally not present a true picture of a transient event such as the change in amplitude when power is removed from an electric motor. In order to see what is really happening, a device such as an oscilloscope must be used.

5

How to Make Measurements

To select the measurement(s) which most accurately represent mechanical condition, several factors must be considered. In addition to the type, nature, and severity of problems that can be anticipated, machine response, response of the measured variable, transducer characteristics, and the frequency range of interest must be examined.

In terms of vibration measurement, machine construction, the purpose of the measurement, and the frequency range of interest will determine which type of transducer is best for the task. Machine construction and dynamics will dictate transducer location, while size, criticality, operating experience, and the type and extent of anticipated problems will determine how many transducers are installed.

Recall that noncontact displacement transducers measure relative motion; if an absolute motion measurement is best for the amplication, a velocity or acceleration transducer must be used. Likewise, a displacement or velocity measurement generally has advantages at lower frequencies, while acceleration measurement has advantages at high frequencies. On occasion, the type of measurement which must be made will force compromises in the measured variable and the transducer which must be used. Take, for example, measuring the natural frequency of a tower, structure, or piping which may be on the order of 1–2 Hz. Displacement is the best variable to measure at low frequencies, yet it is difficult—perhaps impossible—to establish a fixed reference on which to mount the transducer. The second choice, a velocity pickup, won't operate at such low frequencies. As a result, accelerometers may be the only choice to make low-frequency vibration measurements on structures.

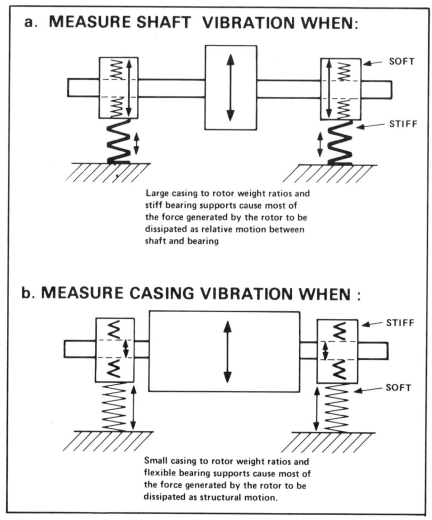

a. MEASURE SHAFT VIBRATION WHEN:

SOFT

STIFF

Large casing to rotor weight ratios and
stiff bearing supports cause most of
the force generated by the rotor to be
dissipated as relative motion between
shaft and bearing

b. MEASURE CASING VIBRATION WHEN :

STIFF

SOFT

Small casing to rotor weight ratios and
flexible bearing supports cause most of
the force generated by the rotor to be
dissipated as structural motion.

5–1—What to measure depends on construction.

Since the signal level is so low, particular attention must be given to
mounting, cabling, and signal conditioning; nevertheless, the measurement can be and is made very successfully.

The decision of what to measure depends to a great extent on the
machine itself. When the machine has a relatively light rotor operating
in a heavy stiff casing (figure 5-1a), most of the force generated by the
rotor is dissipated as relative motion between the shaft and the bearing.

On machines of this type such as high-pressure centrifugal compressors with casing-to-rotor-weight ratios of 30:1, the relative displacement between shaft and bearing measured with a noncontact probe is the best indicator of a rotor's condition.

With the opposite configuration, a relatively heavy rotor running in stiff bearings supported on a flexible structure (figure 5-1b), most of the force developed by the rotor is dissipated as structural motion. On this type of machine (fans, aircraft-derivative gas turbines, and machinery fitted with rolling element bearings), casing vibration, measured with velocity or acceleration transducers, is the best measure of condition.

The response of the measured variable to changing mechanical condition is the second area which must be considered during the selection process. For maximum effectiveness, the measurements which represent condition should display the largest changes or response to a change in mechanical condition. As an example, examine axial position, thrust bearing oil drain temperature, and thrust bearing metal temperature—three measurements which are related to the condition and load on a thrust bearing. Of these three measurements, bearing metal temperature is by far the most responsive to changes in load. Illustrated in figure 5-2, it is not uncommon to observe a thrust bearing metal temperature increase of 100 °F (55 °C) from no load to full

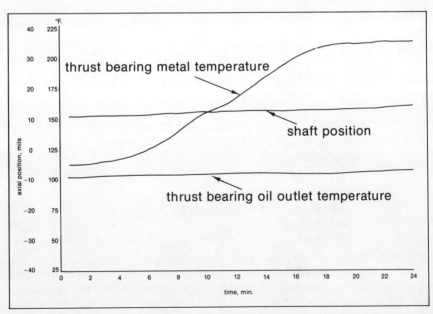

5–2—Response of thrust bearing parameters to increasing load.

load while axial position and oil drain temperature are changing only 2–3 mils (50–75 μm) and 5 °F (3 °C), respectively. Thus, if overload were the only consideration, thrust bearing metal temperature would be the best and only measurement necessary.

Unfortunately, measuring turbomachinery condition is seldom this simple and protection may not be ensured by measuring a single variable at a single location. In the case of measuring the condition of a thrust bearing, the best and most conservative approach uses metal temperature as the most responsive anticipatory measure of load with an axial position measurement to warn of a shift in position caused by something other than overload, such as etching from electrostatic discharge or wiping caused by impurities in the lubricating oil.

The frequency range of interest is a third area in selecting a variable for measurement. If, for example, the range includes high frequencies such as gear mesh, an acceleration measurement would be the best choice. On the other hand, if the measurement is limited to running frequency, either displacement or velocity, depending on the specific application, would be the best choice.

The frequency range of interest may also dictate the transducer. Vibration transducers are like windows through which sections of a vibration spectrum may be viewed. As shown in figure 5-3, noncontact displacement transducers are limited to an upper frequency of about 2,000 Hz by force limitations. Within that range, noncontact displacement measurements on moving shafts between 1,000 and 2,000 Hz are highly suspect due to the difficulty of eliminating surface imperfections appreciably below the values of displacement being measured.

A velocity pickup is limited by construction to a band of frequencies from approximately 10–1,500 Hz. Accelerometers have by far the broadest frequency response of all the vibration transducers. They are able to measure vibration at frequencies below 1 Hz to frequencies in excess of 50 kHz.

Thus, several areas must be considered in order to select a vibration measurement and transducer for a particular application. Machine construction and response, type of measurement, its response to changes in condition, whether the measurement is relative or absolute, and the frequency range of interest are a few of the factors to consider when selecting a measurement system best suited to represent machinery condition.

SHAFT DISPLACEMENT

A typical noncontact shaft-displacement measuring system consists of two transducers mounted at each bearing spaced 90° apart (figure

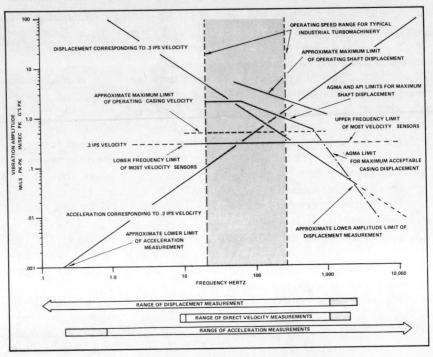

5–3—Measurement limitations.

5-4). In order to facilitate use of the system, shaft displacement probes should be mounted in the same plane, facing the same direction at each bearing of a multicase machine string. To obtain the correct orbital rotation on an oscilloscope, the horizontal probe used with a vertical probe mounted on top of a shaft looking down should be located on the right side of the vertical centerline looking in from the driver end (figure 5-5). This convention is used with an oscilloscope where a positive-going voltage (movement toward the probe in noncontact displacement measurement systems with a minus supply) directs the beam in an oscilloscope upward and to the right. Thus, in a conventional horizontal-vertical orientation, locating the horizontal probe on the right side of the vertical probe looking into the machine from one direction gives the same direction of motion on the oscilloscope screen as is occurring at the bearing.

If it becomes necessary to mount the vertical probe on the bottom of a shaft looking upward, this orientation is rotated 180°. The horizontal probe is then on the left side of the vertical viewed from the driver end

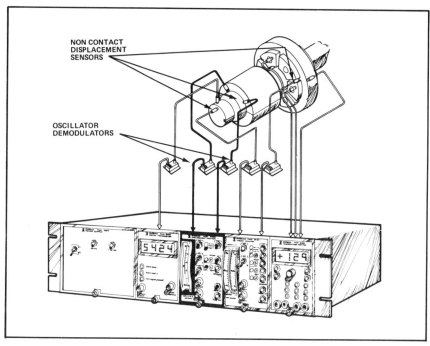

5–4—Typical shaft displacement measuring system.

and the resulting orbit is upside down. If the horizontal probe is placed on the right of an upward-looking vertical probe, the direction of the orbit viewed on an oscilloscope will be reversed.

Since it is often impossible to mount a displacement probe in the horizontal plane due to interference from the horizontal splits of the bearing and casing, current practice favors mounting each probe in the upper half of the bearing 45° either side of the vertical centerline. In this configuration, the probe on the right is arbitrarily called the horizontal probe and is applied to the horizontal axis of an oscilloscope to establish the correct orbital rotation. One must of course remember that the oscilloscope display is tilted 45° from actual shaft motion.

Displacement probes must also be positioned correctly in a longitudinal axis if the measurements are representative of machinery condition. As illustrated in figure 5-6, the shaft-bending mode and response at the point of measurement must be evaluated by calculation to ensure probes are not located at a nodal point. Additionally, probes should be located in the same position relative to their nodal points, either inboard or outboard, so that an end-to-end phase reversal repre-

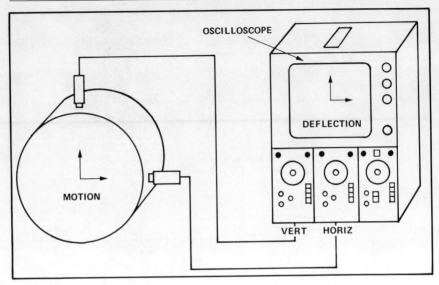

5–5—*Probe orientation for proper motion on an oscilloscope.*

sents the system's dynamic mode shape and not simply probe position.

A third consideration is implied in figure 5-6. As probe position is moved away from a nodal point, the measured displacement for a given rotor deflection increases. Although a probe location immediately adjacent to a radial bearing is preferred by most machinery manufacturers and forms the basis for their recommended vibration limits, it is sometimes impossible to achieve due to interference from components such as a thrust bearing. When this occurs, the probes must be moved away from the radial bearing where shaft amplitudes are likely to be much higher. Even though higher amplitudes can be safely tolerated with the probe in this position, it is a confusing situation which should be avoided whenever possible.

Before leaving the subject of shaft displacement measurements the desirability of installing a phase reference probe on each shaft should be mentioned. The phase reference probe is a standard displacement probe, located so that it observes a once-per-revolution mark on the shaft such as a keyway or a hole. The width of the mark should be at least twice the probe's tip diameter and a minimum of 1/8 in. (3 mm) deep. The probe should be gapped closer than a standard displacement probe, about 0.040 in. (1,000 μm), so that, as the mark passes, a spike of at least 10 volts DC is generated at the output of the oscillator demod-

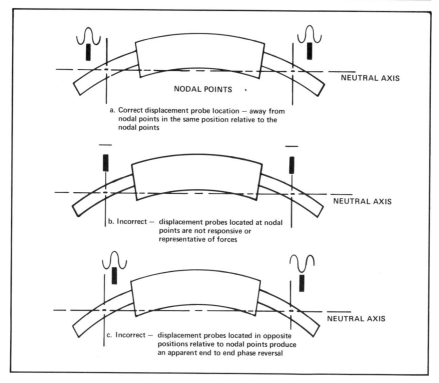

a. Correct displacement probe location — away from nodal points in the same position relative to the nodal points

NODAL POINTS   •

NEUTRAL AXIS

b. Incorrect — displacement probes located at nodal points are not responsive or representative of forces

NEUTRAL AXIS

c. Incorrect — displacement probes located in opposite positions relative to nodal points produce an apparent end to end phase reversal

NEUTRAL AXIS

5–6—Shaft bending mode determines measurement locations.

ulator. The spike may then be applied to the Z axis of an oscilloscope to produce a blank spot for a phase reference in the waveform and orbital presentation similar to that shown in figure 5-7. Note that a hole produces a negative-going pulse in the standard eddy-current displacement system, while some oscilloscopes may require a positive-going pulse for blanking. In this situation, either an inverting amplifier can be placed between the oscillator demodulator and oscilloscope or the oscilloscope can be modified to utilize a negative pulse.

The phase mark may be used for several purposes apart from referencing a waveform and orbit (figure 5-7). It can be fed to a tachometer for speed indication, used as a reference for the horizontal axis of a spectrum plot to construct "order" plots, used for phase measurement in balancing, and used to calculate a correction for shaft runout. How the latter is accomplished is explained below:

1. One cycle of a phase-referenced waveform obtained at a slow speed when the entire signal is assumed to be runout is divided into

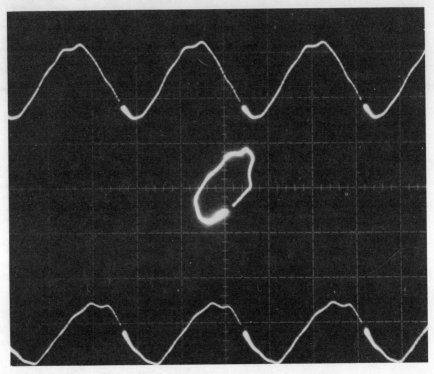

5-7—*Shaft displacement waveform and orbit.*

8–10 equal divisions. The cycle should begin at one phase mark and end at the next (figure 5-8a).

2. A second shaft waveform is obtained at speed and divided into the same number of divisions from phase mark to phase mark as the slow roll waveform (figure 5-8b).

3. The slow-roll amplitude at each division is subtracted from the at-speed waveform by reversing its direction to produce the corrected waveform (figure 5-8c).

A common mistake is to assume that runout always adds to vibration, and therefore the vibration read on a meter is higher than actual shaft movement by the amount of runout present. This assumption can be false and misleading. Depending on the phase relationship between runout and shaft motion, the two may add, subtract, cancel, or anything in between. Until the actual subtraction, one never knows.

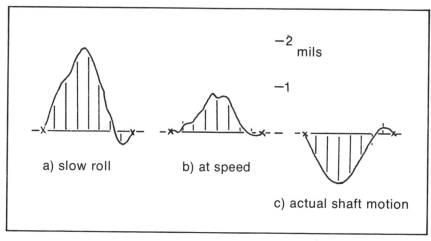

a) slow roll   b) at speed

c) actual shaft motion

5–8—Manual runout correction.

ROTOR POSITION–AXIAL AND RADIAL

Measuring the DC gap voltage obtained from a noncontact displacement probe mounted axially is a common method of measuring and monitoring a rotor's axial position. For best results, the axial position probe should be mounted as closely as possible to the thrust bearing to minimize the effects of temperature changes (10 in. or 25.4 cm is the maximum recommended by the American Petroleum Institute Standard 670). The axial position probe must be mounted to a solid part of the machine not subject to thermal transients and should observe a portion of the shaft or rotating thrust collar.

When measuring axial position from the thrust collar, the collar's position within the thrust bearing is unaffected by temperature. With this configuration, the only thermal changes to affect position measurements are those which occur in the housing between the bearing and the point of sensor attachment. In addition, the collar has a good surface for measuring with a noncontact eddy-current probe, and collar runout measurements are an excellent indicator of a shaft bow—as long as the collar itself is not warped.

When making an axial position measurement to the thrust collar, the measurement will not show the rotor's movement if the collar loosens or becomes detached from the shaft. In order to warn of a shaft movement if the thrust collar loosens, install a second axial position probe. The second probe provides redundancy for this vital measurement and should be positioned so it observes an integral part of the shaft, either the end or a step.

Regardless of the axial position probe's exact location, the measurement of axial vibration can be very important in analyzing problems such as misalignment and coupling lock-up. Thus, the surface observed by axial-position probes should have the same finish and runout tolerances required for radial probes.

In addition to thermal expansion of the shaft and bearing assembly, axial position measurements often drift in operation due to bearing deflection in response to changes in thrust load. In order to eliminate as much of this drift as possible and to provide a direct measure of bearing wear, a position probe may be attached to a thrust pad, observing the thrust collar (figure 5-9).

Some care must be exercised in setting the gap voltages on axial-position probes. Although there are several recommended methods, the basic objective is to ensure that the probe is at the approximate center of its linear range when the rotor is at the midpoint of its thrust movement. In figure 5-10, assume a total thrust movement of -0.018 in. and a probe linear range of 0.065 from -2 vDC to -15 vDC. Further assume that the direction of normal thrust is into the probe.

In this example the center of the linear range is -8.5 vDC $[(15-2)/2]$ from which the shaft will move 0.009 in. either side. At 200 mv/mil,

5–9—*Pad-mounted axial position probe.*

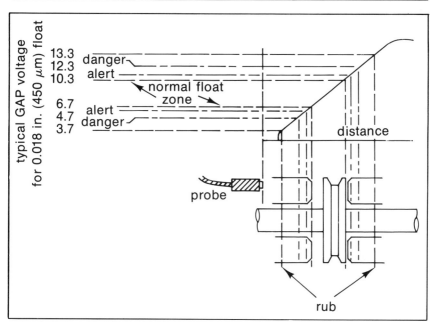

5–10—Position probe typical gap and alarm adjustments.

0.009 in. equals 1.8 volts movement. It is generally best to set axial probes with the shaft against the thrust bearing in the normal direction of thrust. With this accomplished, set an axial probe gap voltage equal to -6.7 vDC $[-8.5 - (-1.8)]$. As a final check, the voltage remaining should at least equal the babbit thickness on the thrust bearing so that a minor wipe will not move the probe out of its linear range. In this example 0.023 in. are left in the active direction before the probe goes out of the linear range which should be adequate. If not, open the probe gap slightly.

In cases where thrust clearance is large, make certain there is at least 0.015–0.020 in. of linear range remaining when the rotor is at the extreme end of its travel in the direction of normal thrust. The remaining linear range ensures the probe won't quit functioning during a thrust bearing problem, assuming that a thrust bearing problem or failure will be in the direction of normal thrust.

Radial position, measured with the DC gap voltage from a shaft displacement probe, can be an important measurement but it is often neglected. This is unfortunate, for radial position is an extremely valuable indicator of a gradual loss in bearing material. Although most hydrodynamic radial bearing failures are either caused or accompanied

5–11—Bearing failure unaccompanied by vibration.

by vibration, some fail with little or no change in vibration (figure 5-11). Static electric discharge ofen causes this type of failure. There have been numerous cases where measuring radial position saved costly damage following an interruption in the lubricating oil supply by allowing a quick assessment of whether or not bearing damage had occurred.

CASING VIBRATION

The major precaution in making measurements of casing vibration is to ensure that the transducer mounting is solid and does not have a natural frequency within the frequency range to be examined. There have been numerous cases of erroneous casing measurements caused by a resonant mounting where the measurement was in fact that of the mount's response and had nothing to do with machinery condition.

In general, cantilevered mounts should be avoided and single-point mounts such as shown in figure 5-12 used wherever possible.

Casing transducers are usually located at or on bearings on the stiffest section possible. Here again one must be concerned about natural frequencies. Casing transducers should never be mounted on inspection covers, unsupported areas of bearing caps, or on other light structural members where excessive excitation could exist at a natural frequency.

One word of caution about excitation at a natural frequency: even though it may be outside the frequency range under examination, a high excitation can produce nonlinearities in the system which will distort signals in other areas of the spectrum. Thus, always check to ensure there is nothing either within or outside the frequencies of interest which could overdrive and distort the measuring system.

High impedance cables from accelerometers are another concern when making casing measurements with accelerometers. The cables must not move to any great extent or else they can generate signals which add to the vibration signal obtained from the transducers.

Generally, the signal from a casing vibration transducer, especially an accelerometer, is much more complex than the signal obtained from a shaft transducer (figure 5-13). As a result, conditioning techniques which work well with shaft signals may not be effective or accurately represent machine condition when used with a casing transducer. For example, it is customary to perform an AC-to-DC conversion step on a shaft signal then display the result on a meter. In most cases, by the very nature of the signal, there will be little difference between the value filtered to running frequency and the unfiltered value. Since the velocity parameter introduces frequency and therefore will extend the range of measurement to higher frequencies, there may be a greater difference between filter in and filter out readings measured in terms of velocity.

The combination of its wide frequency range and dependency on frequency squared generally means that there will be a large difference between acceleration filtered to running frequency and unfiltered acceleration. Measuring acceleration is a little like trying to talk in a crowded, noisy room. One must use the signal conditioning techniques to separate and focus the information. This can be filtering, integration, or spectrum analysis, but it must be some method capable of sorting a complex signal into its component parts.

5–12—Recommended mounting for accelerometer.

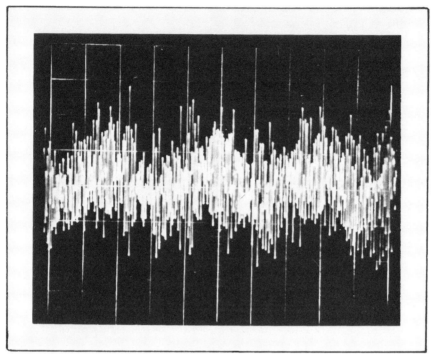

5–13—Accelerometer signal displayed in time domain.

BEARING TEMPERATURE

Of the measurable variables indicative of bearing load and performance, temperature is the easiest to measure and use. Over the years,
oil-drain temperature has been expected to provide external indications of bearing condition; however, tests have shown that a change in
oil-drain temperature may be an inadequate reflection of what is happening to the bearing itself. To cite an earlier example, thrust bearing
metal temperature measured with a thermocouple imbedded in a thrust
pad rose 100 °F (56 °C), approaching failure from overload. At the same
time oil-drain temperature and rotor position changed only 5 °F (3 °C)
and 0.002 in. (50 mm), respectively. Thus, thrust metal temperature was
the only one of three measured quantities which displayed a true
picture of what was occurring.

Tests run by various organizations have verified this observation.
Metal temperature, measured with a temperature transducer (ther-

mocouple or RTD) imbedded in a bearing, is a fast, responsive, easy-to-measure variable which provides an accurate picture of bearing condition and performance.

For best results, bearing temperature measurements should be re-recorded or trended, especially when changes are likely to occur, such as on startup and shutdown. A change in thrust temperature is probably one of the best indications of a locked coupling. It can also warn of unusual operating conditions which might alter the thrust balance of a machine and overload the thrust bearing.

Journal bearing temperatures often spike when a wipe occurs, but the condition is so transitory (often lasting only a few minutes) that it may not be observed unless the temperature is being recorded. Typically, a wipe is accompanied by a sudden temperature rise followed by a decrease to a value which is often less than the original temperature due to the larger clearances and increased oil flow.

Thrust bearing temperature

Measuring the metal temperature of a thrust bearing is most often accomplished with two or more temperature transducers, thermocouples, or RTDs imbedded in thrust pads about 0.060 in. (1.5 mm) from the surface. The temperature transducers are normally located at 75% of the pad's width and circumference in the direction of rotation (figure 5-14). This 75-75 position approximates the center of load and is far enough away from the edges of the pad so that it is not affected by the thermal gradient which exists to the cooler oil circulating around the bearing.

Figure 5-15, a photograph of a thrust pad subjected to overload, illustrates the necessity of offsetting an embedded temperature sensor if the measurement is to be representative of the highest temperature experienced by the pad. The point of highest load on this particular pad, shown by the blackened area, is centered at approximately 52% of the width and 76% of the circumference in the direction of rotation (clockwise). Despite the slight deviation in width between the location recommended for a temperature sensor and the actual point of maximum load on this specific pad, a sensor placed at the recommended location would have been well within the blackened area and thus close enough to the point of maximum load to warn of the overload condition.

For best protection, three or four temperature transducers should be installed and spaced at approximately equal intervals around the active side of a tilting pad thrust bearing. One or two more in the inactive thrust bearing are handy for a reference and for use if the machine

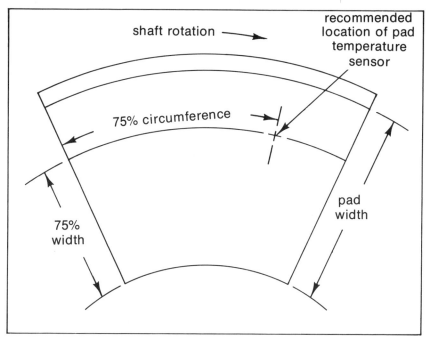

5–14—*Thrust bearing pad showing recommended 75%–75% location for locating bearing temperature sensors.*

operates on its inactive thrust. If only two temperature transducers are installed, they should be 90° apart in case the thrust bearing is tilted slightly, resulting in an unequal load distribution.

As mentioned in an earlier paragraph, thrust metal temperature generally varies directly with load. Most manufacturers will place an upper limit on bearing metal temperature at 230–240 °F (110–115 °C), and this value should not be exceeded without specific authorization from the thrust bearing manufacturer. Normally one should become concerned about thrust bearing temperature when it reaches 200–210 °F (90–100 °C). A spread of 20–30 °F (10–15 °C) is often observed between temperatures measured in the active side of a loaded thrust bearing. In addition to differences in load caused by one or more pads slightly higher than the rest, such a temperature spread could be due to slight differences in the depth of the temperature transducer itself.

A certain amount of care must be exercised in leading the temperature-sensing wires out of the machine casing as they often must be routed around the bearing in areas of rather tight clearance. It should go without saying that the exit fitting from the machine must be oil-tight.

5–15—*Discolored thrust pad illustrating point of maximum load.*

Journal bearing temperature

Journal bearing load is often an indication of misalignment. Here again metal temperature, measured with a temperature transducer imbedded in the bearing, is an easily measured, responsive variable which indicates load as well as bearing performance.

The temperature transducer should of course be mounted in the bottom half of the bearing in the area of maximum load. This is generally about 20° off the vertical centerline in the direction of rotation.

The same mounting considerations and temperature limits discussed in the previous section for measuring thrust metal temperature apply to the measurement of journal bearing temperature.

PRESSURE

Pressure measurements are generally straightforward and easy to make. One precaution, however, particularly when measuring the differential pressure on a centrifugal compressor balance drum: the pressure gauge should have its own static port into the low-pressure chamber of the balance drum or there may be an error due to a flow-induced pressure drop that can occur at the balance line exit from the machine as flow rates increase.

TORSIONAL VIBRATION

Of the measurements discussed thus far, torsional vibration is probably the least familiar. Torsional vibration is an alternating shaft twist which, unlike many types of lateral vibration, always produces stress reversals. These stress reversals may, in extreme cases, lead to fatigue failures. Since torsional vibration is a twisting motion or instantaneous change in shaft speed, it is generally not evident externally, except possibly in the case of gears where the presence of torsional vibration will produce increased noise. Thus, a serious torsional problem may not be recognized until a catastrophic failure occurs, such as a shaft fracture.

A torsional problem occurs when a natural source of excitation coincides with a torsional resonance. The excitation can be produced by anything causing a pulsating torque (surge, gear teeth inaccuracies, etc.) by shock at startup or by sum or difference frequencies such as occur during startup of a synchronous motor.

Torsional vibration is measured in two principal ways: with strain gauges attached to the shaft, or as a variation in angular velocity sensed by a magnetic or eddy-current probe observing a gear attached to the shaft. The first method is complex, requiring slip rings or telemetry to recover the signal. Since the latter method requires only a gear located such that it can be observed by a noncontact pickup, it is favored for most measurements.

The place along a shaft where a measurement is to be made is more critical in torsional analysis than in lateral analysis because it is much easier to recognize a nodal point when making lateral measurements and the point of measurement can be easily shifted. Whereas the maximum stress typically occurs at a torsional node, a node is, by definition, the point of zero motion. If the measurement is made with strain gauges, it should be made close to the node while angular velocity measurements must be made away from a node where the motion is at a maximum. The method of measurement thus determines its location.

Because of this relationship between position and response, the expected mode shape should be calculated prior to making a measurement; then locate the transducers accordingly.

Prior to analyzing the torsional signal obtained from a gear, it must be frequency demodulated. This step produces an AC output representative of the frequency variation as the gear teeth pass the transducer.

Torsional vibration, measured with a noncontact pickup observing a gear, may have errors due to tooth spacing and runout. Both can be significant and affect the final results of the analysis.

Whether obtained from strain gauges or by frequency demodulation of a tooth-passing frequency, the torsional signal is spectrum analyzed to obtain its principal components. The torsional components, their amplitude and position in the spectrum, are analyzed in exactly the same fashion as lateral vibration. Although allowable amplitudes have not been established for torsional vibration, a Campbell diagram of frequency versus rpm is often useful to locate potential problems.

6

Instrumentation for Recording and Analysis

The newcomer to vibration analysis is often faced with new, perhaps perplexing terms used to describe the instrumentation he will need to master. It is important to know the instruments themselves, the features which are particularly useful in machinery analysis, and some basic terminology. This information should provide a starting point for the selection of the instruments best suited for a specific application.

VIBRATION METERS

A vibration meter (figure 6-1) is an inexpensive and simple-to-use basic instrument which should be a part of any vibration monitoring program. A typical vibration meter is battery powered with replaceable batteries, uses a seismic pickup (generally velocity), and will have provisions for measuring amplitude in either velocity or displacement units in several ranges. It should also have some means for testing the internal batteries so the user can determine when replacement is required. Although vibration meters are available which combine sensor and meter in one housing, the type shown in figure 6-1 with a separate sensor connected by 4–5 ft of flexible cable is somewhat easier to use in confined locations and around obstructions where it may be difficult to view the meter on a combined unit with the sensor in a preferred location and orientation. It should go without saying that a vibration meter should be as small and lightweight as possible, ruggedly packaged for maximum resistance to abuse, and have some means for carrying (such as a neck strap) which leaves both hands free.

Electronically, a typical vibration meter is a simple device consisting of a selectable gain circuit for ranging, an integrator which can be switched in to transform the velocity signal from the pickup to displacement, and an AC-to-DC converter to change the AC signal to a DC value which can be read on the meter.

6–1—*Typical vibration meter (courtesy IRD Mechanalysis).*

TIME VERSUS
FREQUENCY DOMAIN ANALYSIS

Of the four types of analysis instruments to be introduced, three are classified as frequency analyzers while the fourth operates in the time domain. As illustrated in figure 6-2, time and frequency domain simply describe two different vantage points from which a given signal may be viewed. In the time domain there is a two-dimensional picture of amplitude versus time on the vertical and horizontal axes, respectively. In the frequency domain the time domain is seen end on; amplitude is still in the vertical axis, but the horizontal axis now represents frequency. It makes no difference whether the time domain signal is a series of discrete identifiable sine waves, as in the output from an accelerometer, or is a single complex waveform of the type normally

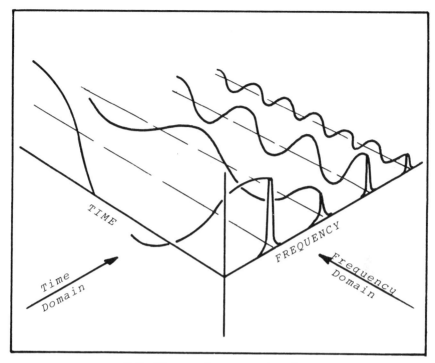

6–2—Time vs. frequency domain.

obtained from a noncontact displacement transducer, for the latter can be represented by a series of sine waves.

Since the frequency of a signal is inversely proportional to its period, it can easily be transformed from one domain into the other if its amplitude and either period or frequency are known. Thus, there is no mystery about amplitude or frequency domain. Simply stated, they are like viewing a signal through one of two windows placed at a 90° angle. Which window is best depends on the purpose of the measurement and what is to be explored.

OSCILLOSCOPES

Of all the instrumentation available to the analyst, an oscilloscope probably gives the best intuitive picture of a machine's characteristics. Although an oscilloscope is primarily a time-domain instrument, that is, one axis represents time, it can also be used to display the lissajou or orbit created by the signals obtained from two shaft sensors spaced 90°

apart. This provides a greatly magnified dynamic view of a shaft's motion in its bearing. The oscilloscope is also used to display the frequency domain output from a real-time analyzer.

Oscilloscopes are available in a range of sizes and are used in a variety of ways in machinery analysis. A small portable unit (figure 6-3) is valuable monitoring data being recorded during field data acquisition and can be very useful troubleshooting machinery instrumentation. For analysis work including oscilloscope photography, a laboratory-type oscilloscope (figure 6-4) is generally best. The laboratory oscilloscope may be a bench unit or configured for rack mounting, depending on preference. A large-screen display oscilloscope is sometimes used in machinery analysis and is particularly useful when several people must view a display simultaneously. It is not, however, a general-purpose instrument nor can it be used for photography.

For use in machinery analysis, an oscilloscope must have at least two channels and four are desirable. With a two-channel oscilloscope one can display both signals obtained from shaft displacement probes at a bearing in either a waveform or orbital format or observe input and output during tape recording to ensure the signal is not being distorted. By adding two more channels, horizontal and vertical waveforms or the

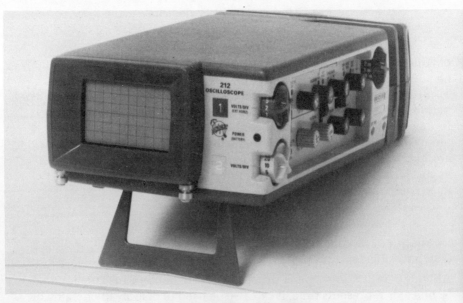

6–3—Portable oscilloscope.

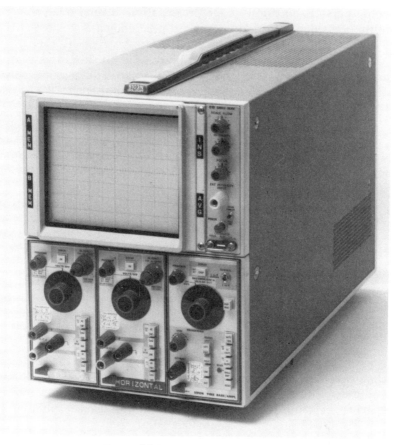

6–4—Typical laboratory oscilloscope.

orbits at both ends of a machine or across a coupling can be displayed. This is often quite valuable in vibration analysis.

Generally speaking, all available oscilloscopes have a frequency response which is more than adequate for machinery analysis. There is certainly no need to pay a premium for the high-frequency response required for electronic testing. Likewise, a dual-beam oscilloscope is not needed in machinery analysis. Even on a four-channel oscilloscope, a chopped single beam provides acceptable results.

In some applications a storage option is very desirable. For example, it is often difficult to observe data at very low frequencies, either from slow-speed machinery or during slow roll, without the ability to hold and store an oscilloscope presentation. Likewise, a storage capability is needed to observe transient phenomena or to sort out a very complex signal which may be varying irregularly with time.

An oscilloscope used for machinery analysis should have an easily accessible means for adding a blanking pulse as a phase reference. Since most phase references will be a slot or other depression observed by a proximity probe, the oscilloscope should blank on a negative-going pulse. If a positive pulse is required, some type of adapter will be needed to achieve the desired blanking. A typical phase pulse produced by a proximity probe is usually 7 volts, so an oscilloscope used for machinery analysis should require no more than 5 volts for full blanking.

Often, one will need to switch between a waveform and orbital presentation. Thus, a specific control is preferred. The oscilloscope in figure 6-4 can be obtained with a three-position switch in the upper-right corner of the time base for switching between a waveform and single sweep or continuous X-Y.

For oscilloscope photography, single-sweep capability is necessary. Most oscilloscopes will have single sweep in the waveform mode; a few will include single sweep in X-Y or the orbital mode. The latter is highly desirable and will greatly improve the quality of the oscilloscope photographs. On the oscilloscope shown in figure 6-4, the duration of the single sweep in the X-Y mode is equal to the setting on the time base. Thus, for a true single sweep the time base must be set at a value equal to the time required to complete an orbit. In most cases, however, leaving the time base at the setting used to photograph the waveform will produce acceptable results.

Oscilloscope photography is very important from the standpoint of maintaining permanent records. It should go without saying that any analysis-type oscilloscope purchased for use with machinery should be equipped with a camera adapter. The graduation on the face of the oscilloscope will photograph most clearly if the oscilloscope is fitted with a side-lighted graticule. An oscilloscope camera with viewing window (figure 6-5) is best, for it permits viewing the signal without removing the camera from the oscilloscope. The camera itself must have provisions for manual shutter control.

To obtain a photograph of the type shown in figure 6-6, the oscilloscope is first placed in the time domain or waveform mode and the two waveforms are positioned in the upper and lower halves of the graticule. When the signals are positioned, the oscilloscope is shifted to single sweep and triggered to verify operation. The camera aperture

6–5—Typical oscilloscope camera.

should be set to approximately 5.6. Next, the viewing window on the camera is closed, the shutter is opened in the time-exposure mode, and a single sweep is initiated. The shutter is then closed. Without pulling the film and with the shutter closed, the viewing window is opened and the oscilloscope is set for an orbital presentation. The orbit is centered, shifted to single sweep, and tested as before. Next, the viewing window is closed, the shutter opened, and the orbit single sweep initiated. Finally, the shutter is closed and the photograph removed from the camera.

If everything is done correctly, a clear, bright orbit and waveform along with clear scope graduations are the result. If the orbit and waveform are not bright enough, increase the intensity on the oscilloscope or open the aperture wider, recognizing that the latter will also make the graduations brighter. Usually, keep the aperture at approxi-

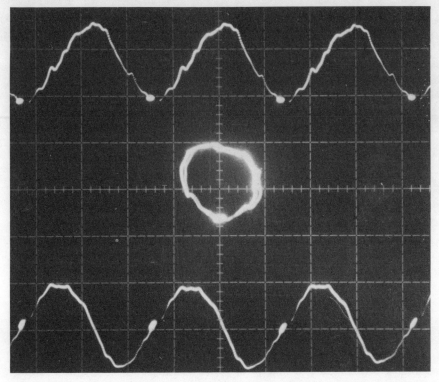

6–6—*Typical oscilloscope photograph of a shaft displacement waveform and orbit.*

mately 5.6 and adjust both the trace intensity and graticule illumination to produce the desired results.

Oscilloscope photography is very important. An oscilloscope photograph is often the only record of a machine's performance; therefore, it must be in focus and clear and display all the necessary information if it has any value. Although thousands of these photographs are taken, most are of poor quality. It is only with practice and patience that one can take high-quality photographs. Finally, don't forget to label the photograph with the amplifier and time-base settings used. A beautiful photograph is not much value without the units.

MANUALLY TUNED FILTERED ANALYZERS

A manually tuned filtered analyzer is very similar to the vibration meter with the added ability to select a specific frequency for measurement. The instrument thus becomes a powerful analysis tool for extracting information to determine the origin of a problem as well as its severity. A typical filtered analyzer (figure 6-7) will have controls to select meter range as well as measurement in either velocity or displacement units. Some analyzers can use the input from an accelerometer and accordingly will allow measurement directly in acceleration units or integrated to either velocity or displacement. Differentiating a displacement or velocity signal to velocity or acceleration does not serve any useful purpose in machinery analysis and is seldom included in an analyzer intended for machinery application.

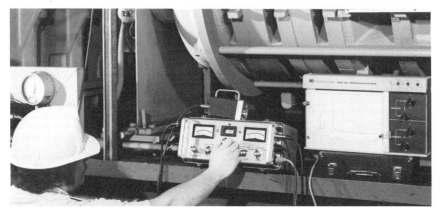

6–7—Typical vibration analyzer (courtesy IRD Mechanalysis).

The analyzer will have a switch for switching the filter either in or out to make overall or narrow-band measurements. Most machinery vibration analyzers will include two filter bandwidths: a broad band for searching and a narrow band for pinpointing a specific frequency. Although not included on all machinery-vibration analyzers, a high-pass or low-pass filter capability in addition to the bandpass filter is very handy searching for signals or when it becomes necessary to clean up a signal prior to detailed analysis.

In most manually tuned analyzers, the filter frequency is read on a graduated dial to some fixed index. A typical vibration analyzer will not attempt to cover its entire frequency range in one continuous step but will have three or more ranges controlled by a range switch. The range switch will typically increase the filter frequency by multiples of 10 or some other convenient value. One thing to look for in this area: it is much more convenient if running speed and its second harmonic for most machinery being analyzed are on a single frequency range.

A vibration analyzer should be battery powered, preferably from rechargeable batteries, to permit long periods of use in the field and as small and light as possible commensurate with the need for rugged packaging to withstand normal use.

For accessories, the analyzer should have a strobe output and strobe for field balancing. A center-zero tuning dial to indicate when the filter is exactly centered is another convenient feature. Finally, some means to accommodate pickups of varying types and sensitivities can be very valuable. It is often desirable to accomplish a frequency analysis on signals obtained from pickups other than that furnished with the analyzer—an installed shaft displacement pickup, for example. In this situation it is much more effective and less costly if one analyzer can be adapted to a variety of pickups and measure the signal from each directly and in the proper units.

An AC filtered output is often handy for oscilloscope viewing of a signal. If the raw and filtered outputs are displayed together on an oscilloscope, one can immediately determine whether or not the dominant frequency has been found, sometimes a difficult task with complex signals. The AC output can also be used to display filtered orbits; however, a dual channel analyzer is needed to accomplish this task effectively.

DC outputs of amplitude and frequency can be used to construct spectrum plots; however, this is a time-consuming and not particularly effective method. Of course, the advantage of a DC output proportional to amplitude is that it can be used to supply a chart recorder and thereby permits continuous close surveillance of a critical vibration value.

AUTOMATICALLY TUNED (TRACKING) ANALYZERS

In addition to manual tuning, an automatically tuned or tracking analyzer has provisions for using an external reference signal to tune the filter to the frequency of the reference automatically. Generally, the reference signal is originated by a once-per-revolution event or mark on the shaft, with the result that the filter remains locked into running speed even though speed may vary. Built-in or separate accessory networks to multiply and/or divide the frequency of the reference signal may be used to allow the filter to track running speed from a reference at a synchronous multiple of once per revolution or to track a multiple of running frequency using a running frequency reference.

In addition to tuning the filter, the reference signal provides a reference from which the phase lag to a point on the vibration waveform can be measured electronically. This is particularly useful in balancing, for with a vibration and reference input the analyzer will provide outputs of frequency, filtered amplitude, and phase.

A tracking analyzer generally has two types of outputs: visual outputs, (usually digital) of amplitude, frequency, and phase and DC outputs proportional to each variable for an X-Y plotter. It is very useful if DC outputs in both rectangular (Bode) and polar (Nyquist) coordinates are available.

In addition to the features described, a tracking analyzer designed for machinery analysis should include a reference input to accommodate either a positive or negative-going signal and to vary the reference signal voltage level required to trigger the tracking circuit. While most reference signals are generated by a proximity probe and pulse in the negative direction, it is sometimes necessary to track a positive-pulse signal. A voltage level offset adjustment is necessary to ensure that the analyzer tracks the reference pulse and is not confused by any vibration or shaft defects which might create additional low-level pulses between the reference marks (figure 6-8). In the left-hand illustration, the too-low trigger level results in more than one pulse per revolution; in

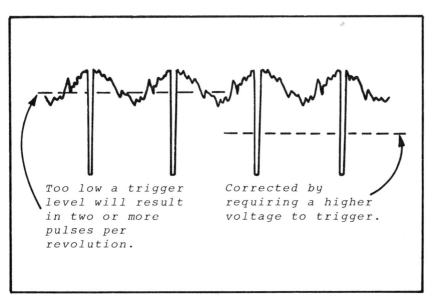

Too low a trigger level will result in two or more pulses per revolution.

Corrected by requiring a higher voltage to trigger.

6–8—*False tachometer triggering due to a scratch or other defect.*

the right-hand illustration, this can be corrected by simply raising the voltage required to trigger. Since trigger signals may vary greatly in amplitude, one fixed value might not always work. One way to solve both problems is to use a reference input circuit which only looks at the absolute value of the trigger pulse and automatically selects a trigger level about 10–20% below the maximum amplitude.

A phase-coherent filtered AC output displays the filtered signal for analysis.

The tracking analyzer should have a means for manually tuning the analyzer as well as a sweep generator which will automatically tune the filter across some frequency band at the maximum rate permitted for accuracy. With this feature, the analyzer can construct spectrum plots although much more time is required compared to a real-time analyzer.

Since phase is a repeating variable like a clock dial and the DC output proportional to phase from a tracking analyzer generally increases from 0–360°, some means must be provided to prevent the large changes in voltage which result if the measured phase happens to swing back and forth across 0–360°. Recognizing this difficulty, most tracking analyzers have a control to shift phase by 180° and thereby move the measurement away from the discontinuity at 0–360°. Another way to accomplish the same result automatically is to have a DC output proportional to phase equivalent of 540° from −90° through 360° to +90°. This way, the discontinuity is eliminated within the overlap.

The ability to adjust the input sensitivity so the tracking analyzer can be used with a variety of pickups is highly desirable, just as it was on the manually tuned analyzer. Likewise, provisions for single or double integration should be included so that the display can be in terms of the desired engineering units.

As another performance specification, the analyzer should be able to track speed changes accurately to approximately 1,000 rpm/sec. Recall that establishing a rate at which a filter is to be swept also fixes its minimum bandpass. As a result some tracking analyzers will have provisions for selecting between a broad or narrow bandpass filter. The broad filter is for use at high rates of change in speed; the narrow filter is available for increased accuracy at low rates of change in speed. This feature can be advantageous.

Finally, in selecting a tracking analyzer be aware of its dynamic range. It is not uncommon to have amplitude changes in excess of 50 dB from a slow-roll condition to the maximum amplitude at a machine's critical speed; if the analyzer is incapable of tracking both amplitude and phase over this range, one might not be able to obtain accurate data.

A dual-channel tracking analyzer capable of tracking two simultaneous signals to the same reference is often very valuable. With a second channel, the analyzer can display filtered orbits or phase and amplitude information at both ends of a machine for two-plane balancing.

REAL-TIME SPECTRUM ANALYZERS

An instrument capable of continuously transforming a time domain signal into its frequency domain spectral components at a rate so the result can be viewed on an oscilloscope and any changes in the time signal will always be reflected by corresponding changes in the spectrum is a real-time spectrum analyzer, RTSA. Thus, both time compression and Fast Fourier Transform analyzers qualify under this definition, but the tuned analyzer capable of presenting the same information on a plotter over a much longer time interval does not. However, most real-time analyzers do not operate in real time over their entire frequency range.

An FFT analyzer employs a mathematical procedure to compute the frequency-domain equivalent of a time-domain signal. The Fast Fourier Transform procedure employed in FFT analyzers differs from a mathematical Fourier Transform in that the FFT is performed on discrete or sampled data and is accomplished with an algorithm or computational procedure designed for maximum efficiency on a computer.

A real-time analyzer is often called a 1,024-line analyzer or a 400-line analyzer. In simple terms, this expresses the number of segments a spectrum is divided or the resolution which can be expected on a given band. For example, if a 500-line analyzer examines frequencies to 20 kHz, the analysis resolution will be 20,000/500 or 40 Hz. Actual resolution as defined by a 3-dB bandwidth will be somewhat broader than the quotient of the frequency range and number of lines, depending on the specific analyzer.

The term *aliasing* and the need for antialiasing filters should likewise be understood. As shown in figure 6-9, a sampling rate that is too slow for the frequencies will create a false low-frequency signal or alias. This phenomenon can be seen in western movies where a slowing stagecoach wheel will appear to rotate backward, stop, and then rotate forward at a decreasing speed as the stagecoach comes to a stop. The backward rotation is caused by a film framing speed which is slower than the time it takes for a spoke to rotate into the position occupied by the adjacent spoke when the previous frame was exposed. The slow backward rotation is thus an alias produced by the framing

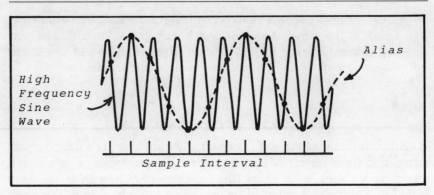

*High
Frequency
Sine
Wave*

Alias

Sample Interval

6–9—*Aliasing.*

speed of the camera. When the frame speed is synchronized with the time required for the spokes to rotate into the same position they occupied on the last frame, the wheel appears frozen. Finally, as the wheel continues to slow, the frame speed becomes high enough to picture the spokes accurately, and the wheel appears to turn in the right direction at the right speed.

The same analogy holds true for real-time analyzers; if the incoming signal contains frequencies in excess of those that can be accommodated at the sampling rate selected for the particular band, a low-frequency alias will be formed. To eliminate this problem, real-time analyzers use a sharp antialiasing filter which is automatically set by the band selector to cut off frequencies above the upper limit of each individual band before the signal is digitized.

Since both types of analyzers operate on discrete or sampled data even though the samples themselves may be continuous, the actual input will be truncated (figure 6-10). In this example, the time-domain signal is obviously a single-frequency sine wave; however, the sample window does not begin and end at the same zero point in the cycle and will introduce spurious frequencies sometimes called leakage. Since most time-domain signals are a mixture of frequencies, it is impossible to adjust the sample window to avoid truncation. However, in order to minimize the leakage effect, a weighting function is applied to the sampled data (figure 6-11). Note that the weighting function progressively attenuates the signal toward the edge of the windows and minimizes leakage.

However, as is usually the case, the correction of one problem requires a compromise in another area, and weighting is no exception. While the weighting function reduces leakage, it does so at the expense

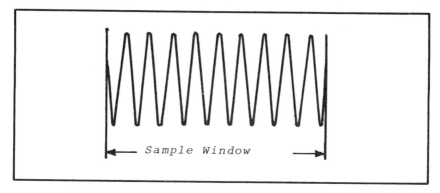

6–10—*Continuous signal truncated through time sampling.*

of resolution; the effective filter bandwidth is increased with the amount of increase, depending on the specific weighting function used.

There are many different weighting functions. A weighting function is generally named after the person(s) who developed the equation, and different analyzers use different weighting functions depending on the manufacturer's preference.

Since an FFT analyzer employs a computational procedure, it is a

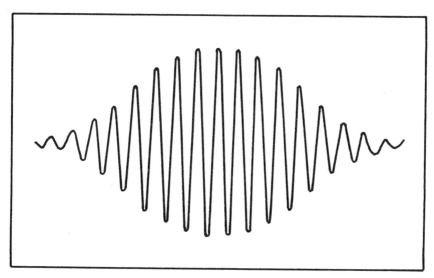

6–11—*Weighted time domain waveform.*

flexible instrument which can do more than convert a time domain signal into its spectral representation. For example, many FFT analyzers have provisions for calculating correlation and coherence functions which can be used in mechanical testing. Perhaps most important, phase is preserved within the FFT and can be extracted on many analyzers.

Real-time rate is another area that should be discussed briefly. Although the present trend appears to be toward analyzers with lower real-time frequency capability, this is not desirable for machinery analysis. In many cases, the fluctuation of a spectral component, whether regular or irregular, and the rate of fluctuation provide valuable clues as to the producing mechanism. If the analyzer is too slow, i.e., its real time frequency is too low, this valuable information is lost. As a word of caution, always check the memory period of the analyzer to ensure the rate of a beat or fluctuation is in fact at the frequency counted and is not being influenced by the speed of the analyzer.

A real-time analyzer must have provisions for averaging in order to obtain statistically accurate data which can be used for comparison. Two or more memories are a valuable feature to facilitate comparing data under different conditions. Some analyzers will permit difference and ratio comparisons between spectra held in memory for a more quantitative assessment of changes.

In addition to facilities for averaging, the real-time analyzer should have a peak hold mode for holding the highest amplitude achieved in any location. This feature is used in three principal ways. First, the envelope produced by connecting amplitude peaks at running frequency as it moves across the analysis range during startup or coastdown is a rectangular coordinate or Bode plot of amplitude response versus speed. Second, it is often quite valuable to determine the maximum amplitude reached by a fluctuating component such as subsynchronous instability. Often the only way to assess the effect of a change is to compare the peak and average values over some time period. Finally, when impacts are involved, the maximum amplitude reached by each component must be known.

Provision for capturing a transient is another valuable feature which should be included in a real-time analyzer. Transient capture is particularly valuable when impact-exciting a component or structure to determine its natural frequency or frequencies.

Four other capabilities can be quite valuable in real-time analyzers. First, the ability to normalize the frequency axis to orders of running speed can be helpful in some situations. Some analyzers will have this function built in, while others will require an auxiliary adapter.

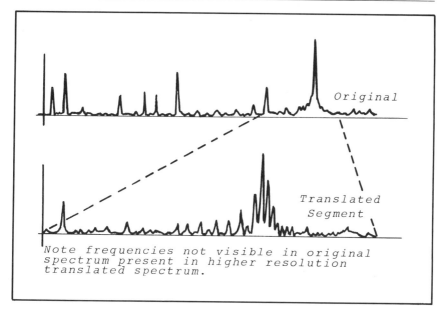

Original

Translated
Segment

Note frequencies not visible in original spectrum present in higher resolution translated spectrum.

6–12—Frequency zoom or translation.

Second, a dynamic cascade or waterfall spectrum where one spectrum is stacked on top of another often provides the only method to observe what is happening during a transient. This can be a particularly valuable feature for accomplishing a large number of startup, shutdown, or dynamic-response analyses.

Third, the capacity to increase resolution at a selected center frequency, sometimes called zoom because of the camera analogy, is often the only way to sort out a complex spectrum with closely spaced components. As shown in figure 6-12, a zoom or translation capability allows an RTSA to expand a segment of a high-frequency spectrum into a lower analysis range and thereby achieve vastly improved resolution. This feature is particularly valuable in gear analysis where individual, closely spaced, high-frequency spectral components must be identified. Finally, a real-time analyzer should be computer compatible for automatic data management or analysis.

DATA ACQUISITION AND RECORDING INSTRUMENTS

Magnetic tape recorders

Virtually every program of machinery analysis will eventually use a magnetic tape recorder to collect and store dynamic data for later analysis and/or comparison. A magnetic tape recorder allows data to be acquired at a remote site then brought to a central location for more detailed analysis. In this way, the recorder eliminates the need to expose expensive analysis equipment to a hostile field environment. Magnetic tape recording is also used at startup and shutdown where it provides the only practical method of collecting and preserving simultaneous transient data from multiple sources for detailed analysis. Two modes of recording, direct and FM, are used in machinery analysis.

Direct recording

In direct recording, an AC input signal is amplified and applied to a winding within the record head, where it appears as a varying magnetic flux across a small gap in the head. As a magnetic recording tape is passed across the record head, the flux variations produce a corresponding permanently magnetized variation in the ferrous-oxide coating on the tape. When the magnetized tape is passed across a reproduce head, the process is reversed; the magnetic variations on the tape induce a voltage in the reproduce head which is amplified and then made available as an output.

Since the reproduced signal level is proportional to the rate of change and not the magnitude of the flux, the response of the direct recording process falls off at low frequencies. For this reason, it is impossible to reproduce low frequencies in the direct mode; the response of most recorders operating in the direct mode will fall off steeply below about 50 Hz. High-frequency limitations occur in direct because the wavelength of the recorded signal becomes increasingly small compared to the head gap. The high-frequency response of a given tape recorder operating in the direct mode can be improved by using higher tape speeds.

By itself, the direct-record reproduce system is not very linear and needs an equalizing network to be of any practical use. The equalizing network is built into the recorder and may be adjustable as part of the recorder calibration procedure to attain maximum linearity.

Compared to the FM mode, direct recording offers a higher high-frequency response for a given tape speed. A typical instrumentation-grade recorder might have a frequency range from 50 Hz to 50 kHz in direct and is thus used primarily for broadband signals from acceleration transducers.

A disadvantage of direct recording is that phase and other nonlinearities are introduced which can distort the signal. Although this is not generally a problem with the type, shape, and frequency of signals commonly recorded in machinery analysis, an analyst contemplating the use of direct recording should be aware of the potential for a problem.

Perhaps the major disadvantage of the direct mode is the amplitude variation which occurs across the frequency range. A typical specified amplitude deviation is $\pm$ 3 dB, which means that the output may vary from 0.7 to 1.4 times the input across the bandwidth of the recorder. While a variation of this magnitude is probably not objectionable when working with high-frequency acceleration signals, it can cause difficulty at the low frequencies where severity is nearly always based on amplitude.

Converted music recorders have and are being used in machinery analysis. Although a music recorder represents a much smaller investment than an instrumentation-grade recorder, it is not designed for this application nor does it have the accuracy required.

Frequency modulated (FM) recording

In FM recording, the tape heads and techniques for magnetizing the tape and detecting flux changes are the same as for the direct mode. Here the similarity ends; in FM recording the amplitude of the input signal is used to frequency-modulate a high-frequency carrier. As illustrated in figure 6-13, the frequency modulation process translates the amplitude and frequency of the input signal to a shift in the carrier frequency and the rate at which the shift occurs, respectively. During reproduction, the amplitude and frequency of the original signal are reconstructed by demodulating the signal received from the reproduce head.

Since amplitude is represented by a shift in the carrier frequency, an FM recorder can record signals down to DC. In fact, this is one way an FM recorder is calibrated: a DC input at a specified amplitude is introduced at the input and the carrier frequency is measured for the correct deviation.

The FM system of recording/reproduction is inherently more linear in both amplitude and phase than the direct system. Because the amplitude of the reproduced signal depends solely on the frequency deviation of the recorded carrier and has nothing to do with the magnetization of the tape, amplitude errors can be kept below 1 dB. For the same reason, partial demagnetization caused by tape wear or poor storage conditions has less influence on FM data than direct data.

Although FM recording offers significant advantages in machinery applications such as excellent linearity and accurate reproduction, it has a

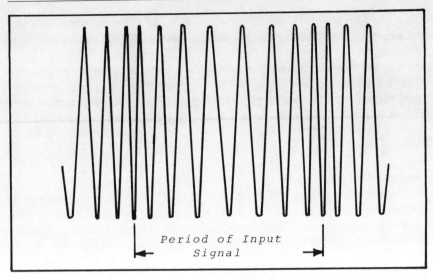

Period of Input Signal

6-13—Frequency modulation process.

frequency response which is generally about 1/5 to 1/10 the direct response at the same tape speed. As in direct recording, the frequency response in FM can be increased by increasing tape speed; however, in FM the change in frequency response is directly proportional to the change in tape speed, e.g., doubling tape speed doubles frequency response.

While FM is largely independent of tape characteristics, the speed stability of the transport is very important; any flutter will cause corresponding changes in the carrier. For this reason an FM tape recorder typically costs more than a direct tape recorder.

Most instrumentation-grade tape recorders using ½-in. and 1-in. tape are built to IRIG (Inter-Range Instrumentation Group) standards, which mean that head gap, track spacing, and carrier frequencies will all be the same, regardless of the manufacturer, to permit tape interchangeability. IRIG standards do not include ¼-in. tape recorders, and, as a result, there are many configurations available ranging from 4 to 8 channels which may or may not produce interchangeable tapes. If one plans on buying a ¼-in. instrumentation tape recorder and wishes to interchange tapes, check the specific recorders to determine if a tape recorded on one can be reproduced on the other.

Portability is an important consideration in the selection of a tape recorder for machinery analysis. Ideally, the recorder should be as light as possible and battery powered; however, this is not always possible. If the recorder is used at a single location, 65 lbs. is the maximum weight that can be conveniently handled by one person. If it is to be carried as baggage on an airplane, it can't weigh more than 70 lbs. packed in a rugged protective container.

There are several cassette recorders available with both direct and FM capability. Although these recorders are smaller, lighter, and less expensive than a reel-to-reel unit, they generally cannot compare in performance with a reel-to-reel recorder. While the cassette recorder may be adequate for recording displacement signals to 1,000 Hz, it is usually not adequate for recording acceleration signals above 10 kHz.

All the instrumentation-grade tape recorders which would be considered for machinery analysis have the required controls for recording, reproducing, and operating the transport. A footage or turn counter is necessary to determine the start and stop of a specific recording within a tape. Some users will annotate the tape on a voice channel; others prefer a written tape log.

A large tape recorder (½ or 1-in. tape) used for machinery analysis should have provisions for simultaneously reproducing a minimum of three channels without sacrificing a record channel. Three-channel simultaneous reproduction, two data channels, and one phase-reference channel are necessary to display a phase-referenced orbit off tape.

A tape recorder which will be used with preamplifiers should likewise have a convenient means of determining the input signal level to each channel. This can be accomplished with a monitor oscilloscope or meter; however, if the unit must be manually plugged into each channel, the process can be time consuming and prone to error. The best method on recorders not equipped with an integral input level device is to manufacture an input switching matrix to which the input-level monitor can be plugged and selectively switched into each channel.

Like so many other things, making consistently good tape recordings requires some experience. It is a good idea to monitor the input signal on one channel of a two-channel oscilloscope and the output on the other. In this fashion, any distortion or clipping within the tape recorder can be immediately detected.

As a final word of caution, a tape recorder is a sophisticated instrument representing a large investment which, perhaps more than any other single unit, can affect the results of a machinery analysis program. Before selecting this or any other major instrument, get comments from people who are using similar instrumentation for the same purpose in the same environment.

Amplifiers

Although amplifier circuits are used in vibration monitors and analyzers, this discussion covers separate, self-contained instrumentation amplifiers used to boost a low-level signal from a transducer to an optimum value for recording or analysis. Many tape recorders have provisions for varying their input gain but most are continuous potentiometer-type adjustments and require some sort of calibration signal to determine the gain setting. For this reason, the recorder should be set for unity gain with a specific maximum input voltage, usually 1 volt rms, and a fixed-gain, step-instrumentation amplifier should be inserted ahead of the recorder to boost the signal from the transducer to this value.

The specifications of a typical FM instrumentation tape recorder with a full-scale input level of 1 volt rms and a signal-to-noise ratio of 45 dB is a good example of why preamplification is often necessary. Translated, these specifications establish the noise floor of the recorder, which limits the lowest-level signal that can be recorded to 45 dB, or a factor of 178 below rated input. Based on a rated input of 1 volt rms, the noise floor is about 5.6 mv rms, corresponding to approximately 16 mv peak to peak. For a recorder to accommodate a displacement signal on the order of 0.5 mil (12 μm) peak to peak at a sensitivity of 200 mv per mil (8 mv/μm), a noise floor less than 100 mv peak to peak will be required. If this signal is recorded without any preamplification, the effective signal-to-noise ratio has been reduced to 100/16 or 6.25 corresponding to 16 dB. While this limitation might be acceptable under steady-state conditions, any lower-level harmonics would probably be lost in the noise. Problems could be expected if the recording included a coastdown for plotting amplitude; phase response for changes in amplitude well over a factor of 6 are normal and are expected on many types of machinery.

This example points out that all recording and analysis instruments have a range of inputs within which they must operate. In the case of a tape recorder, it is very convenient to adjust the amplitude of the incoming signal ahead of the tape recorder in fixed steps so that the amplitude entering the recorder is always as close as possible to the recorder's rated input signal. In this way, the recorder is operated at a signal level which maximizes its useful dynamic range.

Many analysts do not use preamplifiers but simply use the gain adjustments provided at the input of most recorders and set the recorder full-scale level slightly above the maximum amplitude signal they expect to record. This will work acceptably if one can predict the maximum level signal which will be recorded. But problems quickly occur when an unusual signal such as a 10-volt peak phase reference signal or a very low-level acceleration signal must be recorded during the course of one analysis. Based on experience with numerous analyses, the following dynamic range (the ratio between maximum and minimum signals required when recording machinery vibration) can be expected.

TABLE 6.1
Dynamic Range Required for Different Transducers

Type transducer	Minimum dynamic range required, dB
Shaft displacement only	26
Shaft displacement plus phase reference	40
Velocity	34
Acceleration	54
All-displacement, velocity acceleration	70

With some judicious adjustments, one can probably get by without instrumentation amplifiers and record both shaft displacement and velocity at some penalty in noise. However, to record acceleration or certainly all three variables, preamplification will be required.

A typical instrumentation amplifier must have linear-gain steps ranging from 0.2 to 0.5 to at least 500 for machinery work. Typically, these gain steps will follow the sequence 1, 2, 5, 10, 20, 50, etc. This may seem complicated, but it really poses no problems in calibration. As an example, take a signal which must be amplified by a factor of 20 to achieve the recorder input level. Assuming a unity gain through the recorder, divide the output of the analyzer or display device by 20 to return to the original level. To be more specific, if the signal from the recorder fills two vertical graduations on an oscilloscope and 2 volts per division are used, the peak-to-peak value of the original input is 4 volts divided by 20 or 200 mv. Thus, one can easily compensate for whatever preamplification was used in recording without altering the system calibration. Amplifiers with gain steps in terms of dB should be avoided in machinery analysis, for the division to compensate for input amplification is much more difficult and results in scale divisions which are not whole numbers.

Next, be aware of the amplifier's frequency response. Virtually every available instrumentation amplifier will have a frequency response from DC to at least 20 kHz which is adequate for most machinery applications. For investigating the higher frequencies, it costs only a slight premium to obtain amplifiers with a frequency response to 100 kHz. Amplifiers with a frequency response above 100 kHz are available and should be considered if exploring the acoustic emission flaw frequencies.

Third, it is highly desirable for an amplifier to have selectable DC or AC input coupling. The latter permits the amplifier to accept and eliminate the bias voltage present from noncontact displacement-measuring systems and some acceleration-measuring systems. Some method of eliminating a bias voltage is always necessary before this type of signal can be recorded with an FM tape recorder, for FM tape recorders are DC coupled at the input and will be swamped with bias voltages above their rated recording input. As mentioned earlier, an AC coupling network is nothing more than a series capacitor. This, combined with the input resistance of the instrument and the output resistance of the signal source, forms a high-pass filter. Thus, when AC coupled an amplifier will lose some low-frequency response. Here again the analyst must recognize the possibility of attenuation at low frequencies whenever a biased signal must be AC coupled into a display or recording device. To cite a specific example, runout data recorded from a shaft displacement system at slow roll (less than 500 rpm) can be severely attenuated by the AC coupling network necessary to input the signal into an FM tape recorder if the coupling capacitor is too small.

A stable reversed-polarity DC bucking voltage is another, perhaps better, way of eliminating a bias voltage and does not degrade the frequency response of an amplifier. With a stable reversed-polarity DC bucking voltage, a DC bias at the amplifier input can be nulled and thereby maintain the amplifier in a DC-coupled mode for best frequency response. Some instrumentation amplifiers will often have this feature, along with a front-panel control to accommodate varying levels of input bias voltage. An additional advantage of eliminating a bias voltage with a stable DC supply is that changes in position sensed by a noncontact displacement system can be recorded in FM on magnetic tape.

Fourth, there are several small features which can greatly facilitate the use of an instrumentation amplifier. Provisions for inverting the input aid analysis when physical limitations or other restrictions force the installation of displacement probes on the wrong side of a shaft. Two parallel input and output connectors allow connecting display instruments, such as a meter or oscilloscope, without the inconvenience of using coaxial tees. If the amplifier is battery powered, there should be some means of checking battery condition.

Finally, when selecting an instrumentation amplifier one should of course be aware of its electronic specifications such as noise, linearity, and gain accuracy. Typically, these values should be as follows:

Noise	Less than 10 μv rms
Linearity	±0.01% maximum deviation
Gain accuracy	±0.1% or better

X-Y Plotters

An X-Y plotter used in machinery analysis should have a minimum slew speed of 30 in./sec to ensure that it can accurately follow large spectral peaks. Although most real-time analyzers have some built-in means to slow down the sweep when a high-amplitude peak is sensed, a slew speed of 30 in./sec is necessary on some occasions and only costs a little more.

A two-pen or XYY' recorder should be purchased if the plotter will make rectangular or Bode plots of amplitude and phase versus speed. Generally, a plotting surface which can accommodate an 11 × 14 plot is desirable even though most plots may be made on more conventional 8½ × 11 paper. The larger plotting surface allows one to place the 11-in. side of graph paper vertical. This format makes better use of the paper when two or more signatures are plotted one on top of the other.

Finally, calibration controls should be covered and have a means for locking or require a screwdriver for adjustment so they cannot be disturbed unknowingly once calibrated.

Other Instruments in Rotating Machinery Analysis

A number of general and special-purpose instruments are of interest to the rotating machinery analyst. In the first category are test and calibration instruments such as multimeters, function generators, and possibly a frequency counter. These instruments are necessary as a program of machinery analysis is developed, are available from a number of sources, and are purchased directly from a catalog. Rugged packaging, light weight, and battery power are all worthwhile features of general-purpose test instruments used in machinery analysis.

Within the category of special-purpose instrumentation are strain gauge conditioners, filters, envelope detectors, torsional analyzers, and rolling-element bearing analyzers. Most will be purchased for a specific application or test.

Details such as cabling and arrangements for storing cables when not in use, methods of patching one instrument into another, switching boxes for easing the task of selecting one signal out of several for observation, and analysis are just as important as the instruments themselves. Generally, modern electronic instruments are highly reliable and will perform the tasks for which they were intended. How long they take to set up to begin their task and how easy they are to use in a program of machinery analysis depends to a great extent on how much attention is given to the details of system engineering.

7

The Reduction and Display of Mechanical Condition Measurements

Analysis and display instruments can be used to transform an often complex signal into something understandable which can relate to mechanical condition.

STATIC AND DYNAMIC MEASUREMENTS

In machinery analysis, two types of measurements are involved. Static measurements are DC-type measurements; that is, the measured variable is not periodic in nature, can be described in terms of a single property or value, and changes typically occur at relatively slow rates. Examples of static measurements are temperature, radial and axial position, load, and speed.

Dynamic measurements are AC measurements in which the variable is nearly always periodic in machinery applications. As discussed in chapter 2, a dynamic signal can be expressed in terms of three properties: amplitude, frequency, and phase relationship to some known reference. Dynamic signals generated by rotating machinery are generally related to the dynamics of the rotating system or a component part and can change rapidly within a cycle or less. Vibration is by far the best known and most frequently measured dynamic variable. However, dynamic strain is another example which, although generally difficult to extract, is often the best measure of the stress placed on components such as turbine and compressor blades.

Before leaving these classes, the definitions must be modified to include measurements which contain both static and dynamic components. For example, axial position, a static measurement, is generally included in all continuous monitoring systems. Although it is eliminated within most position monitors which are designed to display only the static component, the signal obtained from a noncontact axial transducer also contains a dynamic component, axial vibration, which can be valuable in problem analysis and condition monitoring. Similarly, a signal received from a noncontact radial shaft displacement transducer contains dynamic and static components proportional to radial vibration and position, respectively. Whereas radial shaft vibration is considered a prime indicator of condition on many types of machines, radial position measurement can be equally valuable in detecting bearing deterioration.

Shaft speed can be classified as a static variable. While shaft speed is most often measured from a dynamic or AC signal, shaft speed itself is only one property of that signal, its frequency, and is thus a nonperiodic static quality.

This distinction between static and dynamic measurements is necessary because the type of measurement generally determines the best method of display. For example, static measurements representing a single quantity or value which normally doesn't change very rapidly with time can be displayed and easily comprehended on a digital readout. On the other hand, a dynamic variable, such as vibration, which often fluctuates with time is best displayed on an analog meter or oscilloscope where variations are easily averaged by eye. Digital presentations of raw vibration are generally not preferred, for normal variations in amplitude cause the last digits to change constantly.

The exception to this is axial position; technically a static variable, it is generally best displayed on an analog meter, particularly when two channels are displayed on a single monitor.

Finally, when a dynamic signal is measured in terms of its specific properties, two of those properties, frequency and phase, can be considered static quantities and displayed on a digital presentation. Normal fluctuations in amplitude can produce annoying changes in a digital display. However, if the signal is limited to a single frequency—running speed, for example—with a bandpass filter, the amplitude is generally more stable and thus suited for display in a digital presentation. As a result, most automatically tuned or tracking analyzers will have digital displays of all three measured quantities: amplitude, frequency, and phase.

DISPLAYING STEADY-STATE DYNAMIC MEASUREMENTS

Overall amplitude

By far the simplest way to display a dynamic signal such as vibration is to convert the AC to its DC equivalent then display the result on a meter. Portable vibration meters and most vibration monitors function in this fashion. In use, the overall amplitude is read on the instrument then compared against the severity criteria for an assessment of mechanical condition. Overall amplitudes can be tabulated, graphed, or recorded on a pen or multipoint recorder in order to detect trends. One word of caution: for overall amplitudes to be equal when measurements are made with different instruments, the method of AC-to-DC conversion discussed in chapter 4 and the instrument's passbands must be equal.

Amplitude, frequency, and phase

There are three ways to display amplitude, frequency, and phase: numerically on a meter or digital display, pictorially on an oscilloscope, or a combination of the two such as is possible with the output from a real-time analyzer. (The term "real-time analyzer" describes both time compression and FFT instruments.)

Vibration analyzers equipped with numerical displays, either a meter or digital, are by far the most common in machinery analysis. There are a wide variety of configurations to measure amplitude, frequency, and in some cases phase.

Amplitude is commonly displayed as a numerical value on either a meter or a digital presentation. Most analyzers have switches for changing the amplitude range and selecting either overall amplitude or amplitude filtered to a specific frequency. The latter can be used very effectively to determine the frequency content of a signal by simply comparing the filtered and unfiltered values.

Frequency is measured in one of two ways, depending on the particular analyzer. In the first type, fitted with a graduated tuning dial, the dial is turned until amplitude rises and reaches a peak, indicating the presence of a spectral component. Once an amplitude peak is identified, it may be necessary to tune back and forth to locate its exact center. As soon as the center has been found, amplitude is read on the meter and frequency is determined by multiplying the setting of the tuning dial by a range multiplier. With the second type of analyzer, those equipped with digital displays, the digital display automatically reads the filter frequency so one only has to locate the maximum amplitude then read amplitude and frequency directly.

Phase likewise is measured in two ways. Both require a phase reference mark on the shaft. On analyzers with a strobe light, the analyzer is tuned until the rotating reference mark, which must be readily visible, is frozen or fixed in one position. This indicates that the frequency to which the analyzer is tuned is synchronized with the predominant frequency of the machine's shaft or some whole multiple. At this point frequency and amplitude are read as before. Phase is either read as a clock position of the frozen reference mark or in degrees on a scale marked or attached to a fixed structure adjacent to the shaft (figure 7-1). If the measurement balances or checks phase at rotating frequency for changes, be careful that the frequency of the analyzer is the running frequency of the machine, for the shaft mark will freeze at any whole multiple of running frequency.

In order to measure phase, the automatic or tracking analyzer must receive a once-per-revolution electronic pulse. The pulse tunes the filter within the analyzer to the frequency of the pulse, presumably running frequency of the shaft being analyzed, and also provides a fixed reference from which to measure phase. Phase, or the angle between the reference and some fixed point on the filtered waveform, is then measured electronically and generally displayed digitally. When making this measurement, be careful either to record the position of the 0–180° phase-shift switch on the analyzer or always record phase with the switch in one position.

Analyzers equipped to measure phase can plot the mode shape of a vibrating structure at a specific frequency. When a tracking analyzer is used in this application, the phase-reference pickup is located to observe a phase-reference mark on a shaft rotating at the frequency being investigated. If a phase-reference mark on the shaft is unavailable, it is often possible to find or construct a location on the machine or structure where vibration is at a high enough amplitude to trigger the

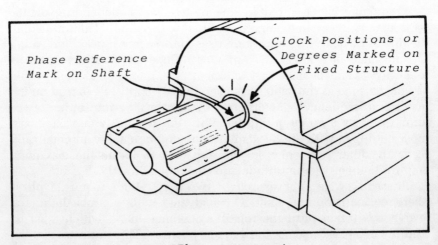

7–1—Phase measurement.

analyzer. When a vibration reference is used, it may be necessary to prefilter the signal before it will properly trigger the analyzer.

Once a reference is established, the vibration pickup is placed at locations on the machine or structure in some logical grid and amplitude and is phase-recorded at each. From this data a plot can be constructed showing the mode shape. The same task can be performed with an analyzer equipped with a strobe, except there must be a mark on the rotating shaft from which to measure phase.

Pictorial displays

Pictorial displays can be of two types: a dynamic display, such as an oscilloscope, and a static or hard-copy display, such as an oscilloscope photograph or plot. All three methods of display have great use in machinery analysis—the oscilloscope display for evaluating dynamic phenomena and the photograph and plot for more accurate measurement, capturing transient phenomena, and recording characteristics for time comparison and trending.

An oscilloscope will accept one or more signals for display. The simplest display is a single amplitude-versus-time waveform. In this type of display (figure 7-2), peak or peak-to-peak amplitude can be measured by counting the appropriate vertical divisions occupied by the waveform then multiplying the number of divisions by the voltage per division setting on the oscilloscope input amplifier. If the oscilloscope has a continuous gain adjustment, be careful that it is in the unity gain or calibrate position before counting divisions. Additionally, while peak or peak-to-peak amplitudes can be measured in this fashion, they can only be converted to RMS or average values if the waveform is sinusoidal. When the waveform is not sinusoidal, the amplitude measured on an analyzer with an average or RMS detector may be signifi-

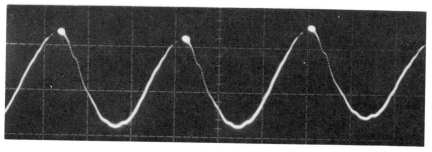

7–2—Simple time domain waveform.

cantly different than the amplitude obtained from an oscilloscope presentation.

Next, the period of a signal can be measured by determining the horizontal graduations in one cycle then multiplying by the millisecond per division setting on the oscilloscope time base. Generally this is accomplished most accurately if the time required by several cycles is measured then divided by the number of cycles to obtain the period. Once the period in seconds has been determined, calculate its reciprocal to obtain frequency.

If a phase-reference mark is applied to the Z or blanking axis of the oscilloscope, the waveform then becomes referenced to the mark's specific position on the shaft. For example, to find the angular difference between the phase reference and the high spot or maximum instantaneous amplitude measured at a particular point, measure the angular distance between the two using 1 cycle = 360° as a basis. In figure 7-3a, the high spot passes a vertical transducer approximately 90° after the phase reference passes its transducer, which, for simplicity, has been placed in the same plane as the vibration transducer. From this example one can observe that the angular location of the high spot can be found by placing the reference mark on the shaft beneath the reference pickup, then measuring from the shaft vibration pickup and against the direction of rotation an angular distance equal to the measured phase angle. In figure 7-3a the high spot is located at the 270° position, 90° behind the vibration pickup.

Figure 7-3b shows another example where phase reference and vibration transducer are not in the same plane. Again observe that the phase mark leads the high spot by 90°. In other words, when the phase

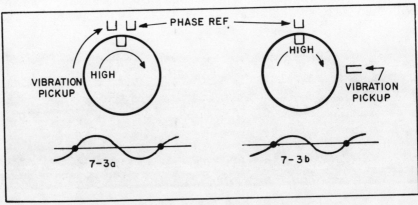

7–3—*Phase measurement to the high spot.*

mark is underneath the phase reference transducer, the vibration sensed by the vibration transducer has 90° more to go before reaching its peak. Since the vibration transducer is 90° from the phase-reference transducer in the direction of rotation, the high spot in this particular example is coincident with the phase reference.

This method of estimating phase lag from an oscilloscope presentation can be used in balancing. Additionally, in machinery analysis, a stationary or changing phase lag over a period of time can often provide valuable insight into mechanical condition. As a result, whenever vibration data, especially shaft vibration, are being recorded for trending, phase lags should be included. The easiest way to do this is to apply the phase-reference pulse to the blanking axis of the oscilloscope, thereby automatically referencing the presentation in phase.

If two vibration signals can be obtained from radial transducers spaced 90° apart, these two signals can be displayed simultaneously as time domain waveforms or the two signals can be combined into a lissajou or orbital presentation (figure 7-4). The orbital presentation has

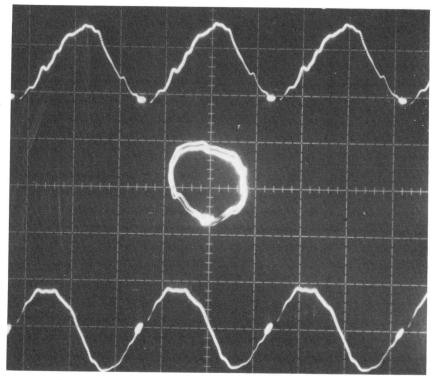

7-4—Phase-referenced waveform and orbit.

gained wide acceptance in shaft vibration analysis, for it is a greatly magnified, easily understood, and highly accurate picture of shaft motion. Many common machinery problems can be identified from the shape of a shaft orbit, and can also be used for balancing.

In addition to being constructed automatically on an oscilloscope, an orbit can be plotted graphically from two waveforms (figure 7-5). Similar to manual runout correction, divide the two waveforms being combined into convenient divisions, establish a reference system with X and Y plus to the right and up, respectively, then determine a numerical value for both at each increment of shaft rotation. The following table is constructed from the waveforms in figure 7-5a:

TABLE 7.1

Shaft rotation	X	Y	Shaft rotation	X	Y
0	0	1.0	7	−0.5	−0.87
1	0.50	0.87	8	−0.87	−0.50
2	0.87	0.50	9	−1.0	0
3	1.0	0	10	−0.87	0.50
4	0.87	−0.50	11	−0.5	0.87
5	0.5	−0.87	12	0	1.0
6	0	−1.0			

Plotting each pair of X–Y coordinates will yield the lissajou or orbital pattern shown to the right of the two waveforms. From figure 7-5 one can see that two pure sine waves of equal amplitude with a 90° phase difference will always produce a circular orbit. In machinery analysis the simple waveforms and circular orbit shown in the figure are often observed in the signals obtained from two noncontact displacement pickups spaced 90° apart observing an unbalanced shaft operating in a symmetrical bearing.

If two sinusoidal waveforms have different amplitudes but retain their 90° phase relationship, the resulting orbit will be elliptical with the major axis in the direction of the largest amplitude, illustrated by the dotted waveform and orbit in figure 7-5. This pattern is also commonly observed in machinery analysis when an outside force such as gravity or a misaligned coupling restrains and reduces the amplitude of shaft motion in one plane.

In figure 7-5, no matter how the amplitudes are varied, the resulting ellipse will always have its axes oriented vertical and horizontal as long as the phase difference between the two waveforms is 90°. Figure 7-6 illustrates the type of orbit formed by two unequal amplitude sine waves when the phase difference between the two sine waves is some-

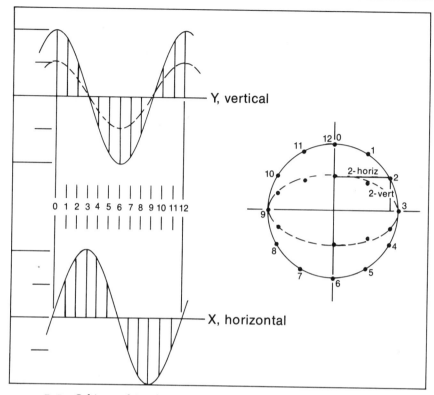

7–5—Orbit resulting from two sinusoidal waveforms with a phase difference of 90°.

thing other than 90°. In the specific case illustrated in figure 7-6, the angled elliptical orbit is produced by two unequal amplitude sine waves with a phase difference of 150°.

If the waveforms contain more than one frequency, the resulting orbit will correspondingly increase in complexity. Figure 7-7 illustrates the type of orbit formed from two complex waveforms, each containing (in addition to a fundamental frequency) a subsynchronous component at 50% of the fundamental frequency. Associated with instability, this type of waveform and orbit were quite commonly observed on older high-speed machinery with cylindrical journal bearings.

With this as a background, one can experiment by plotting different waveforms to gain an idea of how some of the more basic shapes are formed. However, like all signals obtained from a shaft-displacement probe, an orbit can be greatly distorted and lose its effectiveness if the signal includes the effects of shaft defects or runout. Additionally, both

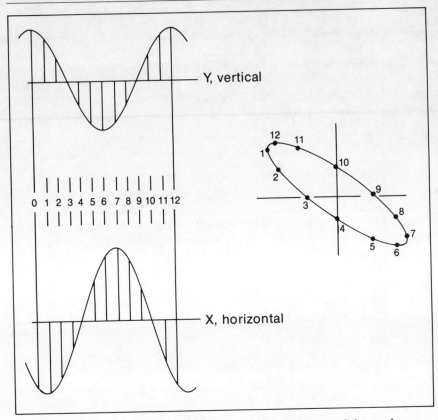

7–6—*Orbit resulting from two unequal amplitude sinusoidal waveforms having a phase difference of 150°.*

the orbit and waveform quickly lose utility if the signal contains more than two or three major components, for its complexity is difficult to resolve by eye alone on an oscilloscope. Of course, filtering can simplify the signal (figure 7-8), but so also can a real time analyzer.

NUMERICAL/PICTORIAL DISPLAYS

The amplitude versus frequency or spectrum plot is the best example of a numerical/pictorial display. In this type of display (figure 7-9), the vertical axis is calibrated to read amplitude in some convenient units, while the horizontal axis is graduated in terms of frequency. At a glance, this is a method by which both the amplitude and frequency of any given component can be quickly and accurately measured. The

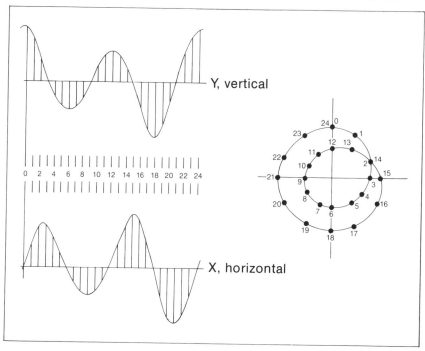

7–7—Orbit produced by two complex periodic signals.

spectrum can be displayed on an oscilloscope for viewing in real time, subject to limitations, or it can be printed in a hard-copy form as a detailed record of vibration characteristics. The spectrum display can be used very effectively to evaluate mechanical condition and in problem analysis. Additionally, a series of spectrum plots taken at regular intervals and compared is an effective method of identifying the early stages of deteriorating mechanical condition.

Within the spectrum plot, individual components are identified by dividing their frequencies by the rotating frequency of the shaft. The quotient of the two frequencies is the harmonic order or multiple of the spectral component. In the low orders, the second, third, and fourth multiples can be easily identified by eye. At the higher frequencies, however, division must be done to obtain the order of a given spectral component. Once the order is known, the component can often be related to the phenomenon which formed it. Examples of this are gear mesh frequency (the number of teeth times shaft speed) and blade pass frequency (the number of blades time shaft speed).

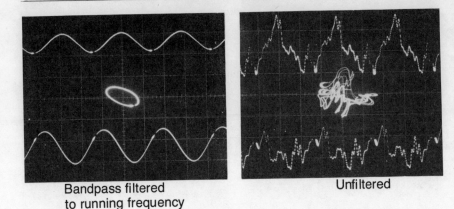

Bandpass filtered   Unfiltered
to running frequency

7–8—Filtered and unfiltered time domain signal.

Most real-time analyzers can be equipped to perform order normalization. In this configuration the analyzer's output is again amplitude on the vertical axis; however, the horizontal axis is now graduated in multiples of running speed (figure 7-10). The advantage of this is that harmonic components will maintain their position through speed changes, a clear asset when comparing the characteristics of variable-speed machines over a period of time. The order normalized presentation does, however, have a disadvantage, particularly at higher frequencies.

The discussion of mechanical impedance in chapter 2 showed how impedance may vary widely with frequency. Within an order-normalized display frequency is a variable which does not appear directly unless it is manually recorded. Thus, as a machine's speed changes, a variation in impedance such as a resonance, which is fixed in the frequency spectrum, moves relative to the harmonic orders,

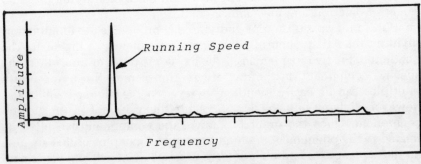

7-9—Typical amplitude vs. frequency spectrum.

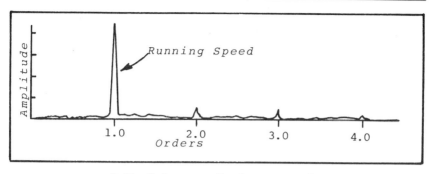

7–10—Order-normalized spectrum plot.

which are held stationary in the order-normalized spectrum. The relative motion between impedance and harmonic order can produce amplitude variations totally unrelated to machinery condition which, in an order-normalized presentation, will take place on a component that appears stationary. To illustrate, assume a 47-tooth gear operating at 100 Hz, 6,000 rpm. Its gear mesh frequency is 47 × 100 or 4,700 Hz. Next assume that the gear has been tested and a minor resonance is found at 4,825 Hz which results in an amplitude amplification of approximately 2. As speed is increased, the amplitude of the gear mesh frequency will increase and reach a peak of twice its normal amplitude at a speed of 6,160 rpm (4,825 ÷ 47 × 60). Of course, if speed is increased further the amplitude will decrease and probably return close to its original value.

Although this phonemenon does not occur often, it can occur and usually causes a great deal of puzzlement. The symptoms are generally a sharp peak in amplitude which occurs over a much narrower speed range than would be expected with a resonance excited by running frequency. Examining a spectrum plot, either a frequency spectrum or an order-normalized spectrum, the affected component can be seen. However, only the frequency spectrum will show the increase to a peak then decrease in amplitude with a change in speed. This is the primary indication of a resonance. Therefore, the amplitudes in an order-normalized plot can vary due to the effects of impedance along the transmission path without any change in the excitation itself. Order-normalized plots taken at periodic intervals at slightly different speeds can contain amplitude variations which have nothing to do with changes in condition. Although comparing amplitudes may be slightly more difficult on an amplitude versus frequency plot, the analyst instantly observes any change in frequency as a possible cause of a change in amplitude.

Most real-time analyzers will include a cursor which can measure the amplitude and frequency of a specific component and display its value digitally. This feature allows very accurate measurements to be made when only an oscilloscope is used with the analyzer. In addition to amplitude and frequency, some FFT analyzers can measure phase lag from a reference input.

REDUCING DATA WITH SPECIAL ANALYSIS TECHNIQUES

Envelope detection

Three special analysis techniques—envelope detection, FM demodulation, and cepstrum—are two-step methods for extracting and enhancing a particular characteristic of a dynamic signal.

The objective of envelope detection is to extract, for more detailed analysis, a low-frequency characteristic or event which is initiating, acting upon, or modifying a high-frequency signal. Its most common application is in gear or rolling element bearing analysis where a low-frequency, generally low-amplitude repetitive event (such as a defective tooth entering mesh or a spalled ball or roller striking a race) excites a high-frequency, high-amplitude resonance.

To obtain the envelope of a complex signal, the signal is first band-pass filtered to some empirical range of interest then passed through an electronic envelope detector. As its name implies, the output of the envelope detector is a signal whose shape conforms to the outline or envelope of the input (figure 7-11).

Displayed on an oscilloscope, the envelope contains the pulse repetition frequency or period of the event producing the envelope as well as its peak and average values. To achieve a more accurate analysis of the amplitude and frequency content of the envelope, it is generally spectrum analyzed and the result is displayed in the amplitude versus frequency format.

Frequency demodulation

A dynamic signal can be modified in a number of ways. If it is amplitude modulated, the envelope detection techniques will extract the intelligence carried by the modulation. A frequency modulation, defined as an instantaneous variation in frequency around some average value, can also occur in the vibration signals generated by operating machinery due to phenomena such as a gear tooth spacing error or torsional vibration. As illustrated in figure 7-12, the average value of a frequency-modulated signal can be calculated by multiplying the

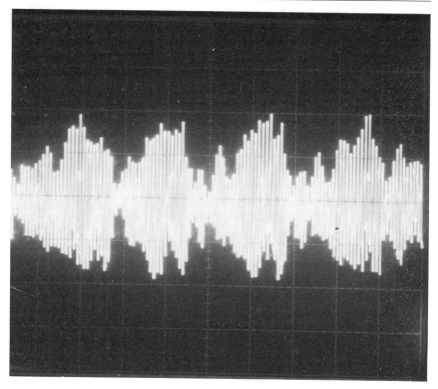

7–11—Raw and envelope detected signal.

number of events per revolution by the number of revolutions per second. If an unequal tooth spacing or torsional vibration is present, the instantaneous frequency will shift back and forth across the average at a rate determined by its generating mechanism. Thus, conditions such as a torsional vibration or a tooth-spacing error can be identified by measuring the rate or frequency at which an average frequency changes.

In practice, a signal suspected to be frequency modulated is fed to a frequency demodulator. The frequency demodulator is tuned to the signal being investigated just as an FM radio is tuned to a station. Within the frequency demodulator the magnitude of the frequency deviation from its average value is converted to an amplitude and its repetition rate is converted to frequency. Its output is thus a time-domain signal with an instantaneous amplitude proportional to the instantaneous deviation in frequency and a frequency proportional to

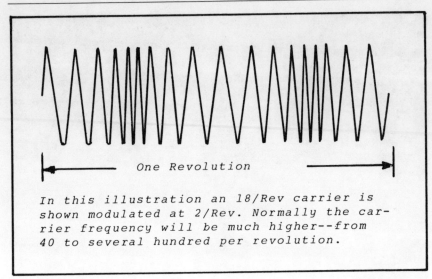

One Revolution

In this illustration an 18/Rev carrier is shown modulated at 2/Rev. Normally the carrier frequency will be much higher--from 40 to several hundred per revolution.

7–12—*Average or center frequency of a frequency modulated signal.*

the rate at which the deviations occur. This signal can be displayed and analyzed in the time domain; however, the analysis task is accomplished more effectively if the frequency demodulated signal is transformed into the frequency domain and displayed in an amplitude versus frequency format.

This procedure for frequency demodulation and analysis is often used in torsional analysis. In this type of analysis, a gear with precisely spaced teeth is installed at a shaft location to be investigated. A noncontact magnetic or eddy current-type pickup is set to observe the gear and generate a pulse as each tooth passes. Since the teeth are equally spaced within very close tolerances, any torsional vibration will produce a frequency modulation of the tooth-passing frequency (number of teeth times shaft speed).

Cepstrum analysis

In cepstrum analysis, the amplitude versus frequency output from a real-time analyzer is treated as a time-domain signal containing periodic components and input into the real-time analyzer a second time. Thus, a cepstrum analysis is like a spectrum of a spectrum. A cepstrum is displayed in a spectrum format with amplitude on the vertical axis and time, called quefrency by some, on the horizontal axis. The strengths of a cepstrum analysis are in its ability to isolate and enhance low-level periodic functions so that their repetition rate can be identified. It has been used successfully in analyzing gears where the amplitude and spacing of sidebands are often difficult to separate using other methods.

Correlation and coherence

To complete this section on special analysis techniques are three other methods of signal analysis, which, although they are not yet used to any significant degree in machinery applications, may be employed in the future. These are auto and cross correlation and coherence.

DISPLAYING TRANSIENT PHENOMENA

Unlike steady-state data which can be accurately depicted with a single plot or photograph, the transient response of a machine during runup or coastdown can often provide valuable information about its mechanical condition and its stability and response at speed. In addition, transient analysis can determine imbalance response, investigate the presence and response of structural and component resonances as well as their coincidence with expected sources of excitation, and in several cases provide information which helps discover shaft cracks.

Rectangular–Bode plot

The first and perhaps most familiar method of presenting machine response is the rectangular coordinate or Bode plot of amplitude (generally at rotating frequency) and phase versus shaft rpm (figure 7-13).

This plot, constructed with the outputs from a tracking analyzer, shows a rotor's response in both phase and amplitude as it approaches and passes through critical speeds. One can identify critical speeds, get some idea of the damping present in the rotor system, and determine the best speeds for making balance corrections from the information contained in the Bode plot.

In machinery analysis nearly all Bode plots are made from the output of a shaft displacement transducer. A word of caution: a Bode plot will be distorted if the signal from the shaft displacement transducer includes any appreciable amount of shaft bow or runout. Both shaft bow and runout (any deviation in the observed shaft surface which produces a transducer output which is not related to motion) will create an initial vector or offset in the phase and amplitude portions of the Bode plot. As shaft speed changes, the bow or runout value (presumably a constant) vectorially combines with true shaft motion to

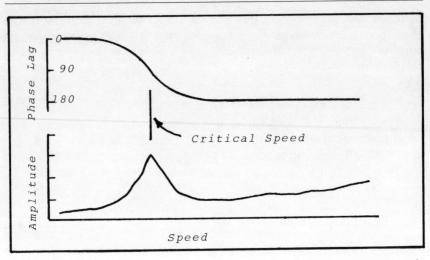

7–13—*Rectangular (Bode) plot of amplitude and phase response vs. speed.*

produce the total signal sensed by the transducer. If bow or runout is a large enough proportion of the total signal, it can greatly alter the appearance of the Bode plot, producing an amplitude peak and phase shift well removed from the actual critical speed, phase shifts through more or less than 180°, dips in amplitude rather than peaks, or no response at all in extreme cases. Thus, if a Bode plot of amplitude response does not approach zero at speeds below 2–5% of maximum operating speed, the information it contains defining response and critical speeds is probably in error and should be used with caution.

Polar–Nyquist plot

Whereas the shape of the Bode plot can be greatly altered by the presence of runout or shaft bow, the form or shape of the Nyquist or polar coordinate plot of a rotating vector, defined by amplitude and phase during a speed change, is independent of and unaffected by both. In this type of plot (figure 7-14) any bow or runout present is represented by an initial vector. To cancel the effect of bow and/or runout, one must shift the origin of the plot to the head of the initial vector. With the new origin, the vectorial subtraction is automatically applied to any subsequent vector and the plot is thus corrected for initial conditions. The Nyquist plot is probably better than the Bode plot for balancing, for the corrected vectorial values needed to apply balance weights can be read directly. It has also been said that structural

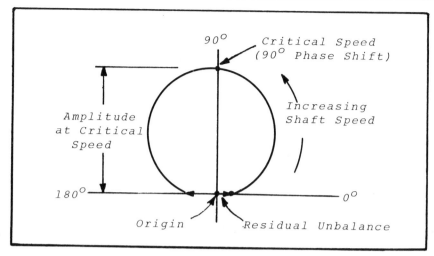

7–14—*Polar (Nyquist) plot of amplitude and phase response.*

phenomena, resonances etc., and amplification factors from which damping can be estimated are more easily observed in the polar or Nyquist plot. The Nyquist plot suffers somewhat compared to a Bode plot in that speeds must be identified manually and amplitude peaks are slightly harder to identify.

Dynamic cascade spectrum

Both the Bode and Nyquist plots are limited, with rare exceptions, to a frequency filtered to running speed. Quite often, however, it is advantageous to observe the dynamic behavior of several components in a frequency spectrum during a speed change. Under these conditions, the dynamic or cascade spectrum, sometimes called a waterfall (a misnomer because it flows up), can provide valuable information. Illustrated in figure 7-15, the cascade spectrum is a series of frequency spectra stacked on top of each other. The interval at which a new spectrum appears in the display can be a function of time or machine speed. Recall from the earlier discussion of the spectrum display that the abscissa or horizontal axis may be frequency or it may be normalized to harmonic orders. Which is selected will make a difference in the appearance of the cascade spectrum. With raw frequency on the horizontal axis, order-related components will shift their position in proportion to the change in speed. If subsequent spectra are recorded at equal intervals of speed during runup or coastdown, order-related

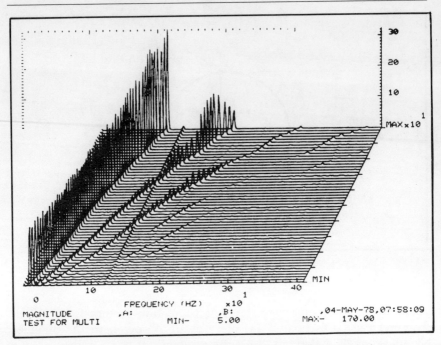

7–15—*Cascade spectrum (courtesy Spectral Dynamics).*

components will be on straight lines with a slope determined by their order. Resonances appear in vertical lines as amplitude increases; they occur when crossed by some excitation such as a multiple of running speed.

The order-normalized cascade spectrum follows the same rules as order-normalized single spectra. Since harmonic orders now appear as vertical lines, resonances, or any other phenomena which occur at a constant frequency, will appear on a sloped line or curve depending on whether the interval between succeeding spectra is determined by speed or time.

Of the two types of cascade spectra, the frequency spectrum seems to display events in a more understandable relationship, e.g., order-related components move in proportion to speed while resonances remain fixed.

Dynamic Campbell diagram

The Campbell diagram type of dynamic presentation, instead of displaying the raw spectrum, includes some arrangement—a code, intensity, or color modulation—which identifies the amplitude of response in addition to its location. In the plot shown in figure 7-16 machine speed in rpm is plotted across the horizontal axis with frequency in Hz plotted on the vertical axis. Orders are shown as dotted lines originating from the lower-left corner of the plot. The crosses indicate a resonant response: increase in amplitude to a peak followed by a decrease. The diameter of the circles surrounding the crosses is proportional to the peak amplitude at resonance. Notice that the Campbell diagram plot uses coordinates which are somewhat different

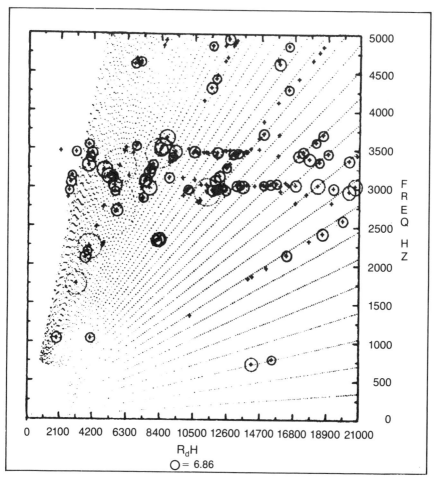

7–16—Dynamic Campbell diagram (courtesy Spectral Dynamics).

than the cascade spectrum plots; however, the same basic information is presented in a little clearer format for judging amplitude response.

Rotated cascade spectrum

Cascade spectra and the Campbell diagram presentation are really methods for displaying three-dimensional data on a two-dimensional surface. To show how this works, imagine taking a cross section of a cascade spectrum along the line at running speed. The result would be a Bode plot of amplitude versus speed. Quite often it is good to have the response of a specific component in the plane of the display rather than appear to be a third or topographical dimension in a cascade plot. In this situation the axis can be rotated (figure 7-17) to place the characteristic in or close to the plane of the display where it can be viewed more clearly. The ability to rotate displays to enhance a specific characteristic is regularly accomplished for computerized structural investigations and will undoubtedly be incorporated in large machinery-analysis systems.

TRENDING TO IDENTIFY LONG-TERM OR RELATED CHANGES

Probably everyone has manually tabulated a series of measurements taken regularly over some period of time to detect changes. A much better method is to plot those measurements as a function of time (figure 7-18). Here again the eye and brain form a powerful combination able to detect a very slight trend which would probably not be recognized at all in a numerical tabulation.

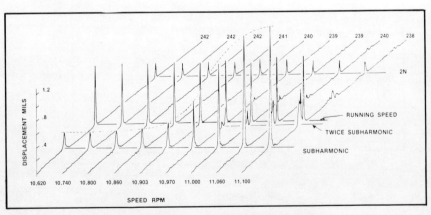

7–17—Rotated axis frequency spectrum.

If the information has more features than can be described by a single characteristic or quality—a complex frequency spectrum, waveform, or orbit, for example—the presentation containing the most concise and quantified measure of its characteristics can be stored and compared over time. This is routinely accomplished in numerous programs of regular predictive analysis. The actual comparison can be a qualitative comparison by eye or a quantitative comparison where the value or amplitude of each component or characteristic is determined and compared against the last. The latter method must of course be used in computerized routines; however, normal variations in machine characteristics often require such a broad tolerance that the first indications of trends may remain hidden.

What one generally looks for to identify a trend is whether all related variables are trending in the same direction. A situation where all related variables, thrust temperature and axial position, for example, are moving in the same direction provides a much stronger indication of a changing condition than a variation in a single variable. This type of analysis can be performed in three ways. First, an analyst should discipline himself to examine related variables for confirming changes even though the levels in themselves may not be of concern. The

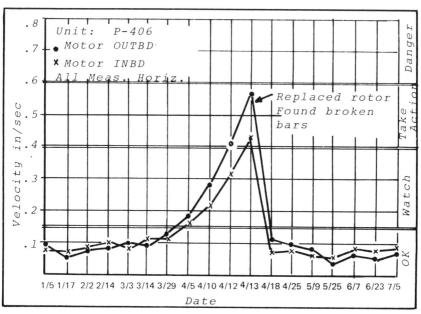

7–18—*Typical predictive analysis plot of amplitude vs. time.*

changes in temperature and position could just as well have been simultaneous changes in shaft and casing vibration or vibration at both ends of a machine which should be looked for in machinery analysis.

A second method by which related changes in single measurements can be identified is by placing them on a multipoint or multipen recorder. Manually graphing measurements on the same time scale is another but much harder method of recognizing related changes. Finally, computer trending can perform the same tasks if the program provides facilities to display measurements as a function of time, to display and compare time-related measurements of different variables against one another, and finally to retain a historical file of past measurements for making it all possible.

8

Machine Condition Characteristics

Operating characteristics which define the health or condition of operating machinery can be classified by groups. The first group is characteristics common to a broad segment of machines such as vibration at a rotational frequency(s) and associated harmonics. The second group contains characteristics common to a particular type of machine such as a centrifugal pump, gear, or gas turbine. In the third group are those characteristics originated by and indicative of the condition of a specific component such as the vibration characteristics of a rolling element ball or roller bearing, the metal temperature of a hydrodynamic thrust bearing, and the differential pressure across a centrifugal compressor balance piston.

Most machinery will generate characteristics in at least two and possibly all three groups; of course, many characteristics are interdependent, that is, a change in one will produce a corresponding change in another. To a large degree, the secret of success in machinery analysis is in understanding a machine, how changes relate to one another, and the ability to use measurements to focus on a specific defect or component.

CHARACTERISTICS COMMON TO A BROAD SEGMENT OF MACHINERY

In general there are four major measurable characteristics which define the condition of operating machinery: vibration, position (both radial and axial), temperature, and pressure. Vibration and position are primarily associated with mechanical condition, whereas temperature and pressure assess performance and efficiency and measure mechanical condition.

131

Vibration

Vibration is generally associated with the dynamics of the rotor bearing system. Conditions such as instability, imbalance, misalignment, loose fits, and in some cases stress on components exhibit specific vibration characteristics. The most common vibration characteristic is at a machine's rotating frequency. Variations in amplitude at running frequency are associated with rotor balance. Next are the harmonics of running frequency. These can be produced in at least two ways; first, by an event that occurs twice during each revolution such as the toggling action of a misaligned coupling; second, by a distortion or deviation from a pure sine wave in the fundamental or running speed component. As illustrated in figure 8–1, truncating a sine wave such as may occur due to increasing force applied to a shaft as it moves closer to a bearing surface produces a series of harmonics which are an outward measurable manifestation of a nonlinear response. Finally, there are higher harmonics generated by repetitive events which occur each revolution such as the meshing of gear teeth, vane, and blade passing as well as the various frequencies generated by rolling element bearings.

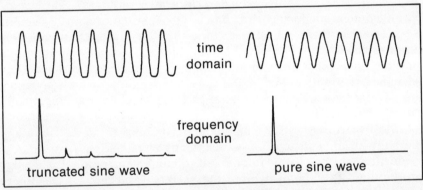

time domain

frequency domain

truncated sine wave   pure sine wave

8–1—A truncated waveform generates harmonics.

Position

Axial position is a common measurement made both on assembly and during operation; it ensures the thrust bearing is functional and operating properly to prevent longitudinal contact between rotating and stationary parts. Radial position measurements can be just as important, for they are often the only warning of a loss of bearing material to phenomena such as electric discharge.

Temperature

Temperature, preferably measured closely to the point of action, is often the best and most responsive indicator of the load applied to the component. In this situation, temperature is a highly responsive anticipatory indicator of a condition, such as overload, which could result in bearing failure. Tests have shown that a gross measurement, e.g., one made in the oil drain, is not as responsive as a measurement made with a sensor such as a thermocouple or resistance temperature detector implanted in the bearing itself, nor will it change enough from normal to failure to provide a clear warning. For best results, bearing temperature measurements should be made with more than one sensor placed to account for changes in the position of maximum load of a journal bearing and in several pads of a thrust bearing.

Pressure

Pressure is a third measurement which can be used to assess the condition of a broad range of machinery. First are the pressure characteristics of specific components, such as balance drum differential in a centrifugal compressor where pressures in excess of the manufacturer's specifications usually mean a loss of balance drum seal clearances with a corresponding risk of thrust bearing overload and failure. Here, a change in one variable (balance drum differential) indicates a condition (increasing balance drum seal clearances) which produces a related change in another variable (thrust load) in turn affecting thrust bearing temperature and possibly axial position.

A lower-than-design overall pressure differential across a specific machine for a given rate of flow and with all other conditions normal is often the primary symptom of excessive internal clearances. Likewise, higher-than-normal stage pressures on machines such as steam turbines can be the primary symptoms of a flow restriction such as might be produced by buildup on the blades. In the latter example, an increase in thrust bearing temperature produced by the added fluid force against the rotor would be a secondary confirming observation.

Beat frequencies

Beat frequencies generated at a rate equal to the difference between two closely spaced components are commonly found on a wide variety of machinery. Perhaps the most common is the audible variation in sound generated by a two-pole induction electric motor at a frequency equal to the difference between line frequency and running speed. Beats produced by the interaction of components from two adjacent machines occur occasionally. In this category two electric motors operating at slightly different speeds due to differences in load may produce a beat frequency which is extremely strong at its peak.

The mechanism responsible for a beat frequency is easily visualized. Referring back to figure 2–1, if a second rotating vector is present at a slightly different speed, the two vectors will alternately come in and out of phase with each other as one overtakes and passes the other. The rate at which this occurs is equal to the difference in frequency between the two vectors. In the case of two electric motors operating at slightly different speeds, the beat frequency may be as low as 1–5 cpm, while the beat between running speed and the line frequency on a typical two-pole induction motor is usually 30–40 cpm.

With two vector quantities moving in and out of phase with one another at a relatively slow rate, there is ample time to produce significant amplitude variations. This alternate amplitude reinforcement and attenuation can produce a strong excitation which can be heard and measured with a vibration instrument.

When the beat frequency exceeds 150–200 cpm, the variation in amplitude is generally too small to be heard, while the frequency itself is too low to be audible directly. Thus, beats are limited to a narrow frequency range.

Beats often appear in the spectrum presentation generated by a real-time analyzer. These beats are produced when two closely spaced components fall within the minimum resolution of a particular frequency range. If the components are too high in frequency to be resolved directly, the translation or zoom feature provided on many real-time analyzers can separate the individual components. As in the case of motor analysis, it is often crucial to know whether the principal spectral component is at line frequency or running speed.

CHARACTERISTICS GENERATED BY A SPECIFIC COMPONENT

Analyzing the condition of rolling element bearings

The primary example of characteristics associated with a specific component is the frequencies generated by defects and flaws in rolling element ball or roller bearings. The frequencies generated by rolling element bearings can be calculated from the following equations:

$$\text{Defect in the outer race} = \frac{n}{2}\,\text{fr}\left(1 - \frac{BD}{PD}\cos\beta\right)\text{(Hz)} \qquad (8.1)$$

$$\text{Defect in the inner race} = \frac{n}{2}\,\text{fr}\left(1 + \frac{BD}{PD}\cos\beta\right)\text{(Hz)} \qquad (8.2)$$

$$\text{Ball defect} = \frac{PD}{BD}\text{fr}\left(1 - \frac{BD^2}{PD}\right)\cos\beta^2\text{(Hz)} \qquad (8.3)$$

The preceding equations assume rolling, not sliding, contact between elements as shown in figure 8–2.
where:
BD and PD are shown in figure 8–2
fr = relative speed between inner and outer race, Hz
n = number of balls
β = contact angle
These frequencies are directly related to the presence of bearing defects and can be found in several areas of the spectrum. First and most obvious is direct observation and analysis at the calculated location in the spectrum. Although many people have obtained good results with this method, others have reported that bearing characteristics are difficult to separate from flow and other machine-related noise and do not vary greatly in amplitude from a normal condition to failure. Next, the same frequencies are often observed as a modulation or

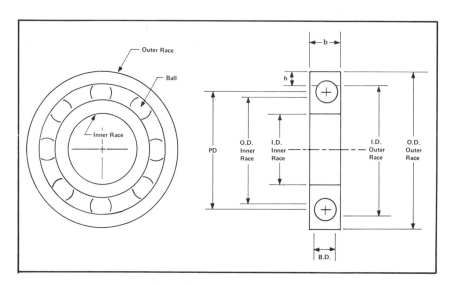

8–2—Basic dimension of a ball bearing.

envelope on a high-frequency signal from which they can be recovered with the appropriate electronic conditioning followed by spectrum analysis. Finally, there are several methods for assessing the condition of rolling element bearings which convert the signal obtained from a high-frequency piezoelectric transducer to a meter reading empirically related to bearing condition.

In direct-spectrum analysis, the complex vibration signal obtained from either a velocity pickup or accelerometer attached to the bearing cap is subjected to spectrum analysis across the range occupied by the bearing characteristic frequencies. With some training and a great deal of experience, an analyst can recognize clear changes as a bearing develops a defect and the defect grows to a point where the bearing must be replaced.

Time domain averaging at the repetition frequency of a specific bearing characteristic is a method which has been used successfully to isolate and enhance the frequencies generated by a rolling element bearing hidden within a noisy signal. With this method, the averaging process strengthens the bearing characteristics relative to the background and the result observed in a normal spectrum presentation.

A third method of extracting the same type of information is based on the observation that the bearing characteristic frequencies may also modulate the high bearing or structural resonant frequencies excited by defect impacts. The basic signal is obtained using a high-frequency accelerometer attached to the bearing or housing; the resulting signal spectrum is analyzed to determine the probable location of resonant frequencies. After the appropriate frequency(s) has been identified, the signal is narrow-band filtered at the particular frequency of interest and the filtered output envelope detected (figure 7–9). Following detection, the envelope is spectrum analyzed to approximately 2,000 Hz to recover the bearing characteristic frequencies. Compared to direct spectrum analysis, envelope detection at high frequencies reduces the amount of noise in the signal not related to bearing condition, thereby enhancing the bearing characteristics that one wishes to observe.

Thus far, these methods have been analytical; that is, a person with skill and experience must interpret some type of presentation and render a judgment. It would be better if the judgment criteria could be simplified to a meter reading to permit less-skilled people to screen operating bearings with a high degree of accuracy. The next four methods of rolling element bearing analysis attempt to simplify the procedure and reduce some defect-related parameter to a meter reading.

The first involves measuring the crest factor or ratio between peak and RMS components of a wideband vibration signal obtained from an accelerometer attached closely to the bearing. As mentioned earlier, defects in rolling-element bearings produce sharp spikes or pulses as the defect contacts its mating member. The larger the defect, the sharper the spike and the larger its amplitude will be in comparison to the normal or RMS amplitude generated by the bearing. Thus, a high or increasing crest factor implies a large or increasing defect. One problem with crest-factor measurements is that in bearings with multiple or spreading defects the crest factor may be low or at least decreasing due to a large or increasing RMS amplitude. Additionally, as bearing speed increases, an individual pulse may not have time to decay sufficiently before the arrival of the next pulse. As a result, at high bearing speeds the pulses become a larger contributor to the RMS amplitude with a corresponding decrease in crest factor and ability to recognize defects.

A second method to measure the condition of rolling-element bearings utilizes the signal obtained from a piezoelectric accelerometer with a resonant frequency in excess of 200 kHz. Within the instrument, generally a small, handheld device, the output from the piezoelectric accelerometer is filtered to a bandpass which has been experimentally determined to represent the condition of most rolling-element bearings. The total energy within the bandpass is displayed on a meter as a measure of bearing condition.

The next two methods, popularly called acoustic flaw detection and shock pulse monitoring, both utilize a high-frequency piezoelectric transducer which is excited at resonance by compression waves produced as a defect contacts its mating member(s). As in several of the methods for evaluating the condition of rolling-element bearings, selecting the proper frequency(s) is a primary consideration. Ideally, one would like to find an area in the spectrum in which flow and machinery noise are at a minimum and bearing-related characteristics are at a maximum.

In acoustic flaw detection (incipient flaw detection or IFD) the band from 80 kHz to 120 kHz is responsive to bearing defects and is being used in most operational applications. This choice is highly empirical, however, and other bands are being used.

Following preamplification and bandpass filtering to eliminate as much noise and extraneous information as possible, the acoustic flaw detection signal is conditioned to produce three outputs which can be measured as numerical values on a meter. First, the RMS amplitude within the bandpass is determined and displayed as a measure of overall condition. Next, the energy content of the spikes or pulses in the high frequency signal above some arbitrary and automatically set multiple, usually 2–4 times the RMS level, is detected and displayed as an indicator of discrete flaws. This measurement can be thought of as the energy content above some fixed crest factor. Finally, the rate at which the signal crosses a given threshold is counted and displayed. Because larger signals will produce more crossings per event or pulse, the count rate measurement can be a second approximation of the energy or severity of the defect. Acoustic flaw detection thus provides three measurements with which to judge overall condition as well as permits recognition and evaluation of local defects. As indicators of bearing condition, field experience ranks the RMS measurement first, followed by SAT with count rate a distant third.

The shock pulse method of rolling element bearing analysis begins in much the same way as the acoustic flaw detection method. Shock waves, produced by the passage of a defect, are transmitted into the structure where they excite a piezoelectric transducer at its resonant frequency. However, the shock pulse transducer has a resonant frequency in the vicinity of 30–40 kHz and the system bandpass filter is set to pass a much narrower band of frequencies centered around the transducer resonance.

Following bandpass filtering, the signal is conditioned and displayed as a shock value above a preset threshold. This measurement is quite similar to the signal above threshold measurement made with the acoustic flaw detection system except that the threshold is either an arbitrary value or is determined by bearing geometry and speed which are set manually on the analyzer. As in the other forms of discrete analysis, the shock pulse system provides a measured value which can be used to assess the performance of new bearings as well as to track the progress of defects.

Based on field experience, both of the last two methods, acoustic flaw detection and shock pulse monitoring, work well on motors and other quiet equipment but may not demonstrate the same effectiveness when used on pumps where flow and cavitation produce impacts that interfere with and mask the impulses produced by bearing defects.

To summarize, there are numerous methods for assessing the condition of operating bearings, both direct and indirect. In nearly every case, a skilled analyst using any one of several techniques can identify bearings in which defects are present or likely. On the other hand, bearing analyzers designed to reduce bearing characteristics to a meter reading may work well in some applications but not as well in others. To be on the safe side, compare the various techniques in his specific application then choose the one demonstrating the best results.

DYNAMIC CHARACTERISTICS OF SPECIFIC MACHINERY

Centrifugal machinery

In centrifugal machinery, the fluid or gas flows through the rotating member radially. Equipment in this category includes pumps, hydraulic expanders, fans, and compressors. In addition to a vibration component at running speed and its associated low-order harmonics, most centrifugal machinery will generate prominent components at the vane-passing frequency (number of impeller vanes times shaft rpm) followed by a series of harmonics.

Figure 8–3 illustrates typical vibration signatures recorded on centrifugal machinery containing prominent components at vane-passing frequency. Note that vane-passing frequency in the top (3b) signature, recorded on the casing of a single-stage centrifugal pump, is considerably higher than the component at running speed. Similarly, amplitudes at vane-passing frequency and multiples of vane-passing

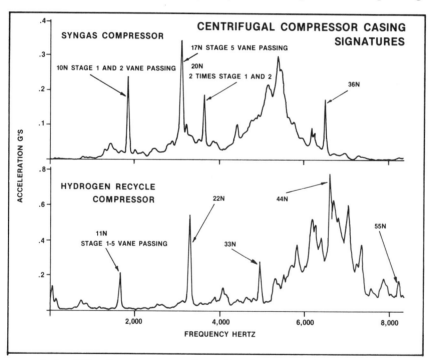

8–3a—Vibration signatures of centrifugal pumps and compressors.

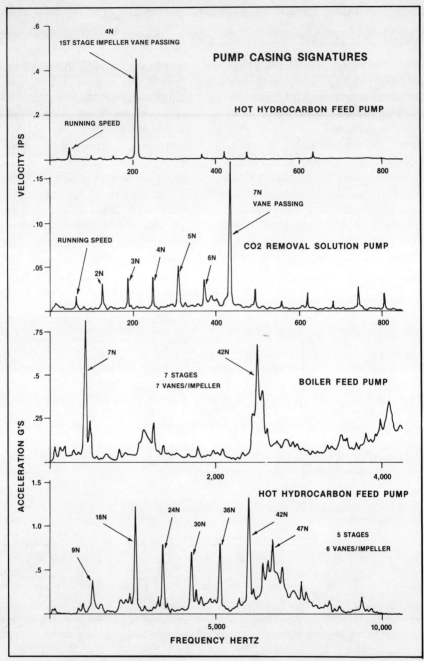

8–3b (cont'd)—Vibration signatures of centrifugal pumps and compressors.

frequency in the lower three signatures, recorded on multistage centrifugal pumps, are also much larger than the amplitude at running frequency. Pumps generating these and similar vibration signatures often appear contradictory in their vibration characteristics for high-velocity amplitudes are present simultaneously with moderate to low values of displacement. This phenomena is expected with this type spectral distribution and is caused by the deemphasis of the higher frequencies when measured in terms of displacement (see Eq. 2.5 and Table 4.1).

Signatures recorded on centrifugal compressors may contain prominent vane-passing frequencies and several harmonics (3a). Amplitudes at vane-passing frequencies may vary widely between compressors and even on the same compressor with minor changes in operating conditions (figure 8–4).

The vane-passing frequencies are probably generated by turbulence or pressure gradients trailing each vane with harmonics caused by deviations in the pressure profile from a pure sine wave. There was some very preliminary information linking the amplitude at vane-passing frequency to cavitation in pumps and surge in compressors or fans; however, the linkage, if it exists at all, is not as clear as first thought and requires more study.

Bladed machinery

Bladed machinery where the direction of flow is parallel to the axis of the rotating member, such as axial compressors, steam, and most modern gas turbines, will usually generate more complex vibration characteristics, particularly in the higher frequencies, compared to centrifugal equipment. Spectral components at blade-passing frequencies (number of blades times shaft speed) are very prominent in vibration spectra recorded from gas turbines and axial compressors, along with multiples and often sum and difference combinations. As a general observation, the blade-passing frequencies observed in steam turbine spectra will be at much lower amplitudes than the blade-passing frequencies generated by axial compressors and gas turbines.

In figure 8–5, the high-frequency signature of an axial flow air compressor, the blade-passing frequency generated by the first four rows containing 37 blades, as well as the blade-passing frequency and several harmonics generated by rows 5 through 11 with 47 blades are prominent. Obtained from an accelerometer mounted on the casing, these components varied significantly in amplitude with changes in speed, pressure ratio, and stator blade angle. The latter is illustrated in figure 8–6, a plot of the amplitude at stator and rotor blade-passing

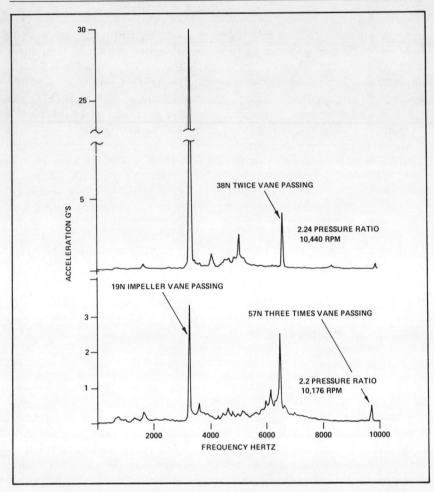

8–4—Amplitude variation of the vane-passing frequency recorded on a centrifugal compressor in response to variations in operating conditions.

frequencies and some harmonics as the moveable first-section stator blades were varied from maximum closed to full open.

The large amplitude variations in figure 8–6 emphasize a precaution which must be observed whenever high-frequency data are recorded for later analysis comparison or trending. Since operating conditions are likely to affect the amplitudes present in the spectrum, variables such as speed, inlet and discharge pressure, flow, density, and stator blade angle, if applicable, must also be recorded and duplicated during subsequent recordings for the comparison to be meaningful.

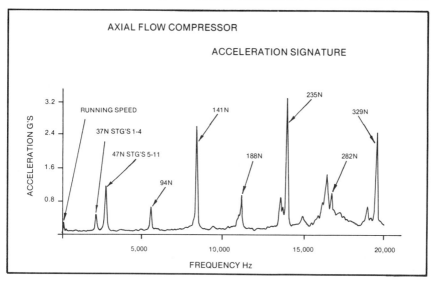

8–5—*Axial flow compressor casing acceleration signature.*

Returning to figure 8–5, also note that stator blade-passing frequencies, if present, are well below the noise level and therefore are hidden from view. This is typical of high-frequency vibration spectra recorded on the casing in which rotor blade-passing frequencies dominate and stator blade-passing frequencies are seldom observed. The reason for this observation is not difficult to visualize. If blade-passing frequencies are created by a wake or pressure gradient trailing each blade, the wakes trailing the rotor blades excite the stator blades at a frequency equal to the number of rotor blades times the shaft speed (rotor blade-passing frequency). This excitation is transmitted mechanically into the casing where it is readily available for observation with a casing-mounted transducer. Similarly, stator blades excite the adjacent downstream row of moving blades at the stator blade-passing frequency. However, in this case the large attenuation across the bearing oil film reduces the signal's amplitude to such a degree that it is not easily recovered in a casing vibration spectrum dominated by the vastly higher amplitude direct-coupled rotor blade-passing frequencies. When a stator blade-passing frequency is observed in a casing signature, it is a reasonably safe assumption that the excitation must be very large.

Before leaving figure 8–6, note that the stator blade-passing frequency was obtained from an accelerometer mounted on the compressor's shaft and the data was extracted through sliprings.

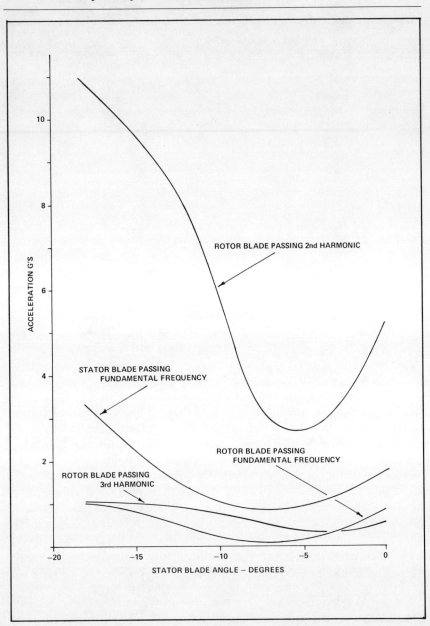

8–6—*Amplitude variations at blade pass frequencies vs. stator blade angle recorded on an axial flow compressor.*

Figure 8–7 illustrates far more complex frequency spectra recorded on the compressor section of three different gas turbines. In each spectrum, most of the prominent components can be related to a specific blade row by simply dividing a specific component's frequency by the shaft running frequency. The resulting quotient will generally match the number of blades in a row and thereby indicate the origin of that particular spectral component.

When calculating a blade-passing frequency, use the total number of blades in one row plus the number of unoccupied spaces, if any, to arrive at the fundamental. As shown in figure 8–8, a blade-passing frequency is determined primarily by the spacing between blades. Missing blades, regardless of the reason, will generate harmonics and perhaps affect the amplitude at blade passing; however, the fundamental frequency is not changed unless the spacing changes. For this

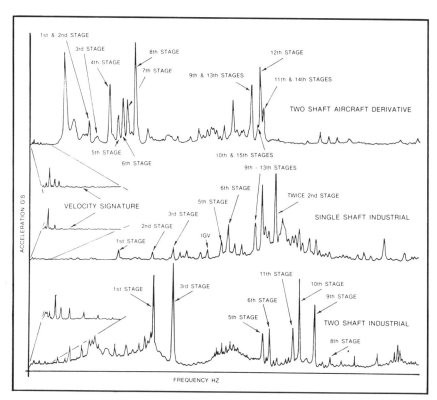

8–7—*Typical casing vibration signatures recorded on the compressor section of three gas turbines.*

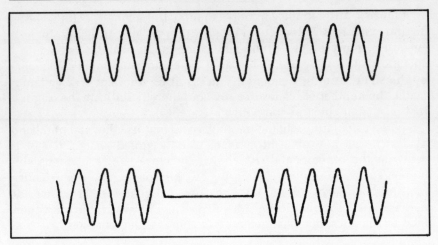

8–8—*The fundamental frequency generated by an interrupted waveform is the same as that generated by a continuous waveform with the same period.*

reason, the blade-passing frequency generated by a steam turbine with 67 blades and one blank space where the blades were inserted will be 68 times running speed, not 67 times as one might expect. Thus, one cannot, from a blade-passing frequency alone, detect missing blades unless so many have been lost that the spacing between blades is altered. Of course in the latter situation there are so many other indications of a serious problem that the blade-passing frequency is little more than academic interest.

Gearing

Gears typically generate a complex, broad vibration spectrum, beginning with frequencies well below the shaft rotational speeds and extending to several multiples of gear mesh frequency (number of gear teeth times shaft rpm). Figure 8–9 illustrates the type of vibration spectrum generated by a typical gear. At the low end of the spectrum are the shaft running speeds and their multiples. By the fourth or fifth order, amplitudes at multiples of the shaft speeds are generally less than 1% of the fundamental and can be ignored for all practical purposes.

The next group of frequencies, intermediate frequencies, generally appear approximately midway between the rotational frequencies and gear mesh. The intermediate frequencies are a series of components synchronous to one or both shafts at multiples of the running frequen-

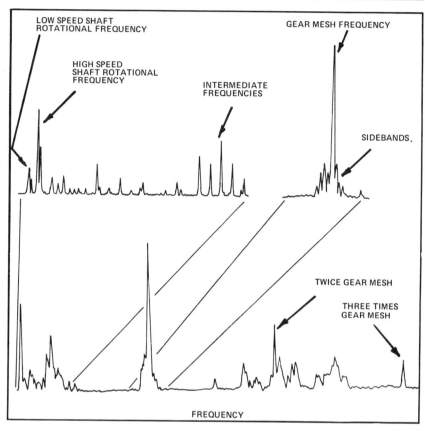

8–9—Typical gear spectrum.

cies which are not easily translated into a mechanical event. In at least
one instance, these frequencies coincided with the natural frequency of
the gear element itself, so it is entirely possible that they are a result
of resonant amplification of a very low-level excitation. In a number of
cases, a change in amplitude at the intermediate frequencies has been a
very sensitive primary indicator of gear failure.

The gear mesh frequency (gear rotating speed × number of teeth)
and its harmonics are generally the most prominent component in both
the casing vibration and sound spectra recorded from gears. The mesh
frequency may be a single prominent frequency or it may be surrounded by sidebands spaced on either side of the mesh frequency at
intervals of the shaft running frequencies. The amplitude at mesh
frequency may vary greatly from gear to gear, depending on number of

teeth, ratio, finish, and load. As a general rule, the larger the number of teeth, lower the gear ratio, higher the quality of tooth finish, and lower the load applied to the gear, the lower will be the amplitude at the mesh frequency. Typical values of the amplitude at mesh frequency will generally fall within the range from 4–8 Gs acceleration; however, it is not uncommon and may not be abnormal to observe gears with an amplitude at mesh frequency well above this value.

The amplitude at mesh frequency has often been cited as a measure of condition; however, normal variations caused by changes in load may mask any trend due to changes in condition. Figure 8–10 illustrates the variation in the amplitude at mesh frequency with changing load. Recorded on the reduction gear of a gas turbine generator, the three acceleration signatures were obtained at rated speed breaker open, approximately one-half load, 9.5 mw, and full load for the ambient condition, 15.5 mw. Note a vast change in the amplitude at mesh frequency from no load to full load. Since the signatures were recorded during an interval of approximately 15 minutes on a unit which was presumably in satisfactory operating condition, the changes could only have been due to load combined with changing temperature of the gear elements themselves in response to changing load.

Also notice that the relative amplitudes of the multiples of mesh frequency change from no load to full load. At 9.5 mw the low amplitude at the second and fourth orders combined with a large third order suggest a square wave, perhaps caused by a sharp force into and out of mesh. At full load this characteristic is gone, replaced by a more normal descending amplitude harmonic string indicating a slightly distorted sine wave. Unfortunately, the recording process was not continuous, so the variation at mesh frequency was not observed across the entire load range.

As was the case in the section on axial compressors, this example emphasizes that large changes in high-frequency vibration characteristics should be anticipated in response to operating changes. Thus, for comparative purposes, it is extremely important to duplicate conditions as closely as possible if the comparison will have any chance of detecting a change in condition. Secondly, it would have been very helpful if a continuous recording had been made so that a cascade spectrum could have been produced to show variations across the entire load range.

The gear mesh frequency is normally followed by a series of harmonics at multiples of gear mesh. Although the strength of the harmonics relative to the fundamental may be a measure of tooth profile

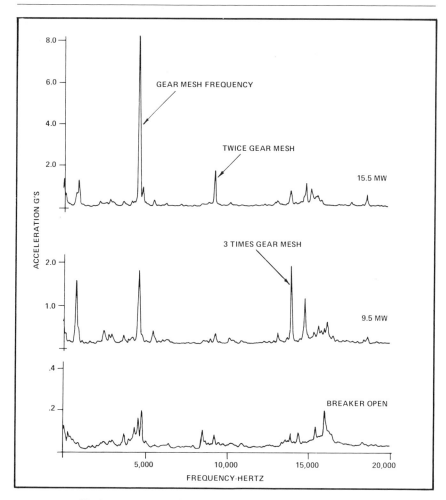

8–10—*Variations in amplitude at gear mesh frequency with load.*

and therefore an indication of wear, the calculations have not been demonstrated by testing.

A fourth characteristic which may be present in the sound or vibration spectrum recorded from an operating gear occurs at the tooth-repeat or hunting-tooth frequency. It is produced when a deformed or abnormal area on one gear meshes with a deformed or abnormal area on the other. The value of the tooth repeat frequency is calculated from the following:

$$F_{tr} \ (Hz) \ = \ \frac{ng}{60Np}$$

(8.4)

where:

ng = speed of the gear, rpm

Np = number of teeth on the pinion

The tooth-repeat frequency generally occurs at a low frequency (1 Hz) and is seldom observed directly. It is, however, often present as a regular audible amplitude variation or modulation of the gear mesh frequency.

Thus far the discussion on gear characteristics has been based on a parallel offset shaft configuration, which is the most common gear found in industrial applications. There are, however, some significant advantages of planetary gears. The schematic of a planetary gear is shown in figure 8–11. Illustrated as a speed increaser, the input shaft drives the planet carrier. The planets engage a stationary ring gear and a sun gear which is attached to the output shaft.

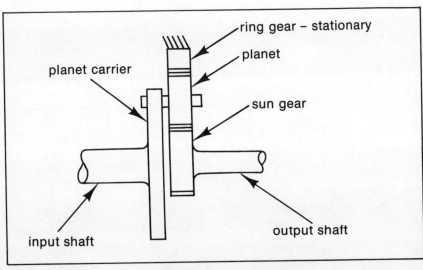

8–11—Planetary speed increaser.

The overall speed ratio of a planetary gear is defined by the following equation:

$$\frac{Ns}{Nc} = \frac{Ts \ + \ Tr}{Ts}$$

(8.5)

where:
    Ns = speed of the sun gear (output)
    Nc = speed of the carrier (input)
    Ts = number of teeth on the sun gear
    Tr = number of teeth on the ring gear

The rotating speed of the planet gears is given by the following equation:

$$Np = Nc\frac{Tr}{Tp} - Nc \tag{8.6}$$

where:
    Tp = number of teeth on a planet

In addition to the foregoing equations which define the rotating speeds of a planetary gear, it is also helpful to know how to calculate tooth mesh frequency and other frequencies generated by a defect on a specific component of a planetary gear.

$$\text{Tooth mesh frequency} = \left(\frac{Ts \cdot Tr}{Ts + Tr}\right)\ Ns = Tr\ Nc \tag{8.7}$$

$$\text{Defect on sun gear} = \left(\frac{np \cdot Tr}{Ts + Tr}\right)Ns = np\frac{Tr}{Ts}Nc \tag{8.8}$$

where:
    np = number of planets

$$\text{Defect on planet} = 2Nc\frac{Tr}{Tp} \tag{8.9}$$

$$\text{Defect on ring gear} = np \cdot Nc \tag{8.10}$$

9

Judging Overall Condition—The Development and Use of Severity Criteria

Guidelines help translate a measurement into some idea of mechanical condition and can be placed in two categories. First and perhaps the easiest to understand are the limits which represent some physical constraint such as the maximum change in axial position which can be allowed before contact occurs. These limits are usually obtained or derived from information supplied by the machine manufacturer. Second, there are qualitative limits on parameters such as vibration. In this category the limit does not generally represent a physical constraint but is a value determined largely from experience, dependent on the type of machine, where and how the measurement is made, and several other factors. Standards are published by industry groups such as the American Petroleum Institute (API), American Gear Manufacturers Association (AGMA), and the National Electric Manufacturers Association (NEMA). In addition, there are a number of national and international standards published by organizations such as the American National Standards Institute (ANSI) and the International Organization for Standards (ISO). However, in the final analysis, the best guidance for the working machinery analyst is probably obtained from the charts published by the instrument and machinery manufacturers.

GUIDELINES AND LIMITS BASED ON PHYSICAL CONSTRAINTS

Quantitative limits

Physical limits predicated on axial clearances must be imposed to prevent metal-to-metal contact. In figure 5–10, an axial movement in excess of 19 mils (460 μm) is made at the expense of thrust bearing material. That is, if the measurement is accurate and the starting point is known, one can predict by measurement alone when losing bearing material. The same logic applies to radial bearings; a change in radial position in excess of the clearance within the bearing means some bearing material has been lost.

Although the concept of axial and radial position changes have been introduced together, the two generally behave very differently. For example, once a thrust bearing is loaded, the only additional change in position in the loaded direction short of failure is the combined effect of pressing the thrust bearing components more tightly together and thinning the oil film, seldom more than 1–2 mils (25–50 μm). In practice, this means that a loaded thrust bearing subjected to an increasing load will not allow much shaft movement right up to the point of failure. When failure occurs, it is usually catastrophic, with movements of 0.250 in. (6.25 mm) or more within a matter of seconds and severe internal damage. Thus, even though absolute limits for axial position can be established, the small movement which occurs up to the point of failure, combined with the rapid shift at failure, will generally allow thrust bearing damage even on machines protected with continuous-position monitors on automatic shutdown. The best the monitor can do is prevent contact between rotating and stationary parts such as wheels and diaphragms.

Before discussing radial position, note this method for anticipating a thrust bearing failure due to overload soon enough to prevent damage to the bearing itself. Thrust bearing temperature, measured with a temperature sensor embedded in the bearing, is an excellent anticipatory method for warning of a thrust failure due to overload. With this method, an increasing load is seen as an increasing metal temperature. Although there may be some exceptional bearings where higher temperatures can be tolerated, setting a limit of 230 °F (110 °C) on bearing metal temperature should prevent most thrust failures due to gradual overload. Thus, metal temperature is an example of another limit related to a physical constraint. In this case, the physical constraint is the temperature at which a typical tin babbit begins losing strength and, accordingly, its ability to carry load.

Radial position usually behaves quite differently than axial position. Whereas a thrust bearing failure is generally a catastrophic event, a radial bearing typically fails over an extended period of time. Regardless of whether a bearing is being pounded out by excessive vibration or etched away by electrical discharge, the damage and corresponding shift in radial position is gradual. With a knowledge of clearances and thickness of the bearing material, one can establish limits based on physical measurements which will tell when a shaft begins dropping and when there is danger of contacting a stationary component (figure 9–1). During this particular failure, experienced on a high-speed steam turbine, there were no changes in vibration characteristics even though the change in radial position indicated the shaft had rubbed into the seals by 0.010–0.012 in. (250–300 μm). When the machine was finally shut down, the depth of seal rub was confirmed.

Another situation where measurements of radial position are quite valuable is after a loss of lube oil. If radial positions are unchanged, the bearings are probably intact.

Although radial and axial position measurements and bearing metal temperature are absolute measurements directly related to a physical

9–1—*Bearing failure unaccompanied by vibration but noted as a change in radial position.*

constraint, be careful. When making position measurements, be aware of the potential for thermal growth to alter the measurement. For example, on a steam turbine it is common for radial position measured with a noncontact probe looking down to decrease due to a shaft which expands more than the bearing. To compensate for this phenomenon, some favor an upward measurement. The same caution holds true for axial measurements; however, probe location can accomplish a great deal to minimize the problem.

Second, when proximity probes are attacked by ammonia in the presence of water, the gap voltage typically decreases. Regardless of the cause, however, in the event all gap voltages in a machine string are trending in a direction that indicates movement in the same direction relative to the probes, there is a good possibility something besides actual motion is the cause. Finally, a radial bearing failure is often accompanied by a sharp increase in temperature followed by a decrease to a temperature below the original operating value. Thus, without some history or another measurement, such as radial position, a normal radial bearing temperature may or may not indicate normal conditions.

Although limits based on physical constraints may vary somewhat between machines, they all can be derived from manufacturer's instructions and should not be exceeded. There are, of course, other such limits: turbine stage pressures, centrifugal compressor balance piston differential pressure, maximum permitted speeds, minimum oil pressure, etc. Again, all are values which cannot be exceeded without a high risk of failure. These limits should be published and displayed prominently where they will be readily available for those who operate the equipment.

VIBRATION SEVERITY CRITERIA

Casing vibration

Although it would be nice to think of vibration limits as exact, they generally are not. As soon as someone says all machines will operate satisfactorily below a certain level or will not operate above a certain level, exceptions will be cited. Thus, assessing vibration severity is largely a matter of experience aided by other guidelines.

Vibration amplitude severity charts had their beginning in 1939, when T. C. Rathbone published recommended limits based on his experience as an insurance inspector. The Rathbone limits were based on casing measurements taken on heavy slow-speed machines with a 2:1 or 3:1 ratio between shaft vibration and bearing housing vibration. Rathbone's idea of plotting maximum tolerable vibration levels versus frequency was refined over the years by a number of people and finally evolved into the chart shown in figure 9–2.

One feature of this and all vibration severity charts should be im-

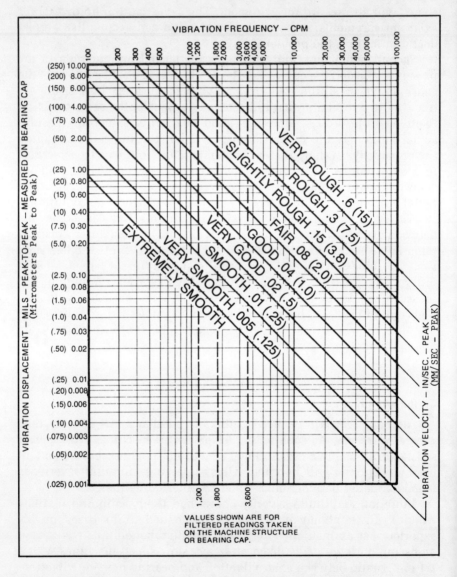

9–2—Casing (bearing cap) vibration severity chart.

mediately apparent: in terms of displacement, tolerable vibration amplitudes decrease with increasing frequency. Recalling the discussion of the relationship between force, displacement, and frequency, it should be obvious that the increasing contribution from velocity and acceleration with frequency requires a decreasing displacement to maintain a given level of force. In recognition of this fact, many have proposed constant velocity criteria over a broad frequency range as the best indicator of machine condition. Note that in figure 9–2 the boundaries between categories of machine condition are constant velocity lines.

The severity chart presented in figure 9–2 and most similar vibration severity charts based on constant velocity are designed for casing measurements taken on typical machines with casing rotor weight ratios on the order of 5:1. Before using any limit, one must know what the limit applies to and how the measurement must be made. Failure to observe these precautions can lead to erroneous conclusions.

Two standards for judging vibration severity are published by the ISO. Widely used in Europe, ISO Standards 2372 and 3945 are respectively a general standard designed primarily for shop testing and acceptance and a more specific standard designed for evaluating the vibration of larger machinery in situ. Both standards contain criteria for judging machine condition from casing velocity measured at a specified location at each bearing. The standards (figure 9–3) apply to machines operating within the speed range from 10 to 200 Hz, 600–12,000 rpm, and specify a measurement limited to a frequency band of 10 to 1,000 Hz.

These two standards require a true rms amplitude measurement and specify that the more common rectified value scaled to read rms with a sine wave is not acceptable unless the vibration is a pure sinusoid. This is probably one of the most controversial aspects of the ISO casing velocity standards; many believe that a peak amplitude is a better measure of severity than an rms value. Favoring rms amplitude measurement is the fact that rms amplitude is more closely related to the energy content of the signal. A signal can have a high peak value without much energy content if the duration (width) of the peak is small.

Both standards make a distinction between flexible-support and rigid-support machines and recognize that a support system may be rigid in one direction and flexible in the other. As in rotor dynamics, a flexible support is defined as a support having its first natural frequency below the main frequency of excitation, presumably machine running speed. Conversely, a rigid support is one in which the first

Ranges of radial vibration severity		Quality Judgement for separate classes of machines			
Range	rms velocity In The Range 10-1000 Hz at the range limits MM/S IN/SEC	Class I	Class II	Class III	Class IV
0.28	0.28 ——— .011 —	A			
0.45	0.45 ——— .018 —	A	A		
0.71	0.71 ——— .028 —	B	A		
1.12	1.12 ——— .044 —	B	B	A	
1.8	1.8 ——— .071 —	C	B	A	A
2.8	2.8 ——— .11 —	C	C	B	A
4.5	4.5 ——— .18 —	D	C	B	B
7.1	7.1 ——— .28 —	D	D	C	B
11.2	11.2 ——— .44 —		D	C	C
18	18 ——— .71 —			D	C
28	28 ——— 1.1 —			D	D
45	45 ——— 1.8 —				D
71					

MACHINE CLASSES

CLASS I   Small Machines to 20 HP
CLASS II   Medium Size Machines 20 to 100 HP
CLASS III Large Machines 10-200 rev/sec, 400 Hp and Larger Mounted on Rigid Supports
CLASS IV   Large Machines 10-200 rev/sec, 400 HP and Larger, Mounted on Flexible Supports

ACCEPTANCE CLASSES

A   GOOD   C   UNSATISFACTORY

B   SATISFACTORY   D   UNACCEPTABLE

9–3—*International standards ISO 2372 and 3945.*

natural frequency of the support structure is higher than the main excitation frequency.

The ISO standards also recognize that machine casing vibrations can be transmitted from the environment and are not applicable when the transmitted excitation is greater than ⅓ of the operating value.

Although several velocity limits are in use, there is good agreement between the various limits as shown in figure 9–4, a plot of some

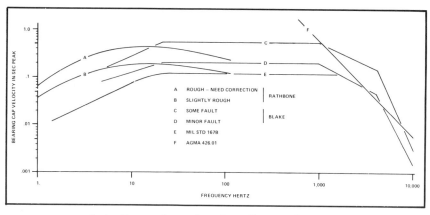

9–4—Comparison of casing vibration limits.

common criteria expressed as a peak amplitude versus frequency. With the exception of the standard applied by the U.S. Navy, which is the most conservative, the remainder all consider anything below 0.1 in./ sec (2.5 mm/sec) peak velocity as a tolerable level of vibration; anything above 0.6 in./sec (15 mm/sec) peak is intolerable. Since the limits of figures 9–2 and 9–4 are expressed as an amplitude at a specific frequency, a filtered reading is implied. This is always true with displacement measurements where one must know the frequency at which the amplitude occurs in order to assess its severity. In figure 9–2, while 4 mils (100 μm) would be tolerable at 1,800 rpm, only about 0.6 mils (15 μm) at 10,000 rpm can be allowed.

The big advantage of velocity measurements is that frequency is included in the measurement itself; therefore, a constant velocity criterion, independent of frequency, can be established for overall unfiltered measurements. Basically, the limits of figure 9–2 are increased slightly because a typical vibration signal contains several components which add vectorially. Naturally, some constraints must be set on the use of such broad criteria. Measurements are limited to those taken on the casings of typical equipment such as electric motors, pumps, fans, steam turbines, and horizontally split centrifugal compressors with external bearings supported through approximately 180°. Operating speeds should be from 900–6,000 rpm and the bandwidth of the measurement itself should be limited to approximately 1,000 Hz. Recognizing these restrictions, the following guidelines for overall, unfiltered velocity can be established:

TABLE 9.1
Recommended Limits for Overall Unfiltered Casing Velocity

Peak Value	Quality
less than 0.15 IPS (3.8 mm/sec)	Acceptable
0.15 to 0.25 IPS (3.8–6.3 mm/sec)	Tolerable
0.25 to 0.40 IPS (6.3–10 mm/sec)	Probably tolerable for moderate periods of time, but increase the frequency of surveillance to warn of changes
0.4 to 0.6 IPS (10–15 mm/sec)	Failure probable; watch closely for changes and be prepared to shut down for repairs
above 0.6 IPS (15 mm/sec)	Danger of immediate failure

To repeat the conditions under which table 9.1 is applicable, the measurements are limited bandwidth casing measurements made on typical general-purpose industrial machinery. With atypical equipment, the principles are the same; all that must be done is modify the severity criteria to fit the specific conditions. For example, it is often necessary to take casing measurements on vertically split compressors with casing-rotor weight ratios of 30:1 or higher and bearings supported through 360°. The impedance from shaft to casing is quite high on this type of equipment, with the result that casing vibration amplitudes will be very low. A reasonable approximation of the casing velocity limits that should be applied to vertically split machinery can be obtained by multiplying the values of table 9.1 by 0.2.

Sometimes the opposite is the case—the recommended limits are too low for a specific machine. Examples in this category are aircraft-derivative gas turbines, gearboxes, and pumps whose normal characteristics include a high excitation at vane-passing frequency. Generally, multiplying the limits of table 9.1 by about 1.25 will result in more realistic limits for the equipment mentioned. Increasing limits should not, however, be accomplished without studied consideration, for even though the limits of table 9.1 are empirical and can probably be exceeded for short periods without damage, they have withstood the test of time and been excellent guidelines. A vibration limit should never be increased until a thorough study proves that the high level is a normal characteristic due to design on support structure and is not the manifestation of a problem such as resonance, and that the machine can tolerate the higher levels without distress.

In practice, the late discovery of a design defect such as a structural resonance requiring major redesign at great cost occurs fairly frequently. Typically, the manufacturer will study the situation, determine that stresses are not being exceeded, and propose an increased vibration limit to eliminate the problem. While the specific nature of the particular problem may permit a higher limit, allowing the problem to exist within an increased limit has two unfortunate side effects. First, the onset of any other problem will be difficult to recognize amid normal excitation. Second, permitting any high vibration to exist as a normal characteristic ultimately causes those exposed to lose respect for vibration as an indicator of condition. Once an operator is convinced that an obviously high vibration is acceptable for one machine, why should he be concerned when another machine begins to vibrate at the same level?

Vibration amplitudes exceeding limits in the severity charts are also significant to human physical senses. For example, 0.5 in./sec (12.5 mm/sec) feels bad to the touch and causes concern. Even though vibration of this magnitude feels and is too high on most machines, a manufacturer sometimes allows 1.0 in./sec (25 mm/sec) and higher in a particular situation. This can present problems, for it desensitizes people and makes them distrust vibration as a measure of machinery condition. This observation certainly does not preclude minor refinements such as allowing 0.35 in./sec (8.8 mm/sec) instead of 0.25 in./sec (6.3 mm/sec) as an upper tolerable limit. These adjustments are certainly permitted and recommended as experience is gained with specific equipment.

Shaft vibration

Although somewhat more definitive than casing vibration, shaft vibration limits nevertheless depend on several variables such as measurement location and shaft mode. In general, figure 9–5 provides the best guidelines for shaft vibration. Here again, observe that tolerable displacement decreases with speed.

A few words of caution: the amplitudes shown on the chart are measured adjacent to a bearing and must be corrected for runout. Recall that the signal received from a noncontact displacement probe is a summation of actual shaft motion and any defects or runout on the shaft. Thus, the chart must be entered with actual shaft motion which can be more or less than the value read on a meter, depending on the phase relationship between runout and actual motion. Another point to recognize is that the severity chart is generally entered with machine running speed to determine a tolerable level of overall vibration. Generally this is a safe assumption, for in most cases running frequency will be the dominant component present in a shaft vibration spectrum. For example, if shaft motion is predominant at another frequency because of misalignment or instability, a limit based on running speed may be too high or too low for the particular conditions. To be more

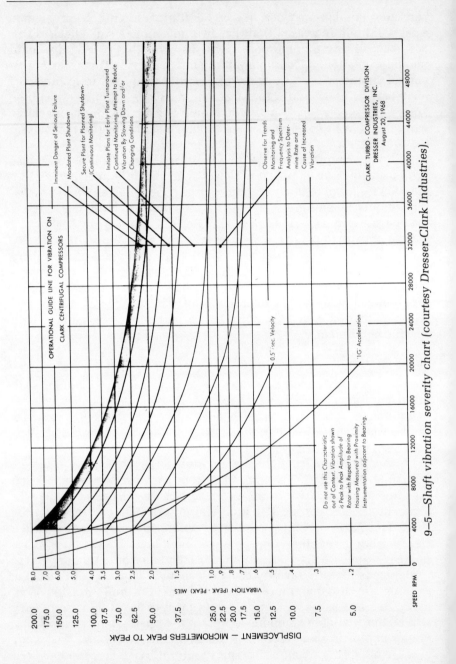

9–5—*Shaft vibration severity chart (courtesy Dresser-Clark Industries).*

specific, there are numerous examples of high-speed machines which have been operated without any distress for extended intervals with subsynchronous instability present at levels far in excess of what would be tolerable if the excitation was at running speed. Again, the familiar relationship between force, displacement, and frequency.

To eliminate the need to base shaft displacement limits on frequency, at least one organization has seriously considered electronically differentiating the shaft displacement signal to velocity so that they can apply a constant limiting value which would be independent of frequency.

Comparing the values of figure 9–5 with figure 9–2, the allowable shaft vibration is higher than that allowed on the casing. By now the reason should be obvious: vibration developed by the rotating shaft is attenuated by the impedance or resistance to motion of the case and structure. Variations in impedance can cause large variations in the ratio between shaft and casing vibration, in some cases on the same machine. To cite a specific example, the outboard bearings on a large power-generating, low-pressure turbine are typically supported on concrete pedestals and are much stiffer than the inboard bearings which may be supported on structural steel. With this type of design, it is not unusual to observe a ratio of shaft-to-casing vibration in the vicinity of 1:1 where the bearings are flexible, compared to a ratio on the order of 10:1 where the bearings are supported on a stiff pedestal. Here again, do not use these values as representative of a situation but consider the specific conditions existing at the location the measurement is made and adjust limits accordingly.

A word of caution concerning the use of any vibration limit: although severity charts and limits are customarily divided into categories of machine condition, the progression is of course continuous. In other words, an amplitude slightly below a dividing line does not imply significantly better machine condition than one slightly above the same lime.

Industry organizations such as the API and the AGMA specify that for the purpose of acceptance, maximum shaft amplitude in peak-to-peak mils shall not exceed:

$$\sqrt{\frac{12{,}000}{\text{rpm}}}$$

or 2 mils (50 μm), whichever is less. In this criteria, displacement amplitude is measured shaft motion and includes runout which can be no more than 0.25 times the allowed displacement.

If the maximum acceptable amplitudes given by the preceding

equation are plotted against speed, they fall well within the satisfactory range established in figure 9–5. This conservative criterion is intended as an acceptance standard for new machinery and must be lower than what one might be willing to tolerate on operating equipment where production is the primary objective.

Above 600 Hz the AGMA specification shifts to a constant 10 Gs casing acceleration. This value (figure 9–4) is more restrictive than the API specification and establishes a criteria for evaluating high-frequency vibration related to gear quality and conditions at mesh. While most operating gears will meet this criteria, and it appears reasonable if perhaps a bit high as acceptance criteria for new gears, an occasional gear will operate successfully at amplitudes above 10 Gs.

As this is written, there is a draft ISO standard covering shaft measurements. It specifies the measurement of shaft amplitude in peak-to-peak units across a frequency range from 10 to 1,000 Hz from two transducers spaced 90° apart at each bearing. Both absolute and relative measurements are covered. The standard also specifies that total runout will not exceed 10% of the allowed amplitude, a limit which is considerably stricter than the API runout limit of 25% of the maximum allowed shaft displacement or 0.25 mil (6 μm), whichever is greater. The draft standard includes judgment criteria for shaft displacement measured on large turbomachines which are straight lines somewhat more restrictive than those shown in figure 9–5.

RECOGNIZING CHANGING MACHINERY CONDITION

There is of course another factor involved in judging condition: are the measured values stable or are they changing with time, and if so how rapidly? A stable unchanging value of any parameter implies stable mechanical condition, whereas a trend upward indicates a change in condition which will ultimately lead to difficulties if the situation continues unchecked.

Although this should be obvious, it is always worth repeating; for often the secret in avoiding a problem is early discovery. For example, assume that a vibration survey is taken on a machine about to be shut down for a plant turnaround. All vibration levels are within limits, so it is decided not to do any work on the machine. Is this a good decision? Well, it may not be if one or more levels were trending up at a rate where limits would be exceeded before the next scheduled shutdown. Thus, measurements alone are not enough to define mechanical condition. One must also know how the measurements are changing with time in order to reach a valid conclusion.

ESTABLISHING MORE SPECIFIC
CRITERIA FOR JUDGING VIBRATION CHARACTERISTICS

General limits are acceptable for a large percentage of operating machinery. There are, however, situations where it is highly desirable to refine the process and devise specific and perhaps more detailed criteria for a specific purpose or a specific machine. Thus far, the limits that have been discussed don't provide any information about what might be causing a problem nor are they detailed enough to enable early recognition of small changes in condition, especially on complex equipment. In order to accomplish this necessary next step, one must resort to a more discrete method of displaying vibration characteristics, such as an amplitude versus frequency spectrum, and then develop guidelines for evaluating the information.

Recalling the discussion of vibration amplitude severity criteria, note one other limitation. The limiting values of vibration contained in figures 9–2 and 9–4 assume the signal is predominantly at the running frequency of the machine in question. A signal composed of a series of components each at or close to the maximum allowable amplitude for the specific frequency is clearly abnormal, even though the chart limits may not be violated. So now the question reduces to one of how can one evaluate a complex presentation containing numerous individual components?

In the low-frequency region, use limits presented in the severity charts to judge running speed, then compare the relative strengths of the remaining components to the amplitude at running speed for an idea of condition. As a means to evaluate more complex spectra, survey a group of similar machines and pick the vibration characteristics of one known to be in satisfactory condition to serve as a baseline. For even more accuracy, compute statistical median values for each component in the frequency spectra generated by similar machines, as well as list the maximum and minimum values recorded to serve as an envelope of known performance. The same results can be found with data taken over an extended time from one machine.

Relative strength of components

A normal low-frequency vibration spectrum, and some abnormal spectra as well, will be dominated by running frequency (figure 9–6). To gain an idea of machine condition from the simple spectrum shown, apply the severity chart limits modified for the specific machine type.

Most spectra will not be quite as simple as that shown in figure 9–6 but will contain additional components (figure 9–7). If the amplitudes

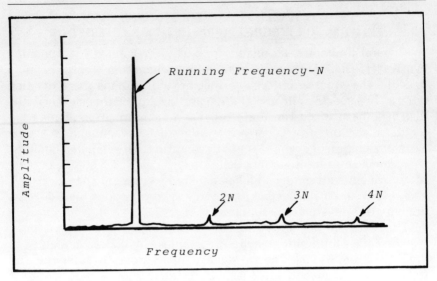

9–6—*Simple low-frequency vibration spectrum.*

of the added components are small, less than about ⅓ the amplitude at running frequency and decreasing in amplitude with increasing frequency, the spectrum is likewise normal and can be judged on the basis of the amplitude at running frequency.

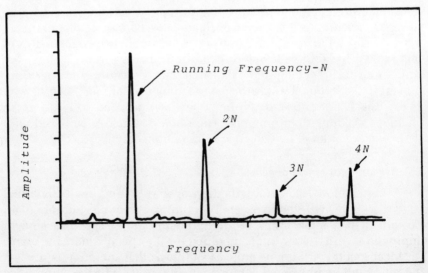

9–7—*Typical low-frequency vibration spectrum.*

If the spectrum contains components either above or below running speed in excess of about half the amplitude at running speed, then some fault may be present and the spectrum will have to be evaluated for an assessment of condition. Another clear abnormality is the presence of a nonsynchronous component above running speed. In the past, this has been connected to a failing auxiliary.

There are a couple of exceptions to the foregoing general criteria which should be noted. The spectrum recorded from a gearbox will normally contain components at shaft running frequencies which should be individually compared to limits. In fact, a gear spectrum might be seen as two discrete spectra superimposed on one another. Following this process, each running speed and its harmonics are evaluated exactly as described for spectra generated by machinery with only a single-running speed.

Gas turbines with two or more shafts fall into the same category; it is necessary to isolate and evaluate the characteristics produced by each shaft.

Finally, some spectral components are transmitted structurally from one machine to another where they may dominate the spectrum. It is not unusual for the casing spectrum of an outboard, gear-driven machine to contain a strong component at the running speed of the low-speed driver. To evaluate the condition of the high-speed unit, the presence of a low speed component can be ignored unless, of course, it is so strong that it is a threat to machine condition.

There are more variations, but these should provide some guidelines for evaluating a low-frequency spectrum. High-frequency spectra are evaluated in the same way except it is much more difficult to establish what a normal signature might be.

Establishing baseline characteristics

There are three principal methods for establishing baseline characteristics. First, the characteristics of a group of similar machines can be compared to the characteristics of one unit in the group in good condition. If more accuracy is desired, statistical medians can be calculated for each major component and the result, along with maximum and minimum values, used as a baseline as well as an envelope of expected performance. Finally, in the event a sample group is not available, the same results can be achieved by comparing the spectra generated by a single machine over a period of time.

The first method (figure 9–8) is relatively self-explanatory. The top signature was selected from about 11 units as the closest to describing

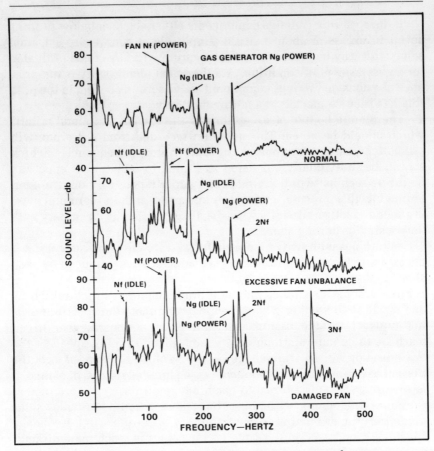

9–8—*Selecting a normal or baseline unit from a sample group.*

normal condition. In the middle signature, note a significantly larger component at fan running speed, indicating the possibility of fan imbalance in excess of the norm. Interestingly enough, the component at the gas generator running frequency in the middle signature is less than the same component in the top or baseline signature, indicating better condition in this area. Finally, the lower signature was taken on an engine with known fan damage. Note that the amplitude of the component at fan running frequency is much larger than the same component in the baseline signature and is followed by a series of prominent harmonics which are not present in the baseline.

The signatures displayed in figure 9–8 were collected on aircraft jet engines using a microphone placed inside the cabin with the aircraft at cruising altitude. Although signatures were obtained from a number of different engines in five different aircraft with varying sound treatments, the engine characteristics themselves were very consistent and repeatable. Thus, with a minimum of sophistication, a standard was developed upon which other identical units in a similar environment could be compared.

The next step is to identify, tabulate, and calculate statistical medians for the prominent components found in a typical signature. Figure 9–9 contains typical signatures and the baseline constructed for a two-shaft aircraft-derivative gas turbine driving a free turbine in power generating service. The lower or baseline signature was constructed from approximately eleven signatures of the type displayed directly above. The horizontal line in the middle of each shaded square represents the calculated median amplitude for each component, while the shaded areas represent the maximum and minimum amplitudes observed in the sample group. A low-frequency signature was used for illustrative purposes; however, the method works just as well with high-frequency signatures recognizing that there will be many more components, the variation of individual components will be greater, and hence the task will be far more complex.

Although a normal or baseline signature may not be representative of any single machine, it provides an idealized, detailed, quantitative model from which to compare the performance of similar machinery. This method establishes a statistical model, providing performance objectives as well as boundaries rather than relying on general criteria which may or may not be correct for the specific machine. Additionally, it provides realistic operating values without the need for a lengthy test program to determine a series of transfer functions. The statistical approach minimizes the effect of varying transmissibility on the assumption that identical machines will, within relatively close tolerances, respond in a similar fashion. For the statistical method to work, however, one must assume that the sample group does not have a common hidden defect. Additionally, extreme care must be exercised to ensure all the data are recorded under identical operating conditions, as many of the high frequency components will vary significantly in response to changes in density, pressure, flow, and speed.

The statistical baseline is most effective as a transparent overlay. In this fashion, one can quickly determine if a specific unit is better or worse than the median. In the event it is worse, the boundaries will tell how close one is to the limits of past experience. Using this method the best and most definitive measure of a machine's mechanical condition can be obtained.

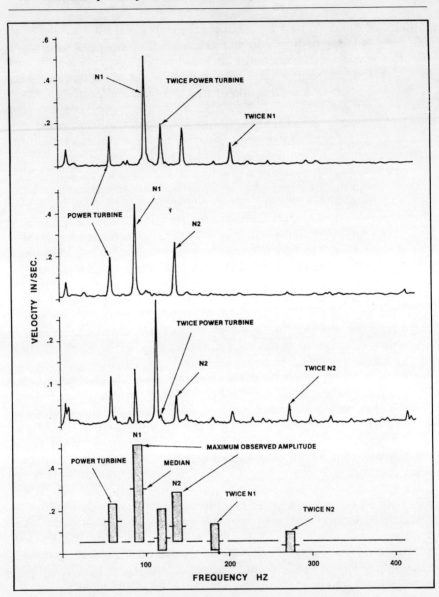

9–9—Constructing a statistical baseline signature.

Before leaving baseline criteria, there is one other salient point. Vibration components, particularly at the higher frequencies, are liable to change in amplitude with changes in operating conditions. Thus, in some cases a baseline signature constructed as described in the previous paragraphs may only apply to one set of operating conditions. Although it is possible to construct a varying baseline to accommodate changes in operating conditions, it is easiest to specify that certain operating conditions must be repeated each time a comparison is made.

In closing, a baseline signature can be used for comparing data with a computer. In this regard two points should be made. First, the deviations from the normal or baseline value must be large enough to accommodate normal variations, yet small enough so that trends can be recognized. Second, the area between components should have some sort of threshold set such that normal low level noise in the signal will be ignored, yet the system will recognize the appearance of any additional meaningful spectral activity.

10

Machinery Diagnostics—Identifying Typical Problems

Assuming that the analyst thoroughly understands his machinery and its dynamic behavior, knows what measurements to make and how to make them, can display the measurements in a variety of ways, and observes something that appears abnormal, now he needs to know what it is, how long can it be tolerated, and what corrective action can be taken either to eliminate the problem or at least reduce its impact.

SUBSYNCHRONOUS INSTABILITY

Subsynchronous (fractional) instability can be generated by several different mechanisms of which oil whirl is usually the most commonly observed. Perhaps the easiest way to visualize oil whirl is to imagine the shaft riding the crest of an oil pressure gradient which is rotating within the bearing clearance at approximately one-half shaft speed. Oil whirl occurs when the bearing is unable to exert sufficient force on the shaft to break the pressure gradient and hold the shaft in position. To correct an oil whirl, install bearings which can develop a greater force on the shaft, such as pressure dam or tilt pad designs.

Apart from oil whirl, subsynchronous instability can be caused by frictional or hysteretic forces generated at shrink or rabbit fits, by uneven clearances around the circumference of a rotating element, and by metal contact, the so-called dry friction whip. All have about the same symptom: rotor precession at a frequency approximately one-half rotational speed.

In a simple time-domain display on an oscilloscope, subsynchronous instability will cause the running frequency to wander or snake (figure 10–1a). If the subsynchronous frequency is exactly 50% running frequency, the waveform will be stationary; otherwise, instability will appear as flutter superimposed on the running frequency waveform. A shaft orbit with an inside loop and two-phase reference marks in a single revolution of the orbit (Figure 10–1b) is sometimes observed accompanying instability. This orbit requires a subsynchronous frequency at eactly 50% running speed. Since this is rarely the case, the typical orbit with a low-level fractional frequency is the multiple loop unstable appearing trace (figure 10–2). Although the orbits in figures 7–5, 10-1b, and 10–2 are considerably different, the waveforms all have the characteristic wander associated with subsynchronous instability.

The presence of two timing marks in a single orbital revolution such as in figure 10-1b indicates the shaft makes two revolutions while the orbit completes one, or the orbit is traveling at one-half shaft speed. In all but the case of dry frictional whirl, orbital precession or motion is forward in the direction of shaft rotation. Dry frictional whirl causes the rotor to precess backward against the direction of shaft rotation.

Although an orbit shows the actual shaft movement within its bearing and is valuable in studies of rotor dynamics, subsynchronous

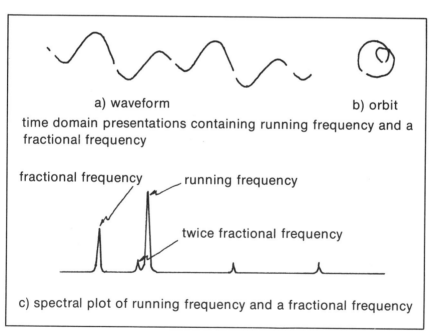

a) waveform   b) orbit

time domain presentations containing running frequency and a fractional frequency

fractional frequency   running frequency

twice fractional frequency

c) spectral plot of running frequency and a fractional frequency

10–1—*Characteristics of subsynchronous instability.*

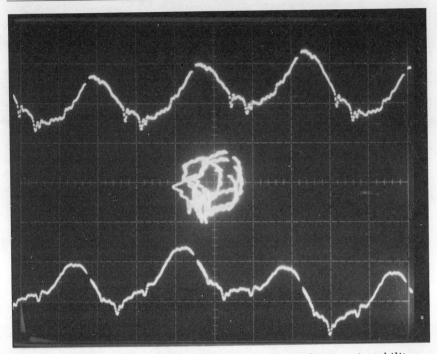

10–2—Waveform and orbit illustrating slight subsynchronous instability.

instability is generally identified from an amplitude versus frequency (spectrum) presentation. As shown in figure 10–1c, the subsynchronous component is clearly visible, its frequency can be quickly and accurately measured, and dynamic properties which may be difficult to quantify in the time domain and orbital presentations are clearly visible. The ability to recognize a low-level spectral component and observe its dynamic characteristics can be extremely important; for in most cases the subsynchronous frequency that identifies instability will first appear at a relatively low amplitude fluctuating irregularly with time.

When the forces restraining the instability are reduced or lost, its amplitude may suddenly increase significantly and stabilize at a value much higher than the amplitude at running frequency. At this point the subsynchronous instability is the dominant vibration, with the result that both the observed waveform and orbit are predominantly at the subsynchronous frequency. The subsynchronous frequency can be calculated from the waveform and will be noted in what is now a circular or nearly circular orbit with two timing marks per resolution.

The destabilizing force producing the instability can be external or internal (figure 10–3). In this example, a cascade vibration spectrum recorded on a compressor during surge, a subsynchronous frequency is excited during the transient which occurred as the reversal in flow jolted the rotor. Fortunately, the bearing system controlled the instability; however, this may not always be the case, as illustrated in figure 10–4 where instability initiated by prolonged surge resulted in a rub and destruction.

Figure 10–4 is another cascade spectrum constructed from the shaft vibration signal recorded on a centrifugal compressor during surge. The plot begins at the lower left with the compressor operating normally. As the compressor begins surging, the speed changes caused by the large variations in load produce wavy lines at running frequency, 2N and 3N, which begin about one fifth the way up the left cascade. As surge continues, the shocks accompanying the violent flow reversal excite the rotor. In turn, the rotor responds at a subsynchronous frequency which can be seen to the left of running frequency, beginning about one-third the way up the left cascade. The amplitude of the instability increases as the surge continues and begins to form its own harmonic orders. Also note that the frequency of the subsynchronous component remains essentially constant and does not track speed.

At the bottom of the right-hand cascade, the instability has progressed to where the compressor is rubbing. Since continued operation is futile, the compressor is tripped about one-fifth up the right-hand cascade. Note that even though speed decreases rapidly, as shown by the leftward curve of running frequency and its harmonics, the subsynchronous component remains essentially constant in frequency until it suddenly drops out about one-third of the way up the right cascade with compressor speed reduced to about 75%. This phenomena is quite common in cases of instability due to the fact that it is self-excited and will maintain itself at a considerably lower speed than the speed required for initiation.

As the compressor continues to coast down, an amplitude increase can be observed as the running speed passes through the frequency at which the subsynchronous instability had appeared. In this case, the amplitude increase and the subsynchronous excitation occurred at the critical speed of the compressor.

The specific frequency at which subsynchronous instability occurs may vary up or down depending on what is producing the instability. Pure oil whirl occurs at 43% of shaft speed; however, instability may

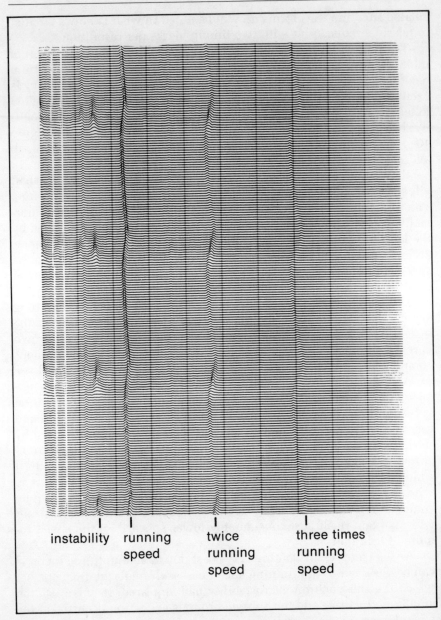

instability   running   twice   three times
               speed   running   running
                               speed   speed

10–3—Instability during stage.

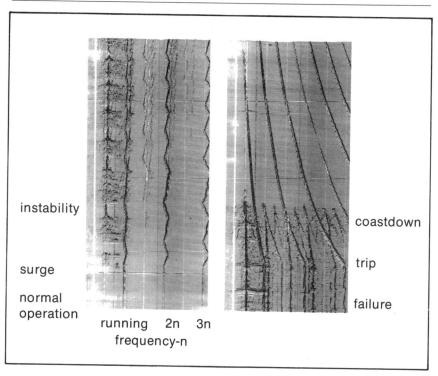

instability

surge

normal
operation

running   2n   3n
frequency-n

coastdown

trip

failure

10–4—Cascade spectrum during machine failure.

occur at the first critical speed, as was the case in figure 10–4, or at
some intermediate point between the two. Thus, subsynchronous instability may be observed from approximately 35% of running speed to
something above 50% of running speed.

What causes subsynchronous instability? The most common example, oil whirl, is caused or perhaps allowed by a bearing which cannot
exert sufficient preload on the rotating shaft to hold it in a stable
position. When a bearing is prone to instability, any outside force
which upsets the bearing load may provide the conditions necessary
for the onset of instability. Surge, a change in oil temperature, or even
changing alignment during a heavy rainstorm is often enough to
produce instability which, since it is self-exciting, remains after the
initial conditions are restored. On rare occasions, minor operating
changes such as a change in oil temperature may eliminate instability;
however, it is often necessary to reduce speed by a significant amount
to eliminate the condition. When the excitation is eliminated, speed

may be returned to its original value and the bearing will usually remain stable at least until upset again. Instability is like a coin balanced on edge; it will remain standing until disturbed, at which time it falls over, requiring outside assistance to restore its original balanced state. The only saving grace associated with instability is that it occurs at a frequency much lower than running speed, where larger displacements can often be tolerated.

Subsynchronous instability can be caused by a number of factors, the most common of which is an inadequate bearing design. Even with a good bearing design, however, it can be caused by oil seals or oil dams—anything which will allow a rotating oil film to exist and apply a force on the shaft. Corrective measures under these conditions nearly always require a change in design, such as decreasing the axial length of the seal or cutting grooves to break up the oil film. An external force such as may be applied on a shaft by coupling misalignment is another possible cause of instability. Although flexible couplings are not supposed to transmit shear forces, they do and in severe cases can produce instability. In fact, in the opposite condition, deliberate misalignment in a direction to load instead of unload, a bearing has been used on numerous occasions to eliminate instability and permit continued operation while a more permanent solution was devised. Condenser vacuum, probably because of its effect on alignment and hence bearing preload, is another operating variable which is associated with instability.

If changes in operating variables and alignment followed by minor changes in design are insufficient to eliminate the instability, major changes will probably be required. Changing to a more stable bearing such as a tilt pad is generally the first and most common design change. Quite often a change in bearings will be accompanied by a seal change in which the seals are designed to exert a minimum amount of force on the shaft. Finally and the most drastic is to increase the diameter of the shaft, shorten the bearing span, or both.

IMBALANCE

Imbalance is nearly always observed as a high radial amplitude of vibration at running frequency (figure 10–5) and may be accompanied by a high axial amplitude. The latter is often confusing and may lead to a false conclusion that misalignment is present. Where the bearing or structure is not equally stiff in all planes, it is not uncommon to observe a large variation in amplitude, depending on where the measurement is taken. To cite a specific example, a pressure dam bearing restraining an

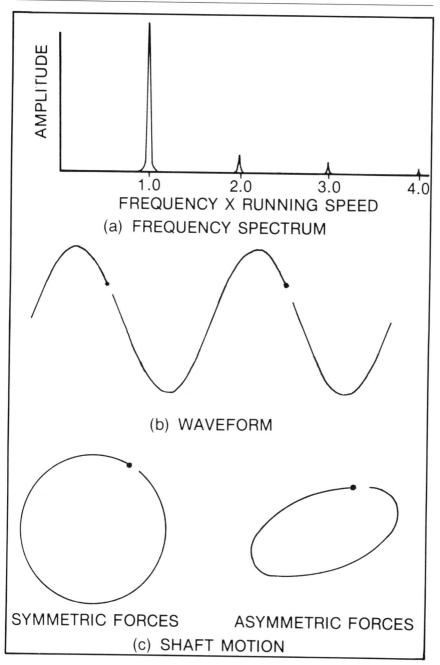

(a) FREQUENCY SPECTRUM

(b) WAVEFORM

SYMMETRIC FORCES   ASYMMETRIC FORCES

(c) SHAFT MOTION

10–5—Characteristics of imbalance.

unbalanced rotor will usually produce a tilted elliptical shaft orbit (figure 10–6). In this situation the minor axis coincides with the line of action through the pressure dam where the bearing applies maximum force on the shaft.

In general, imbalance can be caused in two ways. The most common is that produced by a physical difference between the mass center and rotating center of a rotor. Imbalance caused by movement or a shift in the rotor produced by centrifugal or magnetic forces or by temperature gradients is less-often observed but usually easy to diagnose. As an example of the latter, uneven heating will cause a rotor to bend, producing imbalance. It is not uncommon to observe this phenomenon while starting large steam turbines where uneven heating from gland steam produces a thermal bow which must then be run out at low speed before the unit can be placed in operation. Thermal distortion can also occur during operation, producing an imbalance condition that changes with load or perhaps time.

As implied by the previous paragraph, a bent or bowed shaft will exhibit most of the same characteristics as imbalance. About the only way to tell the difference between the two is to observe the Bode or amplitude versus speed response of the rotor as it is brought to speed. In cases where the rotor is bent or bowed, shaft amplitude, corrected for any runout, will decrease at some speed as the forces developed by the bow and mechanical imbalance cancel each other. If the bow is less than the imbalance, the decrease in amplitude will occur below the critical speed. If the bow is greater than the imbalance, the decrease in amplitude will occur above the critical.

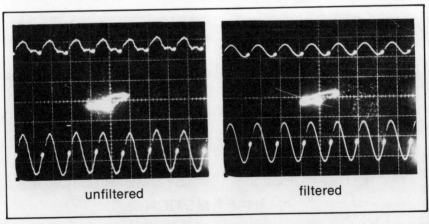

unfiltered   filtered

10–6—*Imbalance waveform and orbit.*

Pure mechanical imbalance will also cause a change in response at the critical speed. As shown in figure 10–7, excessive imbalance will often produce an abnormally high peak amplitude at the critical speed and, while it will decrease as the critical is passed, the reduction will not be as great as with a balanced rotor. In addition to a larger amplitude following the critical speed, the vibration amplitude observed on an unbalanced shaft is likely to increase rapidly with shaft speed. Besides an increased peak amplitude at the critical speed with an unbalanced shaft, the location of the critical may be shifted several hundred rpm due to a nonlinear response at large amplitudes of shaft vibration.

A discussion on imbalance would not be complete without mentioning couplings and the effect of overhung weight. By itself there is nothing to stabilize a coupling except the shaft's resistance to bending. Large overhung weights must be avoided on high-speed machinery; hence, stub shafts are generally as short as possible with the center of gravity of the coupling located close to its inboard end. In extreme cases, machines could not be tested uncoupled with coupling hubs attached without the stabilizing influence of an adjacent coupled shaft. In this situation the only way to perform an uncoupled test was to

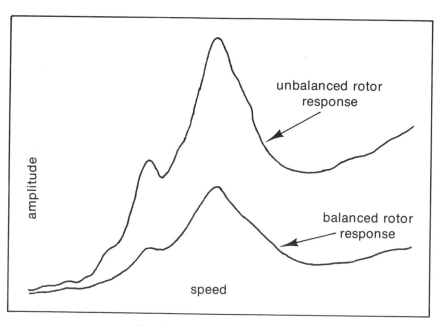

10–7—Amplitude response of an unbalanced rotor.

fabricate a light sleeve to hold a half-key in place for the duration of the test.

Excessive overhung imbalance may in rare cases produce a strong vibration component at twice running frequency. The overhung imbalance can be caused by a coupling or by imbalance of the rotating element itself on pumps and compressors where the impeller is overhung.

COUPLING PROBLEMS—MISALIGNMENT

The vibration characteristics associated with misaligned flexible couplings are not a direct measure of the amount of misalignment but of the coupled system's ability to accommodate misalignment. Thus, the external symptoms of misalignment, in addition to being a function of the offset between shafts, are also affected by speed, torque, or any other condition such as corrosion or sludging which may alter the coupling's stiffness and hence its ability to accommodate a given offset. Due to the angles involved, a long spacer can accommodate more misalignment than a short one; however, a long coupling spacer will usually present dynamic problems on high-speed machines due to overhung mass. For this reason, the coupling spacers used in most high-speed machines will seldom exceed 18 in. (45 cm) in length. As a general rule of thumb, most operating organizations consider alignment offsets up to ½ mil/in. (5 μm/cm) of spacer length to be a safe value which can be tolerated in continuous operation.

As illustrated in figure 10–8, vibration at twice running frequency is the symptom associated with misalignment. A high axial amplitude at rotating frequency is another symptom. However, there are other conditions which can cause a high axial vibration. As a rule of thumb, if the amplitude at twice running frequency is 30–75% of the amplitude at running frequency, the misalignment can probably be tolerated by the coupling for a relatively long time. When the double-frequency amplitude is 75 to 150% of the amplitude at running speed, some coupling damage is likely to occur and the situation should be closely monitored and corrected at first opportunity. When the amplitude at twice running speed exceeds 150% of the amplitude at running frequency, the misalignment is producing a severe action at the coupling which is likely to produce accelerated wear and ultimately failure.

A failure due to misalignment can take many forms on flexible gear-type couplings. Most obvious is discolored, scored, or worn coupling teeth; however, there have been cases where the coupling proved stronger than the adjacent bearing, which pounded out with little actual damage to the coupling itself.

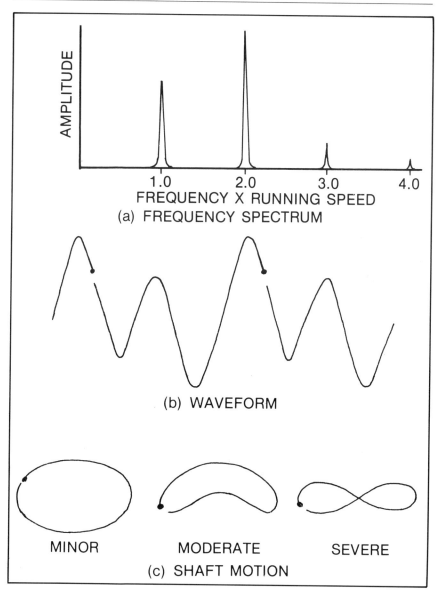

10–8—*Characteristics of misalignment.*

Likewise, the coupling forces may be strong enough to stabilize the system adjacent to the coupling and suppress the symptoms of misalignment. When this occurs, the strongest reaction to misalignment takes place not at the coupling but at the free or outboard end of the machine.

Large offsets in alignment, a relative term depending on the coupling's ability to accommodate misalignment, can result in unloading a bearing enough to induce instability. In this situation, the presence of instability provides valuable confirmation, along with an indication of the direction of misalignment, for obviously the unstable bearing must be low relative to the adjacent coupled bearing.

Bearing temperature and oil-film pressure are other indirect methods of detecting misalignment. Measured through ports sometimes provided for lift oil on large turbine generators, the latter is a measure of bearing load as is bearing temperature measured with sensors imbedded in the bearing metal. With both methods a bearing misaligned low will have a lower pressure and temperature than its higher partner. Since alignment usually changes as a machine is brought to full operating temperature, recording the amplitudes at running speed and twice running speed, as well as bearing temperature and pressure when available, may provide a valuable indicator of the direction and degree of misalignment.

The causes of misalignment are numerous; however, forces transmitted to the machine from piping are probably the most common. Incorrect estimates of thermal growth and uneven shifting or settling of the foundation on which the machines are mounted are other common sources of misalignment.

Another problem common to gear-type couplings is the locked coupling where the frictional force developed at the gear teeth is greater than the applied force causing the coupling to become a rigid member. A locked coupling can cause severe problems and may lead to a thrust bearing failure if it results in the thrust load of two machines being applied to one thrust bearing.

Figure 10–9 illustrates an extreme example of a configuration in which a locked coupling could produce a thrust bearing failure. The driver is a high-temperature steam turbine with its casing held in the axial direction at the end opposite the coupling. The turbine thrust bearing is adjacent to the coupling with the direction of normal thrust outboard or away from the coupling. Although there is little relative motion between shaft and casing at the coupling, the casing moves over 0.250 in. into the compressor from cold to hot, carrying the shaft with it. The compressor thrust bearing is also located at its coupling end and, although there isn't much growth, the direction of normal thrust is toward the coupling.

When the string is started, the turbine immediately begins moving

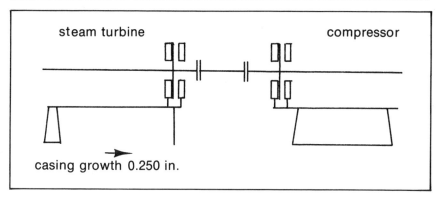

10–9a—Machine string prone to coupling lockup.

toward the compressor. If the coupling between the two locks, the axial movement forces the compressor off its active thrust shoes which transfers the compressor's thrust load into the turbine thrust bearing. As would be expected, the added load on the turbine thrust bearing causes a large temperature increase. In this situation, one must only

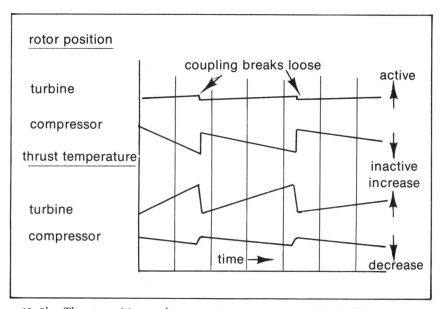

10–9b—Thrust position and temperature response as string in Figure 9a is brought to operating temperature.

hope that the axial force necessary to cause the coupling to slip when combined with the turbine's normal thrust force is not enough to cause a thrust bearing failure.

This actual case illustrates two points: how locked couplings can transfer thrust loads and produce failures, and the necessity of instrumentation. By observing the thrust bearing metal temperature and axial position of the two machines, one knows exactly what is occurring and can safely continue the startup. Without instrumentation or perhaps with partial instrumentation, the problem will either be undetected or its seriousness discounted with the possibility of a catastrophic thrust failure. Although it takes a certain amount of fortitude, deliberately surging a compressor may shock a coupling enough to allow it to slip axially. However, that this is an action of last resort and may damage an already overloaded thrust bearing.

There is another often-used method of detecting stiff or locked couplings on operating equipment. If one compares phase-referenced axial vibration waveforms obtained from shaft probes and finds they are in phase, after accounting for probe orientation of course, the coupling may be locked. If axial shaft movement is out of phase, the coupling cannot be locked.

MECHANICAL LOOSENESS

Mechanical looseness, the improper fit between component parts, is generally characterized by a long string of harmonics of running frequency at abnormally high amplitudes. Although the exact method by which the harmonics are generated is not well understood, they are probably originated by the nonlinear response of the loose part to a dynamic input from the rotor. This type of phenomenon has been observed on machines where the bearing liner was loose in its cap (figure 10–10). Although not observed at the time because the signal was not being analyzed in sufficient detail, indications are that the same general characteristics were present during the last stages of a shaft fatigue failure.

Thus, one can safely conclude that, regardless of their exact origin, a string of relatively high amplitude harmonics is clearly abnormal. Also recognize that a shaft scratch(es) will produce the same symptoms in the signal obtained from a noncontact displacement probe.

RUBS

Rubs are said to be accompanied by a great deal of high-frequency spectral activity; however, in the case of signals obtained from shaft

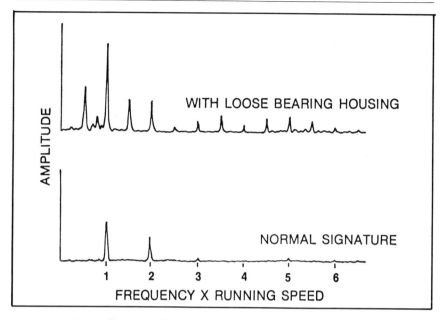

10–10—Spectral characteristics of mechanical looseness.

probes, the same symptoms can be caused by scratches or other defects. Although there have been exceptions, a rub is generally a transitory phenomenon; it either rubs clear or produces other symptoms such as a shaft bow which makes continued operation impossible. While a rub and rub symptoms may be observed on start, it is highly unlikely that the same symptoms observed on a machine which has been operating for several months or years would be caused by a rub. The analyst should keep these thoughts in mind whenever observations suggest a rub.

A flattened waveform and orbit (figure 10–11) are strong indications of a rub. Note that the shaft is restrained and rubbing in the horizontal plane with vertical motion nearly normal. Although such a strong rub usually produces a shaft bow, nearly identical symptoms were observed during the startup of a centrifugal compressor where an improperly installed coupling guard was rubbing on the coupling. In the latter case, even though the rub was not hard enough to cause any damage and eventually cleared itself, it applied enough force to severely restrain the shaft and distort its motion.

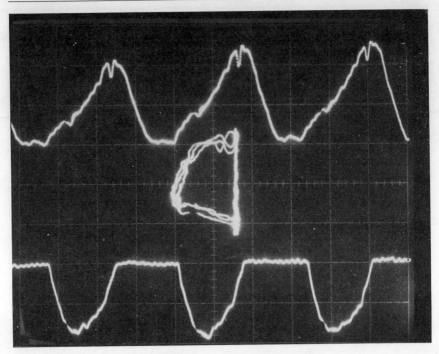

10–11—Waveform and orbit of a rub.

ELECTRIC DISCHARGE

Bearing failure due to a high shaft voltage discharging through bearings or seals is not uncommon on high-speed machinery. This is caused by the buildup of static electricity on a magnetized rotor or a rotor passing through a humid atmosphere. As some potential difference to ground, the static electricity discharges across the path of least resistance at the small clearances at bearings and seals. The discharge initially produces a frosted surface on the bearings, perhaps accompanied by spark tracks, which in extreme cases will lead to pitting and the loss of bearing material. The problem can be difficult to recognize in its initial stages, for it does not alter any of the commonly measured external characteristics. A voltage from the shaft to ground is of course the direct way to identify this condition; however, it may be a difficult task to find an open section of shaft on which to make the measurement.

A loss of bearing material, sensed as a changing DC gap voltage from a noncontact shaft transducer, is often the first real warning of a bearing failure from electric discharge. The condition is corrected by either demagnetizing the rotor or installing grounding brushes at some point along the shaft.

There is speculation that electric discharge can, under some conditions, be observed in the signal obtained from a shaft displacement transducer. Figure 10–12 shows a shaft waveform recorded on a turbine suffering from electric discharge. The irregularity in the waveform was extremely unstable, sometimes present and sometimes not, and continued despite changing pickups, cables, and oscillator demodulators.

RESONANCE

Resonance, or the excitation of a component at its natural frequency, can often be a problem on rotating machinery. When the component is a blade or impeller, the problem is extremely serious and can produce catastrophic failures. More often, however, resonance will occur on machine auxiliaries such as piping, instrument stands, con-

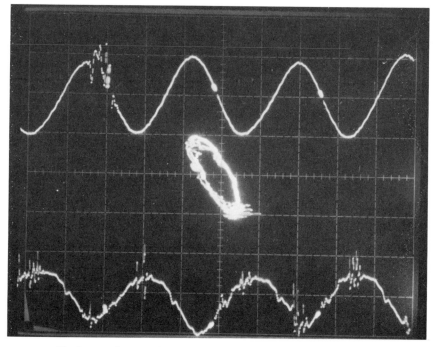

10–12—Shaft waveform and orbit containing irregular excitation which could be related to or caused by electrostatic discharge.

trol linkages, and cantilevered governors. In these situations, resonance is generally an annoyance which can be controlled or corrected by relatively simple changes.

As discussed earlier, a component will exhibit a very high vibration when stimulated at its natural frequency. If the component happens to be a blade or piping with a natural frequency close to a source of excitation from the machine, the vibration will probably lead to failure. With small components such as piping and instrument stands, it is usually not difficult to change characteristics by modifications, such as braces which add stiffness and thereby raise the natural frequency to a point where it is no longer excited. One must be a little careful; for if the original natural frequency was slightly below the excitation, adding stiffness may just make the situation worse.

An easy test to confirm the presence of resonance and determine its exact frequency is to attach a small vibration transducer such as an accelerometer (it must be light enough that it won't affect the component's response) and strike the component with a soft object such as a block of wood. The resulting response, viewed on an instrument such as a real-time analyzer, will be at the natural frequency(s) of the component. This method of shock testing has been used successfully on a wide variety of structures and components, ranging from buildings to small piping.

If it is impossible to alter stiffness sufficiently to correct a resonant problem, the addition of a resonant damper may at least make the situation tolerable.

BLADING PROBLEMS

Blades are subject to a variety of exciting forces, ranging from those at running speed to multiples of the upstream blade or nozzle-passing frequency. They in turn have a number of natural frequencies individually or as groups, depending on the method of mounting, which must not be excited without danger of overstressing and eventual failure. Add to this the fact that many bladed machines must operate through a wide speed range, and one can appreciate the problem faced by the blade designer attempting to ensure that a response and source of excitation can never coincide.

In order to gain an appreciation of how and why blades fail, one must first understand the sources of the excitation to which they are subjected. Beginning with the low frequencies, uneven blade or nozzle clearances can excite blades at running frequency or its low-order multiples. For example, a diaphragm installed at an angle (figure 10–13a) applies more force to the blades where the clearance is least and less where the clearance is greatest. With the angular diaphragm, the blades are subjected to a variation in force at running frequency. If the diaphragm is angled at the center (figure 10–13b), the result is a force on the blades which varies at a frequency of twice per revolution. Similarly, a flow discontinuity such as might occur at a horizontal split can pulse blades twice per revolution.

Thus far it has been implied that the excitation is a sinusoid producing only a fundamental frequency at once or twice per revolution. The excitation, however, is seldom a pure sinusoid and the deviations produce harmonics at multiples of the excitation. Thus, from a one or two per revolution event, the blades can be excited at one or two times running speed and at higher-order harmonics.

Venturing into the higher frequencies, blade and nozzle-passing frequencies are an obvious source of excitation as well as harmonics produced. The spacing or the number of openings which would exist in 360° determines the fundamental frequency generated by partial admission nozzles or blading, not the openings actually present.

Within this menagerie of excitations, is there anything that can be measured externally which will provide some idea of blade condition? Although not yet at a stage where it can be quantified, the answer appears to be a qualified yes. The excitation imposed by stationary blades on rotor blades is transmitted into the rotor as is the rotor blade's response to that excitation. Unfortunately, transmission losses in the path from the rotor to an externally mounted transducer are fairly

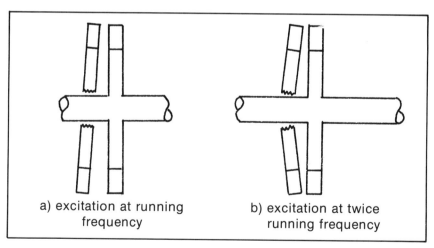

a) excitation at running
frequency

b) excitation at twice
running frequency

10–13—Blade excitation produced by tilted diaphragms.

large—at least 50 dB and probably much greater, based on one limited test. Thus, to examine rotor blades one must either have a very large excitation capable of producing measurable energy at the end of a high impedance transmission path or make the measurement on the rotor itself and bring out the information with slip rings or telemetry.

Although there have been only a few reported cases of blade failures on machines subjected to detailed broadband vibration analysis, in some cases there were clear abnormalities visible in vibration characteristics measured externally on the casing. In one case a relatively high-amplitude nonsynchronous component was noted in an external signature at a location close to an expected blade natural frequency. Over a period of months, the component decreased in frequency and amplitude until it finally stabilized. When the turbine was opened for inspection several months later, a number of cracked blades were found. Reconstructing what had been observed, it was concluded that the blades' natural frequency had been excited by a low-order harmonic of running speed located slightly higher than the natural frequency. The excitation at a natural frequency overstressed the blades and initiated a crack. As the crack grew, the blades' natural frequency decreased and moved away from the excitation until the stress levels were insufficient to continue crack growth. At this point the condition stabilized.

In another case a high-frequency spectra recorded on a steam turbine; the upper spectrum (figure 10–14) was immediately recognized as abnormal due to an excessive number of relatively high-amplitude harmonics between 12 kHz and 15 kHz. Although the mechanism

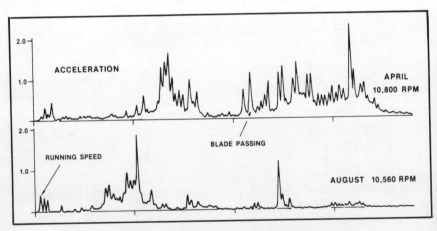

10–14—*Stream turbine exhaust casing signatures.*

producing the harmonics and the method of transmission into an external casing-mounted accelerometer is unknown, the visual evidence led to a prediction of damaged or cracked blades which was subsequently confirmed when the machine was disassembled and inspected. The lower signature is normal, recorded after rotor replacement.

In still another controlled test, the amplitude at rotor blade passing frequency generated by a machine with known blade damage was higher than amplitudes recorded on similar machinery at similar power levels. In contrast a series of signatures were recorded on a turbine which less than two weeks later suffered a blade failure. Nothing could be found which could have led to a prediction of a failure.

Based on this limited experience, it would appear that in some cases there may be external symptoms of an impending blade failure. Although these characteristics may not be quantifiable, they appear sufficient to focus attention on a potential problem area which can then be investigated by other methods.

As stated earlier, the best method is undoubtedly to extract the required data directly from the shaft using implanted sensors and either slip rings or radio telemetry. As machinery grows larger and the cost of a blade failure escalates, emphasis in this area will increase.

GEARING

Like most machinery, gears are subject to common problems such as imbalance and misalignment. There are, however, some significant differences in the symptoms.

Bearing forces are determined mainly by torque rather than element weight. This is particularly true of a light pinion in a high-ratio gear unit. Since torque forces act roughly perpendicular to the line through the gear axes, dynamic forces generated by one or both of the gear elements will generally produce a highly assymetric response. As a specific example, element imbalance will generally produce a much larger response in the plane through the gear axes where the restraining force is least (figure 10–15).

As a general statement, gear radial bearings are usually more heavily loaded than radial bearings on either the driver or driven equipment. Due to the higher loading, gear bearings often run hotter than the bearings in coupled equipment but seldom experience problems with subsynchronous instability.

In high-speed single-increase or reduction-gear units, an up pinion (a pinion which rides in the upper half of its bearing, figure 10–16) is

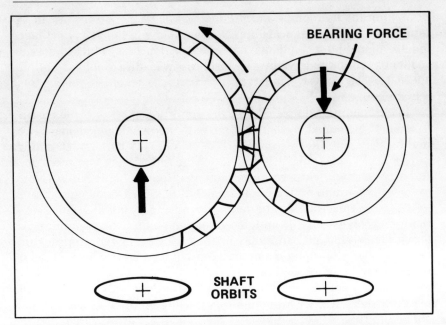

10–15—Gear rotor response due to asymmetrical bearing forces.

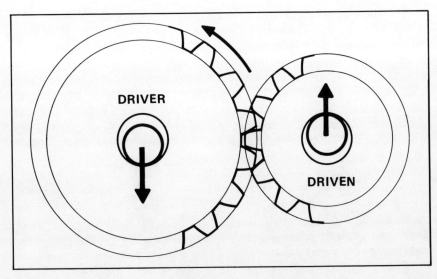

10–16—Gear rotor response due to torque forces.

generally preferred. With this arrangement, the lightweight pinion is lifted into an operating position at very low loads. The point where gravity and torque are more or less in balance may sometimes be observed as an excessive and erratic shaft vibration which stabilizes and decreases as load is applied.

In the reverse situation (an up gear) the unstable region will exist at a higher load due to the larger weight of the gear which must be balanced by applied torque. Failure to provide adequate lubrication and bearing surface for a partial load condition where the gear was actually riding in a 9 o'clock position led to a massive failure on a large speed reducer required to operate at reduced load for extended periods.

In addition, there are several problems unique to gears which may be observed in their vibration characteristics. As shown in figure 10–17, pitch line runout will move one or possibly both gears in the plane through the gear axes in response to the mechanical variations at the point of contact. Defined as eccentricity or offset between the pitch cylinder and the shaft centerline, pitch line runout is most often a

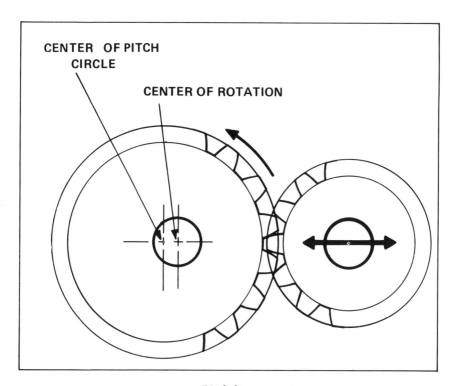

10–17—Pitch line runout.

once-per-revolution variation; however, there have been reports of periodic variations at other than once per revolution. The symptoms of pitch line runout are easy to recognize: a dominant vibration at the running speed of one shaft which is several times higher in the plane through the shafts compared to the plane perpendicular to the shafts. Sidebands, spaced at intervals corresponding to the running frequency of the affected shaft on either side of the gear mesh frequency and caused by amplitude modulation, would likely be present as well. Most easily recognized from an examination of shaft motion, pitch line runout should produce in-phase elliptical orbits on both shafts with the major axis in the meshing plane through the shafts. The orbits will be precessing at the frequency of one shaft, with the larger amplitude occurring on the lighter shaft.

As is usually the case in machinery analysis, these symptoms can be anomalous for the dynamics of a gear system; high vertical preloads and torque forces combined with rotor imbalance can produce the same symptoms as pitch line runout.

Apex runout (figure 10–18) is a second potential anomaly sometimes found on double helical gears which can influence the amplitude at running frequency, this time in the axial plane. Defined as an axial

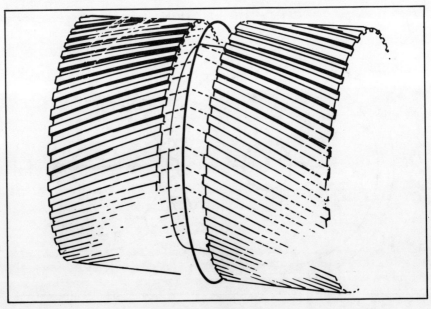

10–18—Apex runout.

variation measured from a plane perpendicular to the gear axis to a surface through the imaginary points of intersection between opposite pairs of teeth, apex runout causes the gears to shuttle longitudinally in their case at a frequency determined by the periodicity of the runout. Excessive axial motion of the pinion at gear-running frequency or some integer multiple is a certain symptom of apex runout on the gear. Depending on the type and location of the thrust bearing, apex runout on the pinion may or may not force the gear to move excessively at pinion frequency; however, if the gear is unable to move, the pinion must.

A tooth-spacing error or variation in the distance between adjacent teeth will cause the gear to accelerate and deaccelerate alternately as teeth with slightly different spacing come into mesh. Tooth-spacing error produces an instant speed fluctuation similar to torsional vibration at a frequency corresponding to the periodicity of the error.

Barreling or uneven heating of a gear element is more of an operating characteristic than an error. Illustrated in figure 10–19, gears, especially the smaller element, have a tendency to heat more in the center than at the edges, causing differential expansion or barreling. Since heating is a measure of load, barreling is a self-increasing phenomena;

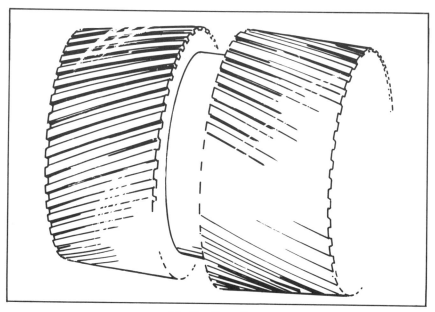

10–19—Barreling.

i.e., as the gear expands unevenly, load is transferred to the center which creates more heat and causes further expansion. Normally, gears are shaped to compensate for small values of differential expansion.

Critical speeds, both lateral and torsional, are likewise gear characteristics which must be understood. Critical speeds, particularly torsional critical speeds, are a system design criteria well beyond the scope of this brief discussion; however, one should be aware of their location, recognize that natural frequencies can be excited by multiples of running speed as well as running speed itself, and realize that any potential excitation is as far away from a natural frequency as possible, at least 30%. Since gears have at least two fundamental frequencies and generally produce a greater number of harmonics than other rotating machines, there is a broad range in which the potential for exciting a critical speed may exist. In this or any case where a resonance is excited by a high-order harmonic, the change in amplitude response will take place across a very narrow speed range. For example, a resonance which has an amplification greater than 1 across 300 cpm (5 Hz) and is excited by a tenth-order harmonic will be traversed with a 30-rpm speed change.

Thus far the primary characteristics of the anomolies discussed occur in the low-frequency range around running speed. As pointed out in chapter 8, gears also generate high-frequency characteristics which are valuable indicators of condition. Figure 10–20 illustrates a progressive failure where the primary symptoms occurred in the intermediate frequencies located approximately midway between rotational speeds and gear mesh frequency. The normal signature shown at the bottom contains both rotational and intermediate frequencies at amplitudes which are about average for this type gear. Although the middle signature contains a vast increase in the intermediate frequencies, neither the rotational frequencies nor the gear-mesh frequency (not shown) changed by any significant degree. Recognizing a condition of extreme distress, the unit was shut down orderly. A visual inspection disclosed the heavy pitted gear elements (figure 10–21). Surprisingly, the journal bearings were undamaged despite the severe excitation.

In an effort to learn the origin and cause of the large increase in amplitude at the intermediate frequencies, both the gear and the pinion were suspended and shock excited. The tests disclosed that the 1,200-Hz center of the intermediate frequencies corresponded exactly to the lowest natural frequency of the low speed gear.

The bearing shown in Figure 10–22 was removed from another speed-increasing gear following a large increase in amplitude at the

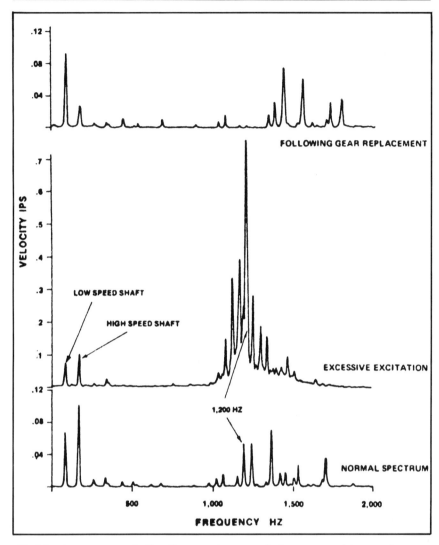

10–20—A sequence of vibration spectra recorded on a speed-increasing gear illustrating normal gear condition (bottom), heavy pitting along the pitch line (center), and normal condition following gear replacement (top).

intermediate frequencies over a six-month period. Although the bearing was heavily damaged and obviously had only a short life remaining, there were no other recognizable symptoms of an impending catastrophic failure nor would those responsible for the gear have

10–21—Photograph of pitted gear which produced the middle spectrum in figure 10–20.

10–22—Damaged pinion bearing removed from a speed-increasing gear displaying similar symptoms to those illustrated in the middle spectrum in figure 10–20.

conducted a visual inspection had not the significance of the change in vibration characteristics been noted. In addition to the two cases where the intermediate frequencies were the primary symptom of an impending failure, there have been numerous nearly identical events reported on a number of similar gears.

Although the exact generating mechanism is unknown, it may well be that the intermediate frequencies represent an external response to excitation at a gear's natural frequency. As long as the excitation is low, normal, smooth entry and exit from mesh, the response—even though magnified by resonant amplification—is also low. However, any change or anomaly which produces a shock at mesh likewise increases the excitation with a corresponding amplified response. Thus, a high amplitude or an increase in amplitude at the intermediate frequencies is likely to be a symptom of uneven or shock meshing which could be caused by tooth or bearing damage.

The gear-mesh frequency is generally one of the most prominent characteristics in the sound and vibration spectra generated by gearing. Although initially thought to be a potentially valuable indicator of gear condition, its use is difficult due to normal variations in amplitude. Amplitude at the mesh frequency may vary greatly from gear to gear (levels from less than 1 G to 30–40 Gs acceleration have been observed on gears which were apparently functioning normally). However, a sudden change in mesh amplitude may indicate problems on a gear when conditions of load and speed have remained essentially unchanged.

Apart from relatively long-term variations in amplitude at mesh frequency such as those caused by changes in load, there may be shorter-term variations generated in the meshing process itself. Important from a diagnostic standpoint, these variations represent differences in mesh characteristics around the circumference of the gear and may be observed as sidebands on either side of the mesh frequency as well as around the harmonics of gear-mesh frequency.

Although the sidebands of mesh frequency can be observed in a direct frequency spectrum, additional equipment often must be utilized to obtain sufficient resolution. As a result, demodulation techniques— both amplitude and frequency—have been used to extract the information which is spectrum-analyzed in the low-frequency area to produce a graphic representation of the dynamic variations occurring at mesh.

The reasoning behind this technique is quite simple. If the process of tooth engagement were identical around the circumference of the gear, the resulting mesh frequency would be stationary in both amplitude and frequency. Any deviations, such as might be caused by motion of the gears relative to one another, tooth profile or spacing errors, fluctuations in load, or variations in tooth stiffness, are likely to produce combinations of frequency and amplitude modulation of the mesh frequency. The so-called hunting tooth phenomenon is probably the most familiar example, for it produces an audible amplitude modulation of the gear-mesh frequency which may be clocked with a stop watch. As a familiar but not often observed example, torsional vibration is known to be a phenomenon resulting in frequency modulation.

Figure 10–23 illustrates how demodulation can be utilized to examine gear characteristics. The lower acceleration spectrum contains the gear mesh frequency surrounded by several sidebands. Directly above, a low-frequency casing velocity spectra is pictured to show the position and relative amplitude of the rotational frequency components and their multiples. The two top signatures contain the spectral components obtained by amplitude and frequency demodulation of the gear-mesh frequency and contain, as expected, the rotational frequencies as well as multiples. It is interesting to observe that the three most prominent components in the frequency-demodulated spectrum are at the high-speed shaft rotational frequency and its fourth and sixth-order harmonics, whereas two of the three most prominent components in the amplitude demodulated spectrum are at the high-speed shaft rotational frequency and its second order.

The relative strength of the harmonics of gear mesh frequency are thought to be indicators of condition, including a measure of the tooth profile; however, the relationship has not been demonstrated to date. At this point, it is safe to say that harmonics of gear mesh most likely represent some anomaly and should be watched carefully for any signs of change.

Because the internal alignment of a gear is so critical to its operation, changes in characteristics, particularly where amplitudes or harmonics increase during the first few hours of operation as the gear is coming up to temperature, should be viewed with suspicion. As stated earlier, most of the characteristics which can be measured externally represent a machine's response to some condition or change. Thus, under ideal conditions, vibration, a machine's dynamic response to alignment, fit, etc., should be at a maximum when the machine is first started and steadily decrease as it comes to full operating temperature. This indicates that compensations for the effects of thermal growth are of the correct magnitude and in the correct direction.

ELECTRICAL EQUIPMENT–MOTORS AND GENERATORS

Problems with electrical equipment may be classified as mechanical or electrical/electromagnetic in nature. The two are easily separated

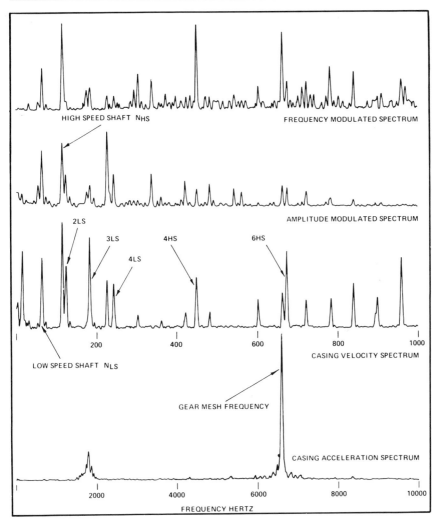

10–23—Demodulated spectra.

when electrical power is removed. If the problem is mechanical, its characteristics will decay slowly in proportion to speed. If, on the other hand, it is electrical in nature, its characteristics will disappear immediately when power is removed. It should be cautioned, however, that an oscilloscope or real-time analyzer must often be used to observe a clear distinction as the inherent damping of vibration meters obscures the instantaneous change of an electrically-induced problem.

Some examples of problems induced by electrical/electromagnetic anomalies are unequal air gaps which pull the rotor more strongly at the location(s) of least gap and cracked or broken rotor bars which move and change rotor balance under the effects of a magnetic field and centrifugal force.

11

Condition Monitoring

Depending on the type of machine, service, and its effect on production, it is often necessary to provide some means for continuous condition monitoring in order to anticipate problems in time to prevent failure.

MONITORING CRITERIA

There are four principal reasons for monitoring mechanical equipment:

Ensure operation within design constraints. As an example, temperature may be monitored to prevent loss of strength and/or damage from overheating. Position monitoring warns of impending contact between rotating and stationary parts. Vibration and speed are monitored to ensure force limits are not exceeded.

Warn of changing or deteriorating conditions to prevent equipment failure and costly secondary damage. Although a monitoring system cannot prevent a problem, it can warn of its presence while the problem is still localized. In itself, this is a significant advantage, for there are large differences in the cost and time required to correct or replace a failing component compared to the cost and time required to correct major damage resulting from a failure.

Provide an accurate description of machine condition in order to determine the frequency and extent of maintenance and overhauls without jeopardizing the integrity of equipment in satisfactory condition by disassembling it for visual inspection.

Warn of an impending failure that could be hazardous to personnel and adjacent equipment.

Since machinery monitoring represents a cost that is not directly reflected in increased production, a compromise must be reached in the choice of equipment to be monitored. Most recognize the necessity of monitoring large critical unspared equipment where an unexpected shutdown or failure is exacerbated by the cost of lost production. On equipment in this category, the cost of an extensive multiparameter monitoring system generally represents only a small fraction of the total cost of the equipment and similarly less than the cost of one day's lost production. The actual method for establishing the cost that can be justified for monitoring critical equipment varies widely among user companies. One guideline considers 0.001 times the annual cost of lost production as the amount that can be justified for a monitoring system to be installed on large critical machines.

In addition to critical unspared equipment, a typical facility will usually have critical but spared equipment where an unexpected failure might be costly and jeopardize production but not cause an immediate interruption. Boiler feed pumps are an example of equipment within this category where a continuous monitoring system is justified but probably not as much as on an unspared machine. The decision depends on the specific machine, its service, probability of a failure, and the cost and effect of a failure on production.

Spared machinery which may be difficult or hazardous to check or which operates unattended will often justify some type of monitoring system. Cooling tower fans and pipeline pumps and compressors are examples of equipment in this category.

The category, modified by factors such as operating experience and degree of manning, will generally dictate the scope and extent of machinery monitoring and protection. For new critical unspared machinery without an operating history, the consequences of an unscheduled outage will easily justify a comprehensive monitoring and protection system along with periodic detailed analyses to detect long-term trends. At the opposite end of the scale, a vibration switch may be all that is necessary to protect spared equipment operating unattended.

In addition to the vital equipment which are immediate candidates for some type of continuous monitoring system, there are less-critical spared pumps, compressors, and solids-handling equipment found in a typical industrial plant. Although all may be candidates for monitoring, the decision to provide a monitoring system depends, to a large degree, on individual plant philosophy, system cost, and the expected return on investment.

Once the scope of a machinery monitoring system has been resolved, the detailed engineering design should start with an evaluation of the machinery itself. Design, construction, support structure, service, type of operation, and response to probable malfunctions must be examined. Potential malfunctions are listed and assigned a priority based on probability and consequences. Next, the measurable health-related characteristics associated with each malfunction are identified and ranked according to response, reliability, and ease of measurement. Finally, a matrix may be developed listing the primary and secondary indicators of each malfunction. Using the matrix as a guide, a method of monitoring and protection can then be chosen to utilize the accessible characteristics most effectively as indicators of changing mechanical conditions.

During the engineering design of a continuous monitoring system, there will be a number of compromises necessary caused by factors such as the practical difficulties encountered in locating transducers, routing wires out of a complex machine case, and the availability of instrumentation. In addition, there is always the temptation to refine a particular measurement beyond the point necessary for the system to recognize abnormal or deteriorating conditions. In most cases the best monitoring system for a given application is one that will accurately, reliably, and inexpensively call attention to a change in equipment condition.

With the engineering evaluation completed and the system conceptualized, sensors, signal conditioning, and the protective scheme can be selected objectively. For example, a simple warning system based on vibration, either displacement or velocity, will probably suffice on relatively slow-speed equipment where symptoms of the most probable malfunctions generally develop slowly and produce easily recognized changes in vibration around running speed. However, if malfunctions can develop quickly or the system warns of incipient, potentially catastrophic problems such as thrust bearing failures, shaft fractures, or the loss of blading or gear teeth, a mixture of sensors combined with carefully selected signal conditioning or an automated diagnostic system will probably be required.

The decision to incorporate automatic protection or rely on a warning which requires manual action can be made in a similiar fashion. Factors such as the probability or suddenness of a specific malfunction and the risks involved if corrective action is not initiated quickly are compared to the probability and consequences of a false shutdown caused by a failure in the protective system itself. In some situations involving a high degree of risk in either case, redundant or confirming parameters may be employed together with a logic system requiring two or more monitored variables to exceed limits as prerequisites for an automatic shutdown.

For best results, the parameters to be measured, transducers employed, their location, and the signal conditioning used should be based on the construction, dynamic response, and problems associated with the specific machine. Using this criteria, an optimum-condition monitoring system will contain a variety of complementary measurements, each employed for a specific purpose.

MONITORING SPECIFIC EQUIPMENT

Centrifugal pumps

In general, centrifugal pumps have flexible supports. With this type construction, much of the dynamic force developed by the rotor is transmitted across the bearings with minimal relative motion and dissipated as structural vibration. These dynamic characteristics, combined with the remote likelihood of a problem involving shaft stability, favor the use of casing vibration sensors, attached to the bearing housings in the plane of least stiffness, to obtain the best response and indication of mechanical condition.

Applied to a centrifugal pump, a casing vibration monitoring system (figure 11–1) employs a single seismic acceleration sensor rigidly attached to each bearing housing as close to the bearing itself as possible. The accelerometer should be selected so it has a reasonably flat response (±5%) across the appropriate frequency bands and should contain integral signal conditioning electronics to transmit its output signal over commercial-grade shielded cable as long as temperatures at the point of attachment do not exceed the operating limit of the sensor's electronics, approximately 125 °C (250 °F).

The often very large amplitude at impeller vane passing frequency must be separated from running frequency and its low-order harmonics. This optimizes the monitoring system's response to common problems such as imbalance and misalignment whose characteristicas may be overwhelmed by the stronger vane-passing frequency in a broadband monitoring system.

Separating frequencies related to specific mechanical characteristics is easily accomplished by filtering the signal derived from the casing sensor into discrete bands within the monitor. The first band, enclosing the frequencies around running speed, should be measured in terms of velocity to incorporate the relationship between force and frequency and be fitted with a low-pass filter designed to eliminate

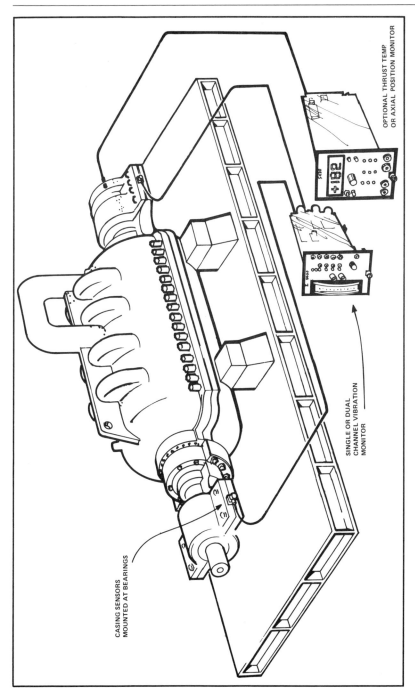

CASING SENSORS
MOUNTED AT BEARINGS

SINGLE OR DUAL
CHANNEL VIBRATION
MONITOR

OPTIONAL THRUST TEMP
OR AXIAL POSITION MONITOR

11-1—Typical pump monitoring system.

interference from the impeller vane passing frequency. If cavitation is considered likely or a potential threat to mechanical condition, a bandpass filter may be used to enclose the vane-passing frequency and one or two multiples into a second monitored band.

On pumps with rolling element bearings, it may be advisable to extend the frequency range upward to 100 kHz or more to monitor bearing condition. The signals needed for this type of system can, in some cases, be derived from the same sensors used to capture the low-frequency characteristics; in others, additional sensors must be added.

In high-head applications where an appreciable amount of thrust force may be developed if internal clearances are lost, include either an axial thrust-position monitor or a thrust-bearing temperature indicator and alarm to warn of an impending problem.

Many high-head process and boiler feed pumps have relatively light rotors operating at moderate to high speeds in a stiff heavy casing. With these physical characteristics, a centrifugal pump monitoring system should be patterned after the centrifugal compressor monitoring system.

Centrifugal compressors

As a group, modern centrifugal compressors operating on sleeve or tilt-pad hydrodynamic radial bearings generally have a relatively large casing-to-rotor-weight ratio and stiff supporting structure. As a result, most of the low-frequency energy developed by the rotor and indicative of bearing stability, rotor balance, and coupling alignment is dissipated by relative motion between shaft and bearing, hopefully within the bearing clearance. In this situation, a noncontact relative-motion displacement monitoring system (figure 11–2) generally has the fastest and most easily recognized response to small changes in mechanical condition.

At the higher frequencies, vane passing and above, there may be significant excitation generated by aerodynamic turbulence or an impeller resonance. Although this excitation is relatively easy to detect as acceleration and might potentially lead to a fatigue failure, its displacement is likely to be well below the minimum detectable amplitude of a typical industrial displacement monitoring system. Fortunately, this occurs so infrequently that the additional instrumentation required for protection is not generally warranted on a permanent basis. If, however, aerodynamic response is of concern, casing accelerometers can be incorporated as permanent or temporary measures to assess conditions related to long-term fatigue failures.

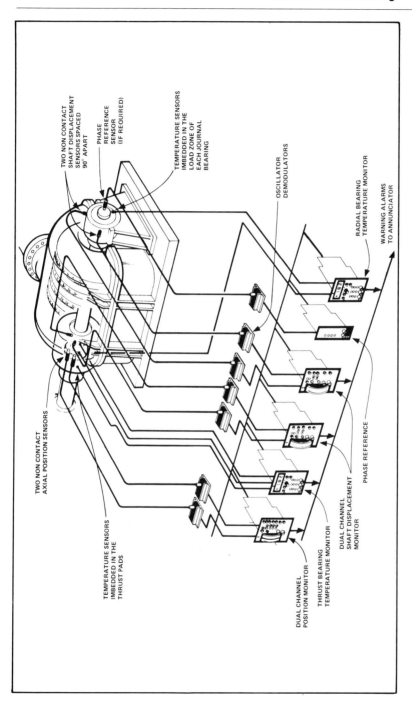

TWO NON CONTACT SHAFT DISPLACEMENT SENSORS SPACED 90° APART

PHASE REFERENCE SENSOR (IF REQUIRED)

TEMPERATURE SENSORS IMBEDDED IN THE LOAD ZONE OF EACH JOURNAL BEARING

OSCILLATOR DEMODULATORS

RADIAL BEARING TEMPERATURE MONITOR

WARNING ALARMS TO ANNUNCIATOR

TWO NON CONTACT AXIAL POSITION SENSORS

TEMPERATURE SENSORS IMBEDDED IN THE THRUST PADS

DUAL CHANNEL POSITION MONITOR

THRUST BEARING TEMPERATURE MONITOR

DUAL CHANNEL SHAFT DISPLACEMENT MONITOR

PHASE REFERENCE

11–2—Typical centrifugal compressor monitoring system.

As illustrated in figure 11–2, thrust-position monitoring should be included as a part of any centrifugal compressor monitoring system. A typical position monitoring system will have one or two axial displacement sensors (the latter in high head or especially critical applications) and an appropriate monitor.

Thrust and journal bearing temperature, obtained from thermocouples or resistance temperature detectors imbedded in the bearing metal close to the loaded surface, should be incorporated in any continuous monitoring system for critical machinery. Thrust temperature is the best anticipatory warning of a thrust overload and is considered mandatory on high-differential head compressors where the failure of a balance drum seal can overload the thrust bearing to failure. The associated temperature monitors should, as a minimum, be able to display temperature and have one or two alarms for warning if temperature exceeds a safe value. Logic requiring two or more thrust temperatures to exceed limits as a prerequisite for actuating a higher level or danger alarm is highly advantageous if thrust temperature is used for shutdown.

Fans

Centrifugal fans used for forced or induced draft and primary air generally have large-diameter rotors running 700–900 rpm in pillow block bearings supported on structural steel or concrete foundations. As a rule, the major problems with fans are imbalance caused by uneven buildup or loss of deposited material and misalignment, all characterized by changes in vibration around rotational frequency which can be monitored effectively with either a shaft displacement or a casing monitoring system.

Without any distinction in this area, the choice of an optimum monitoring system is dictated by type of construction. If the bearings are supported on stiff reinforced concrete pedestals, most of the dynamic force developed by the rotor will be dissipated as relative motion within the bearing clearance, and relative motion shaft monitoring (figure 11–3) will give the best results. With this system, two noncontact X-Y displacement sensors should be installed at each bearing in case it becomes necessary to view shaft motion; however, one dual-channel monitor monitoring one of the two sensors at each bearing will generally provide adequate protection and should be considered as a measure to reduce cost.

If, on the other hand, the bearings are supported on structural steel, the dynamic force is likely to be dissipated as structural vibration and a

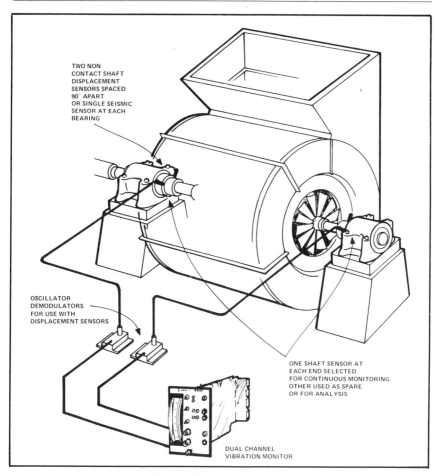

TWO NON
CONTACT SHAFT
DISPLACEMENT
SENSORS SPACED
90° APART
OR SINGLE SEISMIC
SENSOR AT EACH
BEARING

OSCILLATOR
DEMODULATORS
FOR USE WITH
DISPLACEMENT SENSORS

ONE SHAFT SENSOR AT
EACH END SELECTED
FOR CONTINUOUS MONITORING
OTHER USED AS SPARE
OR FOR ANALYSIS

DUAL CHANNEL
VIBRATION MONITOR

11–3—Typical fan monitoring system.

casing seismic monitoring system using sensors attached to the bearing housings will give best results. The latter is slightly less expensive and much easier to install and maintain. For optimum results, the casing sensors should be mounted on the bearing in the plane of least stiffness, generally horizontal. In order to eliminate characteristics such as duct noise or vibration not specifically related to mechanical condition, a fan's casing vibration signal should be filtered within the monitor to a bandpass from approximately 50% of running speed to three or four times running speed.

Axial-flow compressors

Industrial axial flow compressors have much the same low-frequency characteristics as centrifugal compressors except they are rarely afflicted with the bearing stability problems often associated with high-speed centrifugal units. In the high-frequency area, axial compressors usually generate strong spectral components at the various blade-passing frequencies and their multiples (figure 11–4). These frequencies are probably generated by turbulent wakes trailing the blades with amplitudes determined by factors such as blade performance, condition, effective angle of incidence, and cleanliness. The high-frequency characteristics of axial compressors are considered sufficiently important to be included in any monitoring and protective system.

The next question is whether acceptable protection can be obtained with casing sensors alone or whether shaft and casing sensors must be mixed to cover the total frequency range. An axial compressor monitoring system using casing sensors with the resulting frequency spectrum divided (figure 11–4) offers acceptable protection against low-frequency problems such as imbalance and misalignment as well as high-frequency blade-related problems. A more conservative approach has been to combine acceleration monitoring for the blade-passing frequencies with a conventional shaft displacement system.

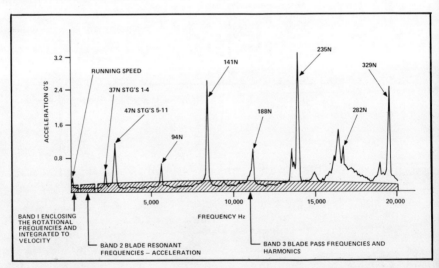

11–4—*Method of dividing the complex frequency spectrum generated by an axial compressor into filtered bands for monitoring.*

If a casing system is used to cover both low and high frequencies, the low frequencies should be limited to a band from approximately 30% of running speed and presented in velocity (figure 11–4) in order to increase the amplitude ratio between low and high frequencies.

Whenever blade problems are anticipated, the high-frequency limit of the band containing running speed components should be lowered and the second band added just above to incorporate the fundamental resonant frequencies of the blades themselves. Although the fundamental frequencies generated by a blade resonance are seldom present in vibration signatures, there have been several cases where a frequency, later identified as a fundamental blade resonance, was present in a frequency spectrum recorded from a casing sensor prior to a blade failure.

In either a total casing or combination casing and shaft monitoring system, the high-frequency band should begin slightly below the lowest blade-passing frequency (number of blades times shaft rpm) and extend to the third or fourth multiple of the highest blade-passing frequency. In a system such as this, a high vibration amplitude in the low-frequency band indicates imbalance or misalignment, while excessive vibration in the high band indicates a blade problem such as foreign object damage, fouling, impending surge, or moveable stator blades which have separated from their turning mechanism and assumed an abnormal angle in the airflow.

A continuous-thrust monitoring system incorporating a single-position sensor generally provides sufficient protection for axial compressors; however, two redundant sensors provide improved protection at little added cost. The decision to alarm only or alarm and shut down on axial position usually depends on the individual. If an alarm and shutdown system is selected, a dual sensor system requiring both to exceed limits in order to initiate a shutdown is recommended. This is particularly important on large critical machinery where an unexpected shutdown can jeopardize other equipment or perhaps a process.

Steam turbines

Steam turbines vary significantly in dynamic response depending on design, construction, application, service, speed, shaft horsepower, and steam conditions. As a general category, steam turbines designed for petrochemical process drive or boiler feed pump applications usually operate between 5,000 and 12,000 rpm and deliver from 6,000 to 30,000 hp with inlet steam pressures to 1,500 psi. On the other hand, power-generating turbines are considerably slower operating at synchronous or half synchronous speed, are generally much larger in size, and may operate on inlet steam pressures above 3,000 psi.

In addition to details of construction, which in turn influence dynamic response and the variables to be monitored, other factors such as the advisability of monitoring blade characteristics must be considered in order to arrive at an optimum means of monitoring mechanical condition. If the turbine has a relatively low casing-to-rotor-weight ratio (5 to 10), a consistently flexible support structure, and blade characteristics to be examined, a monitoring system based on casing acceleration sensors is likely to have advantages. Where bearing stability might be a problem or the turbine and its bearings are mounted on a stiff support structure, a relative-motion shaft displacement system is generally best. A seismically referenced shaft sensor monitoring the absolute motion of the shaft may have advantages in some applications such as large power-generating turbines running at synchronous and half synchronous speeds with significant variations in bearing stiffness.

A relative-motion shaft displacement monitoring system is best suited in applications where most of the dynamic force developed in the rotor will be dissipated as relative motion between shaft and bearing, i.e., moderate to high casing-to-rotor weight ratios and relatively stiff support structures. Most large process-drive turbines and boiler feed pump turbines fall in this category.

A relative motion shaft displacement monitoring system (figure 11–5) provides excellent results at the low frequencies around rotational speed, particularly where shaft instability might be a problem, and is the only way to monitor radial position. In addition, there are at least two reasons for giving serious consideration to a backup casing vibration monitoring system consisting of a single casing accelerometer mounted at each bearing on critical high-speed turbines.

First, and for some unexplained reason, a number of unexpected shaft fractures and bearing failures have been suffered by steam turbines equipped with functioning, calibrated shaft-monitoring systems. In each case, clear symptoms observed in casing vibration characteristics were either ignored or dismissed on the grounds that shaft vibration appeared normal, was well within limits for continued operation, and had not shown any abnormal changes. Whether the conflict was caused by inadvertent placement of the shaft sensors at a nodal point, in-phase motion of the bearing housing, force due to vibration at high frequencies, or a large amount of opposing runout, a casing monitoring system would presumably provide the insight to avoid similar problems.

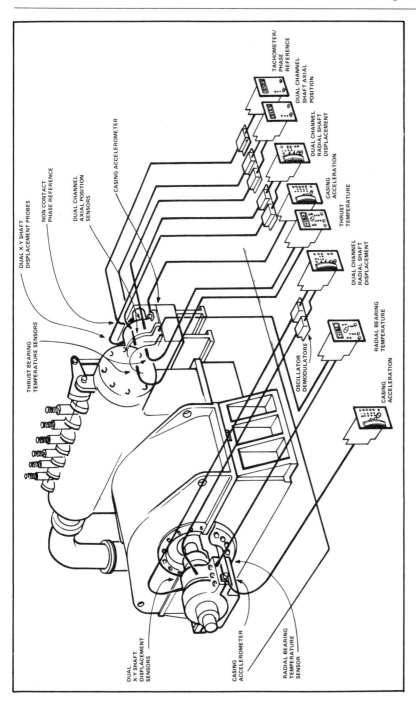

DUAL X-Y SHAFT
DISPLACEMENT PROBES

NON CONTACT
PHASE REFERENCE

DUAL CHANNEL
AXIAL POSITION
SENSORS

CASING ACCELEROMETER

TACHOMETER/
PHASE
REFERENCE

DUAL CHANNEL
SHAFT AXIAL
POSITION

DUAL CHANNEL
RADIAL SHAFT
DISPLACEMENT

CASING
ACCELERATION

THRUST
TEMPERATURE

DUAL CHANNEL
RADIAL SHAFT
DISPLACEMENT

THRUST BEARING
TEMPERATURE SENSORS

RADIAL BEARING
TEMPERATURE

OSCILLATOR
DEMODULATORS

CASING
ACCELERATION

DUAL
X-Y SHAFT
DISPLACEMENT
SENSORS

CASING
ACCELEROMETER

RADIAL BEARING
TEMPERATURE
SENSOR

11–5—*Typical steam turbine monitoring system (mechanical drive).*

Second, with its wide frequency range, a casing acceleration sensor can simultaneously observe the low rotational frequencies as either a primary or back-up means of monitoring, as well as the high blade and flow-related frequencies which are beyond the capability of any system-measuring displacement. To make effective use of a casing acceleration sensor, the associated monitor must divide the complex spectrum generated by a steam turbine into a minimum of two bands so that changes in either the low or high-frequency area can be recognized. The lower band should extend from approximately 20% to 550% of running speed and be integrated to velocity in order to emphasize the low frequencies. The higher band is left in acceleration and is high-pass filtered at the upper limit of the velocity band to eliminate the frequencies being examined within the lower band. In this fashion, the lower band indicates common mechanical problems such as imbalance, misalignment, and instability, while the higher band indicates longer-term problems such as those which might lead to a fatigue failure.

Depending on the design, steam turbines may be susceptible to thrust bearing problems. In addition, conditions such as blade fouling and locked couplings can produce a thrust overload, so thrust bearing performance and condition must be included in any comprehensive steam turbine monitoring system. The considerations outlined for thrust monitoring on centrifugal compressors apply equally well to steam turbines. In view of the vital nature of the axial position measurement and the difficulty of replacing sensors once the turbine is in operation, the installation of two sensors is highly recommended. The decision of whether to use a single-channel position monitor with the second sensor left as an installed spare or to monitor both continuously with a dual-channel monitor can be based on factors such as the size and criticality of the turbine and the potential for a catastrophic thrust failure which might dictate a voting logic automatic shutdown.

Temperature sensors imbedded in thrust pads are the best anticipatory indicator of a thrust bearing overload. Journal bearing temperature obtained from sensors imbedded in the bearings is likewise an extremely valuable indicator of bearing performance and should be included in any comprehensive monitoring system.

In addition to the measurements discussed for process drive and boiler feed pump turbines, the unique nature of large power-generating turbines dictates some modifications as well as some additional measurements.

Illustrated in figure 11–6, power-generating steam turbine supervisory systems may include a means, either a shaft-riding seismic

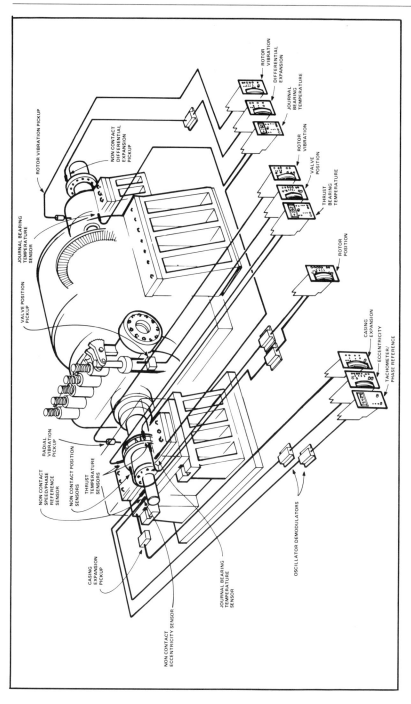

11–6—*Typical steam turbine monitoring system (generator drive).*

sensor or a relative motion, and a casing absolute motion sensor, electronically subtracted, to obtain absolute shaft motion at each radial bearing. In addition to vibration, it is also necessary to measure rotor eccentricity while on the turning gear on large turbines with long bearing spans to warn of a thermal rotor bow which could result in packing rubs. An eccentricity monitoring system will have one or more noncontacting shaft motion sensors and a monitor with either a very long-time constant or a sample and hold circuit capable of displaying the peak-to-peak shaft excursions at turning gear speeds.

In addition to shaft motion and eccentricity, a large steam turbine supervisory system should also include a noncontact phase and speed measuring system, the former for use in balancing; rotor position, measured with a noncontact displacement sensor located at the thrust bearing; valve position, measured with an LVDT or potentiometer; and thrust and journal bearing temperatures, measured with temperature sensors implanted in the bearings.

Large high-temperature steam turbines are subject to several inches of axial growth from ambient to full operating temperature which must be accommodated by some type of slide or sliding shoes. To ensure the slides are free and functioning, a necessity if casing stress is to be maintained within safe levels, one or possibly two casing expansion sensors (usually LVDTs or some other device for measuring a large displacement) are customarily located at the sliding end of the turbine. The sensor(s) has one end attached to a fixed portion of the structure and the other contacting the turbine so that movement between the two can be measured and transmitted to a monitor or recorder.

The rotor and casing can also change temperature and thus dimensions at different rates; hence, a differential expansion measurement must be made to avoid rubbing. As illustrated in figure 11–7, the

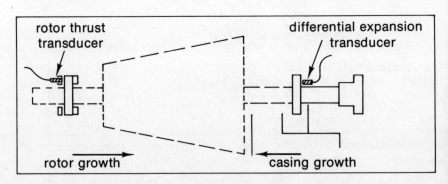

11–7—Location of the turbine rotor differential expansion transducer.

differential expansion measurement is accomplished with a noncontact axial position sensor attached to the casing and observing the rotor at the end opposite the thrust bearing. If the axial differential expansion measurement remains constant, the rotor and casing are either not growing or are growing at the same rate. If the measurement changes one, probably the rotor is changing dimensions more rapidly. In this situation, the clearance from wheel to diaphram must not be exceeded or a rub will occur. Displaying the differential expansion measurement on a monitor and/or a recorder provides the information necessary to recognize and hopefully avoid such a situation.

Gas turbines

Compared to other types of industrial rotating machinery, gas turbines have relatively low casing–rotor weight ratios, light flexible casings, and a flexible support structure. Within this group, aircraft-derivative turbines have the lowest casing–rotor weight ratio and the most flexible casing and support structure. Although speeds vary greatly, gas turbines generally operate at moderate to high speeds from approximately 3,600 rpm to well over 20,000 rpm.

Gas turbines generate a vast number of spectral components spanning a wide frequency range. In addition to several running frequencies, the signature may also contain components generated by power takeoffs, load and accessory gearing, turbine and base plate-mounted auxiliaries, and compressor and turbine blades as well as numerous harmonics and sum-and-difference combinations. With this vast amount of condition-related information available, it is first necessary to decide how much to use and then design the monitoring and protective system accordingly.

Applied to a gas turbine, a shaft monitoring system has three principal limitations and a fourth conditional limitation offsetting its advantage of direct observation of shaft motion. First, a displacement system cannot collect the characteristics which define blade and gear condition due to the intolerable energy levels required to produce a measurable displacement at high frequencies. Second, it is always difficult—nearly impossible on aircraft-derivative turbines—to find suitable sensor locations which are accessible without major disassembly. Third, frequencies generated by components other than the rotating shaft are either greatly attenuated or eliminated altogether in the signature obtained from a shaft sensor. Finally, a shaft sensor is ineffective on machinery employing antifriction bearings due to the limitations imposed on relative motion between shaft and structure by the small bearing clearances. Thus, the signal originated by a shaft displacement sensor is restricted to low-frequency characteristics such as balance and alignment of a rotor supported on journal bearings and is insensitive to other, potentially valuable characteristics of vital auxiliaries, gearing, and blades.

Most gas turbines have a relatively flexible casing and support structure along with a low casing–rotor weight ratio, producing casing vibration characteristics which accurately indicate mechanical condition. Although gas turbine monitoring systems can be based on shaft or casing vibration, a casing system using accelerometers (figure 11–8) may be favored because of its ability to monitor the mechanical condition of more components, its quick response to a variety of problems, its ability to withstand high temperatures, and its ease of installation and replacement. Shaft vibration sensors may be required, however, in special applications involving rotor stability.

In a gas turbine monitoring system employing casing vibration sensors to obtain dynamic information, the problem becomes one of emphasizing and segregating various discrete frequencies or frequency bands within a complex spectrum containing numerous high-amplitude components, particularly at the higher frequencies. As discussed in the section on pumps and axial compressors, separating the complex signal into manageable segments so that small changes are not masked by stronger components is the key to successful monitoring. Referring back to figure 11–4, the broadband signal obtained from casing accelerometers should be integrated to velocity to emphasize the low frequencies around running speed (figure 11–9). This segment can be monitored as an indication of overall imbalance, misalignment, etc., or it can be divided by filtering to separate frequencies related to specific mechanical components. The remainder of the spectrum should be left in acceleration units, high-pass filtered if desired, and perhaps divided to separate a particular part of the turbine such as compressor and turbine rotors on two-shaft machines. Short of a diagnostic system capable of examining each individual component, this arrangement provides maximum certainty that a change can be recognized and localized without additional analysis.

For maximum protection, a gas turbine monitoring system should also include axial position and journal bearing temperature monitoring (figure 11–8). Thrust temperature monitoring may be included, if desired, but is not considered mandatory.

Gears

High-speed industrial gears generally have moderate, torque-induced bearing preloads and comparatively flexible casings. As a

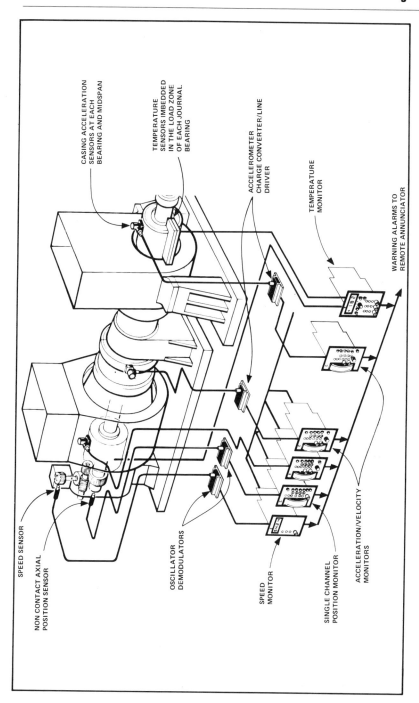

CASING ACCELERATION SENSORS AT EACH BEARING AND MIDSPAN

TEMPERATURE SENSORS IMBEDDED IN THE LOAD ZONE OF EACH JOURNAL BEARING

ACCELEROMETER CHARGE CONVERTER/LINE DRIVER

TEMPERATURE MONITOR

WARNING ALARMS TO REMOTE ANNUNCIATOR

SPEED SENSOR

NON CONTACT AXIAL POSITION SENSOR

OSCILLATOR DEMODULATORS

SPEED MONITOR

SINGLE CHANNEL POSITION MONITOR

ACCELERATION/VELOCITY MONITORS

11-8—*Typical gas turbine monitoring system.*

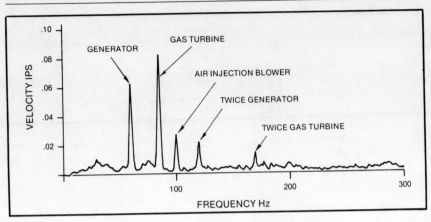

11–9—*Gas turbine casing velocity signature.*

result, most of the dynamic force developed by the rotating elements is transmitted across the bearings with minimal relative motion where it is dissipated as structural vibration. In addition to these physical characteristics, a gear typically generates a broad vibration spectrum, beginning with frequencies well below the shaft rotational speeds and extending to the gear-mesh frequency and its harmonics. The latter constitutes most of the sound generated by a gear and contains a vast amount of intelligence defining gear quality and condition.

In view of these characteristics, a gear vibration monitoring system using casing acceleration sensors in combination with signal conditioning capable of dividing the complex signal in segments has significant advantages and offers vastly improved protection over other types of monitoring systems.

For best results on larger gears, two accelerometers should be attached rigidly to the gear casing in an area of maximum stiffness on or adjacent to the coupling end bearings of both the high and low-speed shafts (figure 11–10). (One acceleration sensor located at the coupling end of the high-speed shaft should provide adequate protection on smaller gears.) The mounted amplitude response of the accelerometers and their associated electronics should be flat within ±5% to the second or third harmonic of the gear-mesh frequency and treated in such a fashion that any additional harmonics which may be present are not amplified significantly by the resonant response of the sensor.

As illustrated in figure 11–11, using filters to divide a gear signature into manageable segments is generally not difficult. The first segment, containing the rotational frequencies of both shafts, will probably begin at approximately 50% of the lowest running speed and extend to the fourth or fifth multiple of the high-speed shaft. In addition to eliminating unwanted frequencies by filtering, the signal should be integrated to velocity as a measure to enhance the lower frequencies indicative of rotor balance, gear runout, and alignment.

The next or intermediate band should be designed to include the frequencies from approximately 1,000 Hz to just below the mesh frequency. As shown in figure 11–11, a typical gear signature generally includes a number of prominent spectral components within this band which coincide with the resonance of the gear element itself. On this occasion, the primary symptom of a gear problem was a sudden increase in amplitude at the intermediate frequencies with both high and low frequencies remaining relatively unchanged. For optimum results, the filter position and its bandpass should be based on operating characteristics to include the required data while rejecting adjacent frequencies such as gear mesh.

The third segment should enclose the gear mesh frequency, ± four or five times the high-speed shaft rotational frequency. This tolerance ensures sidebands, if present, will be included within the filter bandwidth. A great deal has been written concerning the interpretation of the amplitudes at gear mesh frequency as well as its sidebands which

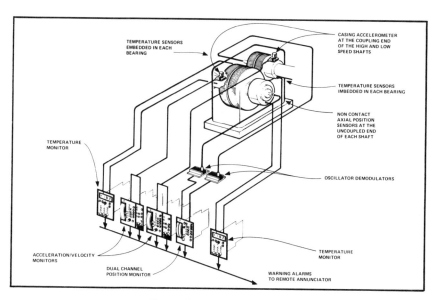

11–10—*Typical gear monitoring system.*

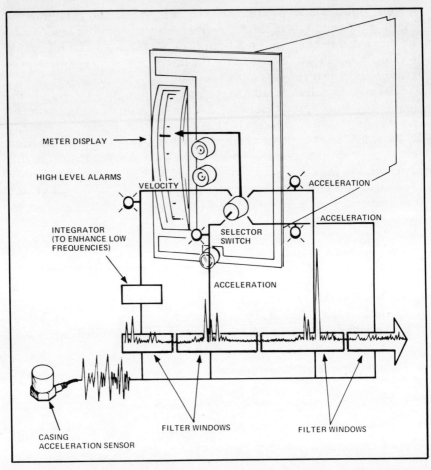

11–11—The division of a typical gear spectrum with filters for monitoring.

have been observed to vary with power and may indicate a condition such as incipient surge within a driven machine.

The ratio between the gear mesh frequency and its harmonics has been reported as a measure of gear condition, and this may be observed by enclosing the harmonics to the third or fourth order within a fourth filtered segment. If this theory proves true in practice, electronically rationing the third and fourth bands and displaying the result may be highly advantageous.

The static and dynamic response of the gears in the axial plane is another valuable indicator of gear condition and performance which should be monitored. For example, on double helical gears malfunctions such as locked or stiff couplings can move the gears axially out of their optimum mesh position. This shifts the load to one helix which, if allowed to continue, may cause tooth damage or possible failure. Axial position monitoring on high-horsepower, high-ratio, double-helical speed increasing gears is thus recommended and may be easily accomplished with a dual-channel thrust monitor supplied from two axial sensors, one observing the outboard end of each shaft (figure 11–10). Since the sensors face opposite directions in this application, the monitor must be configured to reverse the reading from one sensor so that movement of both gears in one direction will produce a corresponding unidirectional meter movement.

Axial vibration obtained from the same pair of sensors is also a good indication of gear quality. Manufacturing errors such as apex and pitch line runout result in axial shuttling of the gears, a condition easily detected with displacement sensors.

In summary, the recommended gear monitoring system consists of one or two casing acceleration sensors mounted at the coupling end bearings supplying multidata path monitors. The monitors must divide the complex spectrum transmitted from the accelerometer into manageable segments, each representing a specific mechanical component or event. Additional axial position probes observing the outboard ends of each shaft are highly desirable to assess gear quality and to warn of difficulties such as coupling lockup which might overload a single helix.

Electrical machinery–motors and generators

Typical electrical machinery will have a relatively heavy rotor supported in bearings mounted on a flexible structure. As a result, most of the dynamic force developed by the rotor results in structural vibration rather than relative motion between shaft and bearing. Apart from rotor bar passing frequencies which are sometimes observed in the vibration signatures of electrical machinery, most of the characteristics which define mechanical condition are found in the low-frequency region to approximately four or five times running speed.

Although both shaft or casing vibration monitoring systems can be used effectively, the latter has advantages on smaller equipment: it is easier to install and is not affected by a rough shaft surface. A casing system has clear advantages on machinery with rolling element bearings due to the restricted relative motion inherent in this type bearing combined with the ability of a casing accelerometer to observe rolling element bearing characteristics directly as a measure of condition. As has been pointed out in other casing applications, the complex signal from a casing sensor must be filtered so only the desired characteristics are being monitored.

Large power generators are generally best monitored with the same type of sensors used on the turbines. On all large equipment, both motors and generators, winding temperatures must be continuously monitored in addition to monitoring mechanical vibration.

COMPREHENSIVE MONITORING SYSTEM

Figure 11–12 illustrates how the recommended monitoring systems for individual machines might be combined on a machine string. The mechanical vibration of both the gas turbine and gear is best monitored with casing accelerometers 6, 7, and 10, augmented with noncontact axial position measurements 1 and 12. A speed-measuring system is installed on the gas turbine 2 and 4 and, although not shown in this particular illustration, the addition of journal bearing temperature should be considered for maximum protection.

Shaft vibration monitoring 18, 3 and 19 is recommended for the

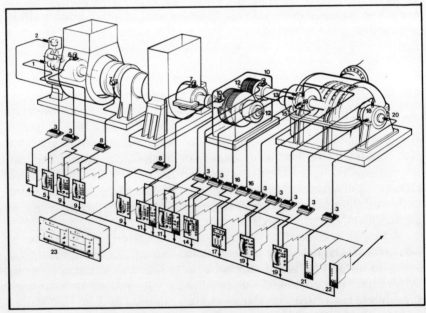

11–12—Multiparameter machinery monitoring system.

centrifugal compressor augmented by dual-thrust position monitoring 13, 3 and 14, and thrust-bearing temperature monitoring 15, 16 and 17. Journal bearing temperature is a worthwhile addition. Since the compressor shaft is operating at a different speed from the gas turbine, a noncontact phase reference 20, 3 and 21 is installed at some convenient location along the compressor shaft observing a once per revolution marker.

Monitors 4, 5, 9, 11, 14, 17 and 19 are all fitted with individual alarms which are then commoned, 22, for transmission to a remote annunciator. In this fashion, an operator is warned of a change in condition which may then be localized by observing the individual monitors.

INSTALLATION

The care and foresight used installing a monitoring system is just as important to the system as its basic design. Proper transducer location and mounting are important as well as the need to protect instrumentation wiring both within and outside the monitored machine. Of particular importance is a means to disconnect and connect the monitoring system at the machine during maintenance periods easily and without hazarding the wiring. A little planning can mean significant savings in cost and time as well as improved reliability.

Instrumentation wires generally exit a machine at or near its bearings, mandating an oil-tight seal. Since an oil-tight seal is often difficult to achieve, especially when a large number of wires must pass through the same exit fitting, there are advantages to providing a means of disconnecting the sensors inside the machine so the machine can be disassembled and the sensors removed without disturbing the seal. Temperature sensors are often installed in this fashion with a barrier strip located inside the bearing cavity to which the sensor is connected after the bearing is installed. Extension wire, connected to the barrier strip, is routed out of the machine and permanently sealed at the point where it penetrates the casing. Illustrated in figure 11–13, this arrangement is the easiest to connect and disconnect and provides the best insurance against an embarrassing and messy oil leak.

A second terminal strip located in a suitable enclosure outside the machine is highly desirable for convenience and troubleshooting and is necessary if the part in which the exit fitting is located must be removed when the machine is disassembled.

Cables from noncontact pickups installed inside a machine are generally routed so connectors are located outside the machine (figure 11–14). Wiring inside the machine must be protected from chafing and

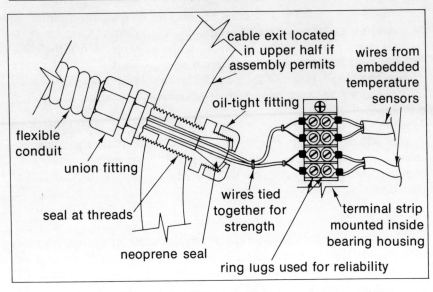

11–13—Recommended cable exit for temperature sensor wires.

windage which will eventually cause failure. In some cases it may be advisable or even necessary to install noncontact pickups with their connectors inside the machine. In this situation, special care must be exercised routing the wire and protecting the connector. Excess wire must be held securely with clips or attached to piping or through holes provided for the purpose with nylon tie wraps. Connectors should be supported at both ends and, for added protection and reliability, a protective covering of heat shrinkable tubing should be considered.

A point of interfacing between facility wiring to the monitoring system and machine wiring is also highly advisable. In a noncontact displacement system, the oscillator demodulators, mounted in a box on or adjacent to the machine as shown in figure 11–15, automatically serve this purpose. A dual-row barrier strip mounted in a suitable enclosure provides a convenient interface between facility wiring and a machine-mounted casing vibration or temperature sensor. In addition to an access point for troubleshooting, this arrangement provides an easy and convenient means to replace a machine-mounted cable which has been damaged.

Although connections can degrade the performance of a temperature monitoring system, practical considerations generally make some type of interface highly desirable. Again, barrier strips mounted in a

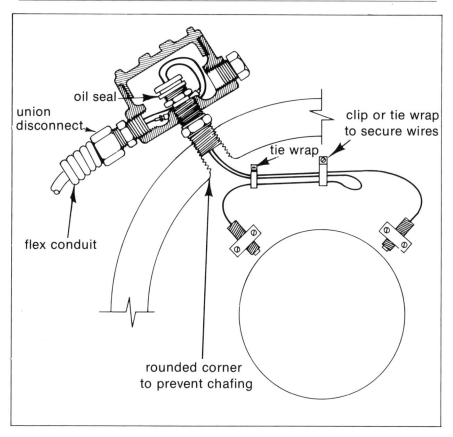

oil seal

union
disconnect

clip or tie wrap
to secure wires

tie wrap

flex conduit

rounded corner
to prevent chafing

11–14—*Typical method for exiting noncontact displacement pickup wiring
from a machine case.*

box located on or adjacent to the machine provide a convenient location for connecting and disconnecting the system.

The type and location of the interface box is important to reliability.
It must be large enough to house the necessary components with ample
working clearance, protect its contents against the environment, and
remain undisturbed and out of the way yet be accessible during
maintenance periods. Conduit from the box to the machine should be
equipped with unions for easy disassembly.

Proper grounding to avoid picking up stray or spurious signals
must not be neglected in a monitoring system. Grounding instructions
should be provided by the system manufacturer and followed for optimum results.

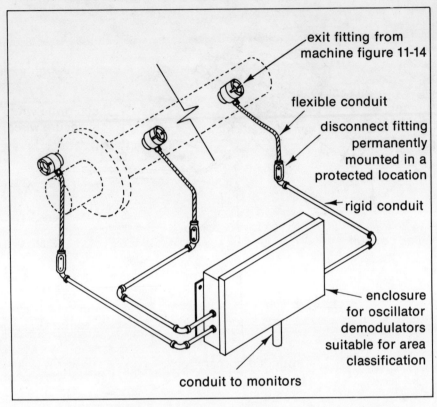

11–15—Interface wiring from noncontact displacement pickups.

Additional features of a monitoring system

In a comprehensive machinery monitoring system of the type shown in figure 11–16, a multipoint or multipen recorder, capable of being patched into any monitored variable, is valuable for observing long-term trends. The addition of an oscilloscope, tape recorder, and analysis equipment is likewise advantageous and extends the use of the monitoring system to more detailed predictive analysis. A spare power supply with automatic transfer to the primary supply in the event of a failure should be considered for improved reliability on systems which depend on a single central power supply.

11–16—Typical comprehensive machinery monitoring and analysis system.

EXPANDING THE CAPABILITIES OF A MONITORING SYSTEM

Unfortunately, vibration, position, and temperature do not describe condition but require varying degrees of interpretation. Where interpretation is a comparison to limits, the task is easily quantified. On the other hand, except for catastrophic failures, most machinery problems appear as a number of gradual changes, no one of which clearly dictates an immediate shutdown. With the natural tendency to condition oneself into accepting increasingly higher values, it is easy to lose track of how far deterioration has progressed. Along with the need for a reference or baseline to which current measurements can be compared, an effective monitoring system should recognize changes in confirming parameters and assess rate of change.

As the first step to a truly comprehensive machinery monitoring system, consider incorporating operating variables such as power produced and absorbed, flow, and pressures. With this information, the monitoring system can note efficiency, an increasingly important value as energy costs escalate. Along with monitoring the efficiency of mechanical equipment, performance variables might be used to recognize conditions which affect mechanical parameters. For example, vibration may increase as a centrifugal compressor approaches surge. In this situation, rather than having the change in vibration actuate an alarm indicating a change in mechanical condition, the process measurement would allow the system to recognize the underlying cause of the change and either suppress the vibration alarm or identify it as an expected result of an operating problem and temporarily allow higher limits. With the latter scheme of indexing limits to operating variables, the limits themselves can be made much tighter, thereby enabling earlier recognition of changes in condition.

Related variables can be used effectively to confirm and add weight to small changes which might go unnoticed. Balance drum differential pressure, thrust bearing pad temperature, and axial position are three confirming measurements which can identify a specific problem. Likewise, casing and shaft vibration or shaft vibration at opposite ends of a machine can confirm one another. In this situation, do not necessarily look for two values above limits but for a confirming change which would validate a more pronounced change measured elsewhere on the machine. Such a concept, similar to the voting logic employed in thrust position monitors, also minimizes the possibility of a false alarm due to an instrument malfunction. This can be taken a step further if the monitoring system is programmed to recognize and call attention to two or more confirming changes even though the individual values do not exceed limits.

To extend the concept of grouping related variables so that confirming changes can be quickly recognized, the assignment of a weight to each variable in relation to its significance should be considered. With this concept, variables most closely related to mechanical condition would be weighted the highest with secondary and confirming variables assigned lower weights. Such a weighting system would ensure that small changes among primary variables would automatically assume precedence over similar magnitude changes to secondary variables.

In this discussion, the term variable is purposely used instead of measurement or parameter to indicate the monitored value could be a measurement or it could be a specific property of one or more measurements. A specific frequency or band of frequencies related to a particular mechanical component or condition would be one example, while a derived or calculated quantity such as rate of change, phase lag, and efficiency would be another.

Rate of change is an important measure of the severity of a problem as well as the time frame in which action must be taken. A slow rate of change generally indicates that time is available for a carefully thought-out plan of action, whereas a high rate of change always dictates fast action to avoid a catastrophic failure. Following this line of reasoning, a monitoring system should be able to identify rate of change and attach such a high weight that its significance is immediately recognized.

Assuming that recognizing rate of change is primarily a short-term task, a monitoring system should also be able to collect and store the data necessary for establishing long-term trends. It probably isn't necessary for the monitoring system itself to include provisions for actually constructing trend plots. However, the data should be readily available in a recoverable form for input into another system in which the trend information could be displayed and converted into a permanent record if desired.

In attempting to analyze a problem, it is often valuable to have an array of data collected immediately preceding and during its evolution. To this end, a moving window or loop file containing constantly updated raw data for the past 20–30 minutes would be a valuable addition. In the event of a transient such as an alarm, protective trip, or even a planned shutdown, the system would continue to collect data for some predetermined time after initiation, then store the entire record for later recovery. In this way a record of the conditions existing for a period prior to the transient as well as the transient itself would be available for later, more detailed analysis.

It is not necessary or perhaps even desirable for the monitoring system to analyze. As operating instrumentation, the prime function of a monitoring system should be to present, as unambiguously as possible, an accurate picture of machinery condition which is easily interpreted by an operator and can be used reliably for automatic protection. As long as the monitoring system can collect and store the raw data needed for analysis, the actual analysis task is best accomplished by a system optimized for this specific function.

This is particularly important, for a monitoring system must be cost effective, that is, the price of protection must be less than the cost of a machine failure. To this end, a monitoring system should not include more than the functions necessary to perform the designated tasks and each function should be fully employed.

In closing, one should consider automatic protection. Although there are varying opinions concerning the advisability of automatic protection a requirement for confirmation by related variables and for incorporating rate of change into the decision process should help convince even the most skeptical the viability and significant advantages to be gained from automatic protection. It is vigilant, never suffers from indecision, always reacts in a predictable way, and is not subject to human error. In a critical situation, these factors can spell the difference between a save and a catastrophic failure.

12

Balancing

Rotating part imbalance is one of the most common sources of excessive vibration. Since every person working with machinery or accomplishing machinery analysis will sometime be involved with a balancing problem, one should be thoroughly acquainted with the various methods of balancing and some of the difficulties associated with balancing.

SYMPTOMS AND CAUSES OF IMBALANCE

Imbalance is nearly always characterized by a high radial vibration at running frequency which may also be accompanied by a high amplitude in the axial direction. Depending on relative stiffness, the amplitude may be much larger in one radial plane than another.

Only balancing can correct imbalance; therefore, before beginning any balancing make certain that the high amplitudes are caused by imbalance and not by another unrelated problem such as misalignment. Additionally, if noncontact proximity probes are used, total runout—both amplitude and phase—must be accurately measured and all subsequent measurements of shaft vibration compensated for runout.

Imbalance is basically a very simple problem caused by an asymmetry in the rotating element which results in an offset between the shaft center line and center of mass. The asymmetry can be an off-center weight distribution or it can be a thermal mechanism which produces uneven heating and bowing of the rotor.

When the problem is pure mechanical imbalance, the objective in balancing is simply to add or subtract a weight(s) so that the forces developed by the weight changes will exactly balance the asymmetry. While this sounds simple and often is, certain factors can complicate the situation and make balancing, particularly balancing high-speed, flexible-shaft rotors, difficult.

DEFINITIONS

Listed are a few definitions of terms used in this discussion:

Heavy spot—position of the imbalance weight.

High spot—the point on an unbalanced rotating shaft with the greatest distance to the center of rotation (figure 12-1). The high spot is produced by the shaft's response to imbalance; it will be the point closest to a concentric stationary surface as the shaft rotates and is observed by a vibration pickup as the point of maximum positive amplitude. The high and heavy spot may or may not coincide, depending on where the rotor is operating relative to its critical speeds.

Static imbalance—imbalance where the force acts in one direction (figure 12-2a). With a condition of static imbalance, a rotor placed in bearings will roll until it comes to rest with the imbalance weight at the bottom.

Couple imbalance—an imbalance condition where the imbalance weights are at opposite ends of the rotor (figure 12-2b). With couple imbalance, a rotor will appear in balance statically, i.e., it won't tend to roll if the opposing imbalance weights are equal in magnitude. However, when rotated, the opposing dynamic forces developed at each end by the imbalance will cause the rotor to rock.

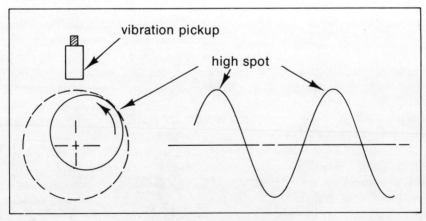

12-1—Definition of high spot.

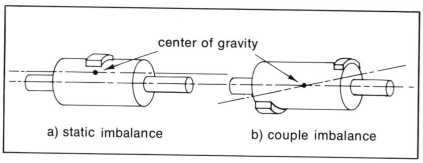

center of gravity

a) static imbalance   b) couple imbalance

12–2—Static and couple imbalance.

Dynamic imbalance–the most general form of imbalance, occurring when a rotor has both static and couple imbalance.

Stiff shaft rotor–a rotor operating below its first critical speed. On stiff-shaft rotors, the high and heavy spots coincide.

Flexible shaft rotor—a rotor operating above its first natural frequency or critical. A 180° phase change occurs as the rotor passes through the first critical and shifts from rotating about its geometric center to rotating about its mass center. As a result of this shift, the high and heavy spots are 180° out of phase on rotors operating between their first and second critical speeds. Since the objective of balancing is either to remove weight from the heavy spot or add weight opposite the heavy spot, the difference between high and heavy spots can be very important from the standpoint of where a weight change is to be applied.

Lag angle–the distance from 0° to 360° a shaft turns between the phase reference and the high spot. This term has a slightly different meaning when used with seismic transducers compared with noncontact transducers.

PHASE MEASUREMENTS

Figure 12-3 shows lag angle measured with a noncontact shaft displacement pickup and phase reference. With this measurement system, the lag angle is the angle measured on the vibration waveform from the point where the phase marker passes beneath the phase reference pickup to the point where the high spot passes beneath the shaft displacement pickup. Remember that the lag angle measured with a noncontact displacement system begins with a signal from the phase reference pickup and ends at a point determined by the shaft displacement pickup. The high spot is located by stopping the shaft with the

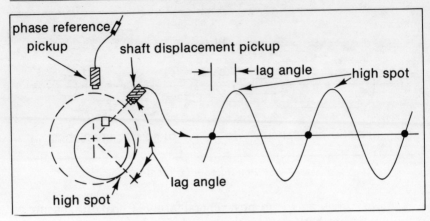

12-3—Definition of lag angle–noncontact convention.

leading edge of the phase mark beneath the phase reference pickup then measuring from the shaft displacement pickup and against the direction of rotation, an angular distance equal to the lag angle.

Although the lag angle estimated from an oscilloscope waveform and the lag angle displayed on a tracking analyzer should be very close to the same value, the tracking analyzer makes its measurement in a slightly different way. In a tracking analyzer it is difficult to identify and make an angular measurement to a peak in the waveform. As a result, lag angle is measured from the phase reference to the first positive-going zero axis crossing. To this value the tracking analyzer adds 90° to arrive at a measurement to the peak of the waveform.

A seismic system using a strobe for phase measurement has only one pickup; therefore, the lag angle must be derived in a slightly different way. Using this system of measurement, a flash angle is defined as the angle between the vibration pickup and the point at which a reference mark placed on the rotating shaft is frozen by the strobe. If it weren't for the presence of time delays in the seismic system, the strobe would flash at the positive-going zero axis crossing observed by the vibration pickup and freeze the reference mark at some point in the shaft's rotation. In this theoretical example, the flash angle and lag angle would be equal and the high spot could be located in basically the same way as proximity probes. Unfortunately, a seismic system has inherent time delays which produce a substantial difference between the flash and lag angles. The total delay is comprised of a mechanical delay caused by the phase difference between shaft and casing motion and delays within the instrument itself.

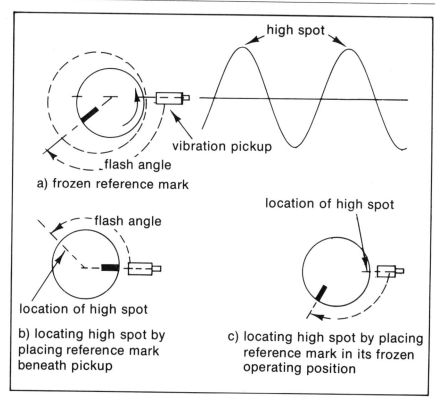

a) frozen reference mark

b) locating high spot by placing reference mark beneath pickup

c) locating high spot by placing reference mark in its frozen operating position

12–4—Locating high spot—strobe/seismic convention—without time delays.

Figure 12-4 illustrates phase measurement with a seismic system without time delays. In this hypothetical situation, recognize that the phase reference and vibration pickups are the same to apply the principles discussed for locating the high spot with shaft pickups. In the absence of time delays, the high spot could be located by placing the reference on the shaft beneath the vibration pickup, then measuring, in the direction of rotation, an angular distance equal to the flash angle (figure 12-4b). Alternatively, with the shaft positioned with the reference in its frozen operating position, the high spot will be located beneath the pickup (figure 12-4c).

While these principles also apply to actual seismic measurements, the flash and lag angles will differ due to time delays inherent in the measurement. As illustrated in figure 12-5, the time delay present in an actual seismic phase measurement produces an angular offset between the position on the shaft defined by the flash angle and the actual high

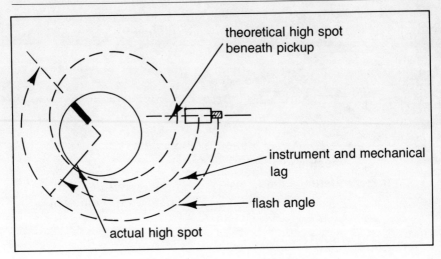

theoretical high spot
beneath pickup

instrument and mechanical lag

flash angle

actual high spot

12–5—Location of actual high spot.

spot which would be observed by a noncontact shaft pickup located in the same position as the seismic casing pickup. Although this angular offset will vary from instrument to instrument and from machine to machine, it will be a constant for a specific instrument and pickup location on a specific machine operating at a given speed. Determined from the final weight position when the machine is balanced, the angular offset between flash angle and high spot should be recorded so that any balance corrections required in the future can be placed at the proper location on the first try.

Thus, the location for a corrective weight can be determined from a noncontact shaft displacement measurement without any appreciable time delay or from a seismic measurement which will always have some time delay. For a given condition of imbalance, the position of the corrective weight must be the same regardless of the measurement system used.

PHASE CONVENTIONS

Shaft pickups

Two conventions are in general use for measuring phase. The first, used with noncontact proximity pickups and phase measurement on an oscilloscope or with a tracking analyzer, produces a measurement which is always against the direction of rotation. The primary advantage of this convention is that it results in a vector plot in which a vector can be rotated by rotating a weight on the machine in the same physical direction. In other words, to move a plotted vector clockwise, move a weight clockwise on the rotor.

To explain this convention, note that phase measurement on an oscilloscope or balance analyzer using shaft displacement probes is the angular distance from the shaft displacement probe to the high spot—measured against the direction of rotation—when the phase mark is beneath the phase reference probe. Said another way, the lag angle measured in this fashion is a measure of how long it takes for the high spot to reach the shaft displacement probe from the time the phase reference mark passes the phase reference probe. In figure 12-6a, showing clockwise rotation, the high spot passes the shaft displacement probe 135° after the phase marker passes the phase probe. If everything is working correctly, one should read 135° on a tracking analyzer and estimate about the same angle from the waveform on an oscilloscope.

Figure 12-6b shows the same system with counterclockwise rotation. The same high spot will now require approximately 225° rotation

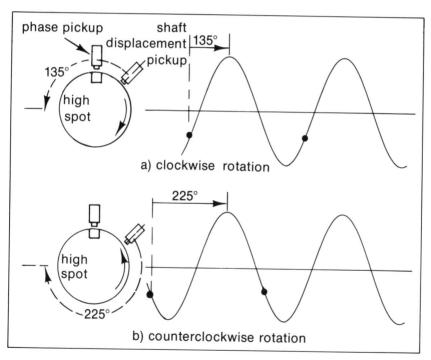

12–6—Phase measurement with shaft probes.

to reach the shaft displacement probe, and this is the value read on a tracking analyzer to estimate from the waveform.

Regardless of which direction the shaft is turning, a tracking analyzer always measures lag angle against the direction of rotation. If the normal left-to-right convention is used on an oscilloscope, lag angle is also automatically measured against the direction of rotation.

Now assume that the high spot can be moved at will in any direction. Regardless of which way the shaft turns, moving the high spot in the direction of rotation decreases the angular distance the shaft must turn before the high spot reaches the shaft displacement probe and accordingly reduces the measured and estimated lag angles (figure 12-7). Conversely, shifting the high spot against the direction of rotation will increase the angular distance the shaft must turn before the high spot reaches the vibration probe and accordingly increases the measured lag angle.

It should be apparent that to shift the high spot, a weight had to be shifted in the same direction on the rotor. Thus, a weight shift in the

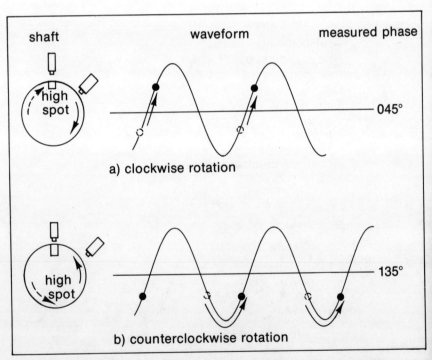

12–7—The effect of shifting the high spot in the direction of rotation.

direction of rotation will move the high spot in the direction of rotation and decrease the lag angle. Likewise, a weight shift against the direction of rotation will move the high spot against the direction of rotation and increase the lag angle.

Next, examine the convention of plotting measured lag angles in a polar coordinate system where the angular reference increases against the direction of machine rotation. Taking figures 12-6a and 12-7a, a shift in weight (high spot) 90° clockwise (in the direction of rotation) resulted in a decrease in the measured lag angle from 135° to 045°. Plotted on polar graph paper with a counterclockwise (against rotation) phase convention (figure 12-8a), the plotted vector moves in the same direction as the weight change. Likewise, the counterclockwise shift in weight on the rotor turning counterclockwise produces a counterclockwise rotation in its polar plot (figure 12-8b).

To summarize, a polar convention with an angular frame of reference which increases against the direction of shaft rotation will result in vectors and weight shifts which move in the same direction, clockwise or counterclockwise, on the polar plot and machine. If this convention is used and one wants to rotate a vector clockwise in the balancing process, shift weight clockwise without regard to the direction of shaft rotation. Conversely, to move a vector counterclockwise, move weight counterclockwise.

To use the convention with shaft probes, phase, and vibration, remember these three simple rules:

1. Lag angles are recorded directly from a balance analyzer or estimated from the angular distance measured left to right between

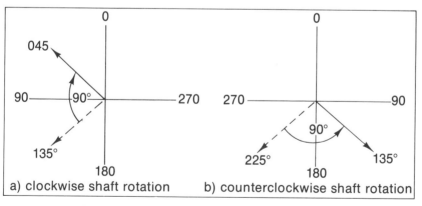

12–8—Vector rotation corresponding to weight change.

the phase reference and the next positive peak on the vibration waveform.

2. Lag angles determined in (1) are plotted in a polar coordinate system where the coordinates increase against the direction of shaft rotation.

3. In the resulting plot, moving a vector either clockwise or counterclockwise is accomplished by shifting a weight in the same direction on the machine.

Casing pickups

Two methods are commonly used to obtain a phase measurement with a strobe light. The first method uses a stationary angular reference with a reference mark on the rotating shaft (figure 12-9a), while the second uses an angular reference system on the rotating shaft and a stationary reference mark (figure 12-9b). In the first method, the angular reference may be expressed in degrees from 0-360 or a clock position. In the second method, the angular reference is always expressed in degrees increasing clockwise. For the purposes of explanation, neglect the time delays inherent in a seismic strobe system and assume the analyzer is properly tuned so the strobe fires and freezes the shaft at the

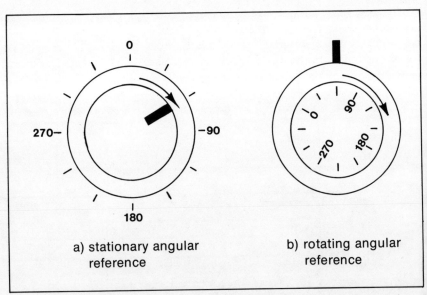

a) stationary angular reference

b) rotating angular reference

12–9—*Statonary and rotating angular reference conventions for phase measurement with a strobe.*

exact point the high spot appears underneath the pickup. Also assume the rotor is operating below its first critical speed where high and heavy spots coincide.

Figure 12-10 illustrates phase measurement utilizing a stationary angular reference. In figure 12-10a, the high spot (also the heavy spot in this example) triggers the strobe to freeze the reference mark on the shaft at an angle of 210°. In figure 12-10b, a trial weight is added 90° counterclockwise from the heavy spot located in figure 12-10a. Thus the added weight will shift the heavy spot to a position somewhere between the original heavy spot and the trial weight.

In figure 12-10b, the added trial weight produces a new heavy spot which, as it appears below the vibration pickup, fires the strobe, freezing the reference mark at 270°. If the trial weight continues to move counterclockwise, the reference mark will move clockwise. Thus, in the fixed angular reference system and regardless of shaft rotation, a shift in weight produces a change in phase opposite in direction to the change in weight.

In the rotating angular reference system, begin with the same physical configuration. In figure 12-11a, the heavy spot, sensed by the vibration pickup, fires the strobe to freeze the shaft at an angle of 210° opposite the fixed reference mark. In figure 12-11b, a trial weight is added 90° counterclockwise from the heavy spot, producing a resultant which is counterclockwise from the original heavy spot and a corresponding counterclockwise shift in phase angle. Thus, contrary to the fixed-reference system described previously, a weight shift in the rotating angular reference system will produce a phase shift in the same direction as the shift in weight.

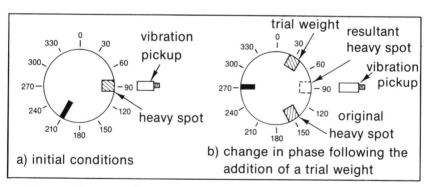

12–10—*Change in phase measurement in response to weight addition. Stationary angular reference convention; no time delays operating below first critical speed.*

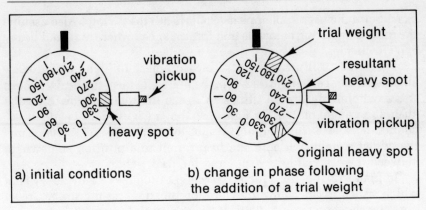

trial weight

vibration pickup

resultant heavy spot

heavy spot

vibration pickup

original heavy spot

a) initial conditions

b) change in phase following the addition of a trial weight

12–11—*Change in phase measurement in response to weight addition. Rotating angular reference convention; no time delays, operating below first critical speed.*

Since both fixed and rotating angular reference systems are in common use, it is extremely important to recognize that the frame of reference determines the direction of weight shift necessary to achieve a given direction of phase shift.

Although the shift in phase was illustrated by its response to a shift in weight, balancing requires a reverse approach. In balancing, the task is to determine the size and position of the weight necessary to oppose exactly the vector defined by vibration amplitude and phase obtained on the initial run.

Before leaving the determination of lag angles, remember an important difference between the angle measured with a seismic pickup and strobe and the angle measured with a noncontact shaft displacement system. Think of the latter, whether the actual measurement is made on an oscilloscope or with a tracking analyzer, as an instantaneous measurement; that is, the measured lag angle is the actual distance on the shaft between the phase reference and the high spot. On the other hand, a seismic pickup attached to the casing is one step removed from actual shaft motion, and the measured lag angle will typically contain an offset determined by the difference in phase between shaft and casing as well as any phase offset of the instrument itself.

SINGLE-PLANE BALANCING

Single-plane balancing addresses imbalance in a single plane and is rigorously true only when a rotor consists of a single thin disc mounted on a perfectly balanced shaft or it has a purely static imbalance.

Single-plane balancing does, however, illustrate the vector techniques which are equally applicable in multiplane balancing.

The first step in any balancing procedure is to record amplitude and phase in the unbalanced condition. Next, apply a trial weight, then bring the rotor back up to its original speed and measure amplitude and phase with the trial weight in place. A simple vector subtraction gives the effect of the trial weight. Once the precise effect of the trial weight is known, it can be adjusted in both position and weight to counteract exactly the original imbalance. To see how this procedure works, note the following example:

In figure 12-12, the initial amplitude and lag angle obtained at operating speed were 3 mils and 240°, respectively. Choose a polar coordinate system where the angles are increasing against the direction of rotation and plot the first or original vector. In this example, the direction of rotation is counterclockwise; choose a clockwise coordinate system and plot the first O (original) vector as shown.

Next, add a trial weight. The weight should be sufficient to make a change but not so large that it could destroy the machine if placed in a wrong position. Several sources recommend a weight which at speed

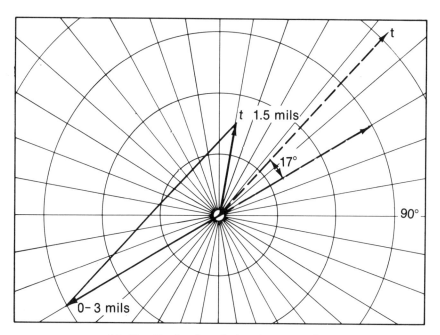

12–12—*Single-plane balancing example 1.*

will exert a force equal to 10% of the rotor's weight on one bearing at rest. This weight can be calculated as follows:

$$W = \frac{F}{KRN^2}$$

where:
- W = trial weight, oz (gm)
- F = 10% of rotor weight on a single bearing, lbs (kg)
- R = radius at which trial weight will be applied, in. (cm)
- N = rpm/1,000
- K = constant 1.77, English (0.011, metric)

The trial weight should always be placed in a corrective position: opposite the high spot below the first critical, on the high spot between the first and second criticals. Assume one is between the first and second criticals and thereby add the weight on the high spot at 240°. Now run the machine a second time.

At speed, record amplitude and phase with the weight in place of 1.5 mils at 010° and plot this as the T (trial) vector on the diagram. Since the objective of balancing is to apply a weight change equal and opposite to the original imbalance, the goal is a trial weight whose reaction is equal and opposite to the original vector. Isolate the reaction of the trial weight by drawing a vector from O to T as shown, then move it into the center by similar triangles or with parallel rules. The trial weight was about 17° out of position and was slightly heavy, determined by ratioing the length of the original vector to the length of the OT vector.

To make a final adjustment, reduce the trial weight by multiplying it by the ratio O/OT = 3/4.2 and rotate it 17° to obtain the final balance correction. Make a third proof run with the correction made with the trial weight before applying a permanent change. This is to ensure vibration is not being influenced by some other factor such as runout (balancing with shaft displacement probes only) or misalignment. In either case, the final move may not reduce vibration, for only imbalance can be corrected by a weight change.

When the results of the third run have demonstrated a satisfactory balance, replace the trial weight with a permanent weight change. In some cases this may consist of permanently attaching the trial weight, while in others the trial weight may be replaced by a permanent weight or by equal weight removal opposite the final position of the trial weight. In the latter case, be certain to remove the trial weight.

In the next example of single-plane balancing, assume the following conditions:

Rotor weight = 4,000 lbs
Speed = 8,800 rpm (above 1st critical)
Rotation = Clockwise
Initial amplitude = 4 mils
Lag angle = 140°
Trial weight radius = 10 in.

$$\text{Trial weight} = \frac{F}{KRN^2} = \frac{4,000/2 \times 0.1}{1.77 \times 10 \times 8.8^2} = 0.15 \text{ oz}$$

Plotting the initial readings, the original vector shown on figure 12-13 is obtained.

Since the machine is operating above the first critical, the high spot is opposite the heavy spot. Thus, add the trial weight in a corrective position on the high spot. Assuming noncontact shaft pickups are used, locate the high spot by placing the phase mark under the phase reference probe and count 140° against the direction of rotation beginning from the shaft displacement pickup. The trial weight will be placed on the rotor at approximately 7:30.

With the trial weight in place, start the machine, bring it up to speed, and record 2 mils at 045°. Plotting this value on figure 12-13 results in a vector OT of 4.6 mils at 346°. Now, make a change in weight and angular position which will rotate the vector OT (transposed to the center of the diagram) clockwise and change its length so that it will be equal and opposite to the original vector. Ratioing lengths O/OT × 0.15, the weight should be reduced to 0.13 oz and rotated 26°. The direction the weight must be rotated will depend on the measurement system; in this example, using shaft displacement pickups, it would be rotated clockwise. After making these changes, run the machine a third time. The vibration will disappear to the point where a tachometer must be used to see if the machine is running.

Before complicating this new knowledge with a discussion of why real balancing problems are seldom this simple, there are a couple of hints which can be helpful.

First, whenever a machine is balanced, a weight change is calculated and applied to compensate for a specific vibration amplitude. If the rotor sensitivity in corrective weight per unit of vibration (oz-in./mil, gm/mil, etc.) is recorded and retained, one can apply the correct weight on the first run when the machine is next balanced. In the last

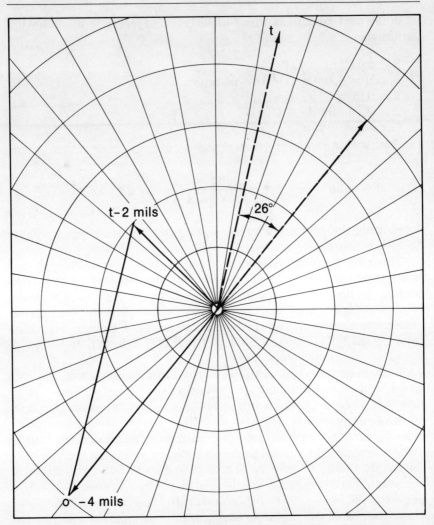

12–13—Single-plane balancing example 2.

example, 0.13 oz at 10 in. were required to correct 4 mils vibration. Expressed another way, the rotor sensitivity for this machine was (0.13 × 10)/4 or 0.325 oz-in./mil. If the next time this machine is balanced the initial vibration is 7 mils, one would add 0.23 oz at 10 in. in the correction position (0.325 × 7)/10 = 0.23 and probably correct the balance with the first shot.

Second, when balancing with a casing pickup and strobe, record the lag angle between the apparent high spot and actual high spot. This information, used along with the rotor sensitivity, will assist locating the trial weight in the proper corrective position when the rotor is next balanced at a vast time savings.

ANGULAR LOCATION OF TRIAL WEIGHTS

Thus far, it has been implied that the location of a trial weight is simply chosen at random. While many balance this way, a satisfactory balance can be achieved much more rapidly if the first trial weight(s) are placed in a corrective position. In fact, if the machine and instrumentation are known well enough and the influence coefficients from previous balancing have been recorded, a satisfactory balance can be achieved with a single run.

Since there are no time delays associated with a shaft displacement system, choosing an optimum location for the first trial weight is not difficult if the definitions are remembered. By now one should know how to locate the high spot physically and also know that the high spot coincides with the heavy spot below the first critical and is 180° from the heavy spot between the first and second criticals. Thus, the optimum corrective position for a trial weight will be opposite the high spot when operating below the first critical and on the high spot when operating between first and second criticals. To check, record the high spot both above and below the critical when balancing flexible-shaft machines and make certain that both define the same weight position.

Although the same principle is just as valid for a seismic strobe balancing system, system lags offset the actual high spot from the apparent high spot defined by the flash angle. Most modern solid-state instruments will have an instrument lag of approximately 90° to which any mechanical lag must be added. If balancing for the first time and the lag angle between apparent and actual high spots is unknown, an estimate of 120°–150° will usually provide a good starting point. Going back to figure 12-5, note that the high spot is determined in a seismic strobe system by subtracting the lag angle from the flash angle.

BALANCING WITHOUT PHASE MEASUREMENT

Often by necessity, sometimes by preference, it may become necessary to balance a rotating machine or part under conditions where a phase measurement is either impossible or unavailable. In this situation, the four-run method can be used to arrive at an amount and position for a corrective weight.

To perform the four-run balancing procedure, one needs a method to measure vibration amplitude and polar graph paper.
1. With the machine in operation, locate and measure the point of highest vibration on a bearing. Either attach the pickup to this position or accurately mark its location so subsequent measurements may be taken from exactly the same place.
2. Measure and record the vibration amplitude—O.
3. Place a trial weight, calculated as before, somewhere on the rotor, restart the machine, and record vibration amplitude—T_1 at location 1.
4. Stop the machine, rotate the trial weight 90° to 120° as most convenient at a constant radius, restart the machine, and record vibration amplitude—T_2 at location 2. .
5. Stop the machine, rotate the trial weight another 90° to 120° in the same direction at the same radius, restart the machine, and record vibration amplitude—T_3 at location 3.
6. From the foregoing data, the location and the amount of a corrective weight may be determined as will be illustrated in the following example:

> Original imbalance = (0) 10 mils
> Trial weight, TW = 50 g
> First trial, T_1 = 7.0 mils @ 0°
> Second trial, T_2 = 12.0 mils @ 120°
> Third trial, T_3 = 18.0 mils @ 240°
> Note: The angles refer to the trial weight positions on the rotor relative to an arbitary zero.

1. On the polar graph paper draw a circle with a radius of 10 mils. On the circumference of the circle mark the trial weight positions (figure 12-14).
2. Using the points marked on the circumference of the first circle as centers, draw arcs with radii equal to the amplitude measured with the trial weight at the location.
3. Draw a line from the origin of the original circle to the intersection of the three trial-weight circles (F); this is the angular position of the corrective weight relative to the trial weight positions.
4. Measure the length of the line drawn in step 3. The correct weight addition may now be calculated from the ratio TW × 0/F = 50 × 10/8.5 = 59.0 g.

TWO-PLANE BALANCING

Unfortunately, balancing is never quite this simple. The reason for the difficulty is not hard to explain: real rotors always have length

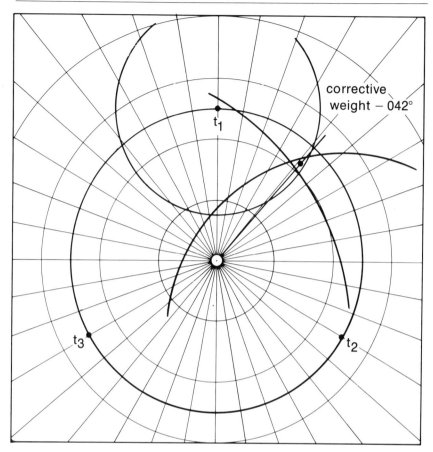

12–14—*Four-run balance without phase.*

along the longitudinal axis with the possibility of imbalance anywhere along that length. Illustrated in figure 12-15, a randomly distributed dynamic imbalance along the length of a rotor cannot be corrected by a single weight correction. In fact, if the rotor is operating in or close to a bending mode, such a distribution will require corrections at each imbalance plane in order to operate with minimum vibration at all speeds. What is generally done, however, is to apply a two-plane correction at the speed the rotor will operate most of the time, then accept some increased vibration at other speeds.

Basically, there are four methods of accomplishing a two-plane balancing: separate single-plane balancing, simultaneous single-plane balancing, the static/couple derivation method, and the influence co-

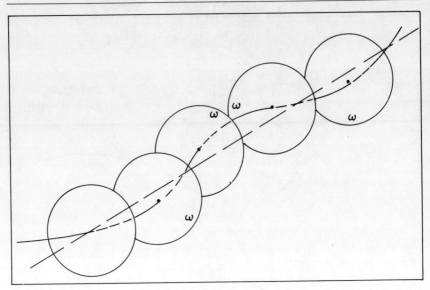

12–15—*Effect of varying imbalance along the length of a flexible shaft rotor.*

efficient or Therele method. The separate single-plane and simultaneous single-plane methods should be reasonably self-explanatory. In the former, correct the imbalance at one end of the rotor using the single-plane method, then move to the other end and repeat the process. This method is the simplest and will work well if most of the imbalance is concentrated at one end of the rotor or the vibration at opposite ends is in phase below the first critical. The reasoning behind the latter is that adding a weight in the corrective position at one end will help at the other as well. When the imbalance distribution is such that adding a weight at one end makes the other worse, the separate single-plane method is difficult to use.

In the static/couple derivation method of multiplane balancing, the two imbalance vectors measured at either end of the rotor are resolved into static and couple components which are corrected separately. On flexible rotors, the static correction is generally applied midspan for maximum effect on the first mode, while the couple correction is applied about one-third of the way in from the ends for maximum effect on the second mode.

In addition to a good method for use on flexible rotors, the static/couple derivation method is very useful for two-plane balancing with large crosscoupling present. Crosscoupling is the change in balance at one end of a rotor produced by a weight change at the opposite end. As an example, a balance correction made on one wheel of a small steam turbine rotor consisting of two closely spaced wheels located near the center of a relatively long shaft will significantly affect the balance measured at both bearings due to crosscoupling. On this and similar rotors, balancing is often very difficult with conventional methods, for a change which improves one end may significantly degrade the other. Two-plane overhung rotors are a second extreme example where large amounts of crosscoupling are best dealt with by deriving static and couple components. Finally, large stiff shaft rotors are often easier to balance with this method, for corrections can be applied simultaneously in two planes without the necessity of compensating for cross-effect.

To illustrate the static/couple derivation method of two-plane balancing, assume a measurement of 6 mils at 180° and 8 mils at 310° in the near and far planes, respectively. Plotting the two vectors and joining their tips (figure 12-16), find the midpoint of the connecting line. The vector drawn from the origin to the midpoint and labelled S_o represents the original static imbalance. The line connecting O_n and O_f becomes two equal and opposite vectors originating at the head of S_o and representing the near and far couple components, respectively. With the static and couple vectors derived in this fashion, they may be corrected individually in any order or all can be corrected simultaneously.

Addressing only the static component, apply a trial weight in a corrective position for the static vector S_o. The corrective weight is generally applied midspan, although it can be divided and applied at the two end planes or distributed across the rotor. If either of the latter distributions are used, remember that it is a static correction, so all the weight is applied at one angular position.

Following the application of the trial weight, the rotor is run up to speed and the near and far-side vectors are recorded. The two vectors, measured with the static trial weight in place, are resolved into static and couple components. The static vector with the trial weight is then compared to the original static vector to determine a weight change exactly as was described in the single-plane balancing examples.

As the static imbalance is corrected, couple imbalance measured in the near and far planes should approach equal and opposite values. At this point, equal trial weights are placed in the near and far balance planes 180° apart, and conventional vector techniques are used to refine the position and amount of weight to minimize vibration.

Although the three methods for two-plane balancing can all be used and may have advantages in certain situations, virtually all two-plane

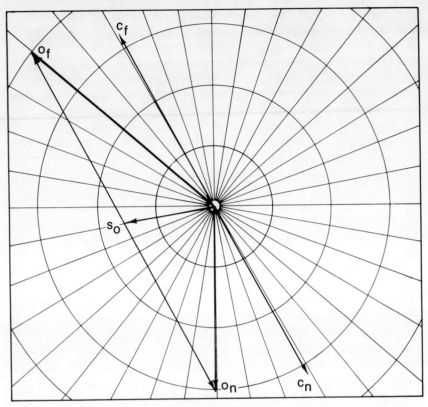

12–16—Static/couple derivation from two vectors.

balancing—certainly that done computationally with computer and hand calculator programs—is accomplished with the Therele or influence coefficient method. In the Therele method, a trial weight is added at one end, the machine is run up to speed, and its effect is measured at both ends. Next, the first trial weight is removed, a second trial weight is added at the opposite end, then its effect is measured at both ends. From these two runs is found a weight's effect at the end which it is added as well as its crosseffect at the opposite end. From this data, a calculator can compute the proper weight change and location at each end of the rotor to achieve an optimum balance. The method is systematic, can be easily mechanized, and works well as long as the crosseffects, i.e., a weight's influence on vibration at the opposite end, do not exceed 50–60%. In a system with large crosseffects, the static/couple derivation method may provide better results.

To use the static/couple derivation method with a Therele computation, simply take and record near and far-end original measurements as for a conventional two-plane problem. Next, define the near-end weight as a static trial weight and obtain the resultant data from the near and far bearings. The static trial weight is removed and a couple trial weight is added as the far-end trial weight. Again, resultant data are obtained for near and far ends. The imbalance and trial weight data are applied to the computer or calculator program. Using this method, the answer for the near end will be the static correction required, while the answer for the far end will be the couple correction.

HIGH-SPEED BALANCING

One problem can be quite perplexing to someone who has not experienced balance problems on a high-speed rotor which couldn't be cured by conventional low-speed post assembly or trim balance techniques. Referring back to the long rotor in figure 12-15, as this rotor assumes a running deflection, the various imbalance weights along its length may vary in the force they exert due to a change in their radial distance from the axis of rotation. Additionally, if corrective weights are not placed in exactly the plane of imbalance, dynamic couples are established along the length of the rotor which can create imbalance at speed. Finally, the rotor deflection may create or alter the action of a couple imbalance. For these reasons, it is not uncommon to find a flexible rotor, balanced to balancing machine tolerances at low speed, incapable of operation at high speeds due to imbalance. This problem is minimized in built-up rotors found on centrifugal compressors by "stack balancing" where the bare shaft is balanced; then impellers are added one at a time and balanced. In this way, balance corrections are made in the plane of the imbalance and do not set up couples which can cause trouble at higher speed.

On solid rotors typically found on steam turbines, stack balancing is impossible and the rotor must often be trim balanced at full speed to reduce vibration to an acceptable level. Since in-place trim balancing is normally limited by access to two or three planes, a trim balance at speed will often represent a compromise with increasing vibration on either side of the balance speed. To minimize the necessity for in-place balancing at speed—a procedure which can often delay a plant startup—several organizations have high-speed balancing facilities and can balance rotors at or close to operating speed outside the machine.

When accomplishing high-speed balancing, the bearing stiffness of the balance machine should be as close as possible to the bearing stiffness on the actual machine. This is so the rotor's performance on the balance machine, location of critical speeds, response, etc., will match its performance under actual operating conditions.

Although it is customary to high-speed balance without coupling hubs, a final run should always be made with coupling hubs in place as proof of the rotor's performance in its operating configuration. Similarly, the shop drive should be rotated 180° to ensure it is not affecting balance.

As one final note, some turbines are extremely sensitive to overhung weight and cannot be balanced in place with the coupling hub installed. In this situation, remove the coupling hub and, if a keyed coupling, install a half key of the proper length held in place with a thin shrunk-on band.

BALANCING TOLERANCES

When machines are being balanced in place, it is customary to use the vibration criteria from chapter 9 to determine when an acceptable balance has been attained.

API Standards 612 and 617 for Special Purpose Steam Turbines and Centrifugal Compressors, respectively, specify that "the maximum allowable unbalanced forced at any journal at maximum continuous speed shall not exceed 10 percent of the static loading of that journal." Both API Standards state that maximum residual imbalance (oz-in.) shall not exceed:

$$\frac{56{,}347 \times \text{(journal static loading, lbs)}}{N^2 mc}$$

where:
$$Nmc = \text{maximum continuous speed}$$

An older standard for rigid rotors defines the maximum permissible imbalance (oz-in.) as 4 W/N where:

$$W = \text{rotor weight, lbs}$$
$$N = \text{rotor speed, rpm}$$

The more conservative standard depends on the specific rotor's speed and weight. The API Standard will be the more conservative for lightweight high-speed rotors. while the 4W/N criteria will be more conservative for heavy low-speed rotors.

The response of a given machine to imbalance depends on its specific dynamic characteristics. Therefore, if balance criteria similar to the preceding are used and measured in terms of vibration, a method of converting from balance units into vibration units becomes necessary. To make this conversion, an individual rotor's response to a change in balance weight is derived from data obtained during the balancing process. Calculating a conversion factor between balance and vibration units begins by determining the vibration amplitude due solely to the effect of the trial weight, represented by the length of the vector OT (figures 12-12 and 12-13). Dividing this value, in amplitude units, by the weight producing the change times its distance from the shaft centerline produces a quotient which, when multiplied by balance units, will provide equivalent vibration units for the specific rotor.

To see how a typical calculation works, refer to the example in figure 12-13. In this example, a 1.5 oz-in. (0.15 oz @ 10 in.) trial weight produced a reaction of 4.6 mils (vector OT). The conversion factor is thus: 4.6/1.5 = 3.07 mils/oz-in. Although calculated in a slightly different fashion, this conversion factor is the reciprocal of the rotor sensitivity calculated at the end of the second single-plane balancing example.

13

Alignment

Together with imbalance, misaligned couplings are a common source of machinery vibration. Like imbalance, misalignment is a maintenance problem since it can be corrected and prevented by using the proper maintenance procedures. Thus, everyone involved with machinery analysis and maintenance must be well-versed in the various alignment procedures and be able to select and implement the procedure(s) best suited to a specific application.

OBJECTIVE AND IMPORTANCE OF ALIGNMENT

The objective of alignment is to have two coupled shafts in perfect coincidence under operating conditions; however, achieving that objective is often complicated. Temperature differences from ambient to operating condition, often several hundred degrees, the effects of improperly aligned and/or supported piping attached to the machine, twisting or uneven settling of the support structure, and a host of other factors can influence the position of one machine relative to its adjacent coupled mate.

In practice, perfect coupling alignment is very difficult to achieve. Although several methods are described for accurately aligning a machine string for a given set of ambient and operating conditions, many machines, particularly those mounted outdoors and subjected to wide variations in both ambient and operating conditions, will undergo corresponding changes in operating alignment. In this situation, the best or optimum alignment will be an average position which minimizes the excursions expected in normal operation. In addition to accommodating normal changes in operating alignment as well as slight offsets due to tolerances in both the measurement and alignment procedures, the coupling between two machines must be able to absorb, for short periods, the offsets applied to compensate for thermal growth. In theory, the latter should be eliminated as the machine attains equilibrium operating temperature; however, the offsets may actually increase for a short time immediately after startup due to variations in the rate at which individual components change temperature.

In addition to unintentional misalignment, there are normal and expected conditions requiring some flexibility between coupled shafts. The necessity to accommodate normal operating misalignment as well as absorb axial growth nearly always requires some type flexible coupling between high-speed machines.

Flexible couplings are available in several styles and sizes. In high-speed, high-horsepower machinery, continuously lubricated gear-type couplings and dry flexible member couplings are most often used. Grease-packed gear couplings, couplings with elastomeric members, and dry flexible couplings are widely used on smaller machines. For each coupling, there should be manufacturer's recommendations for the maximum misalignment the coupling can safely tolerate. Figure 13-1 is one recommendation for continuously lubricated gear-type couplings. For added margin, many users reduce these limits to a simpler 1/2 mil offset per inch of spacer length (5 μm/cm).

Flexible couplings do not absorb misalignment. A well-aligned machine will generally operate more smoothly, reliably, and with fewer maintenance problems than one which is misaligned. On rare occasions, however, misalignment can help reduce instability. In addition, a perfectly aligned gear coupling may experience fretting and accelerated wear caused by a breakdown of the lubricating oil film due to insufficient relative motion between teeth. Since these are special circumstances which rarely occur, every maintenance organization should strive to achieve the best coupling alignment possible.

TASKS IN MACHINERY ALIGNMENT

Two general tasks are involved with machinery alignment: determining the amount of alignment change from ambient to an average operating condition, then applying the proper offsets under ambient conditions so that shafts will be coincident at operating conditions.

AMBIENT (SHUTDOWN) ALIGNMENT

The face and rim method and the reverse indicator method are commonly used for accurately measuring the shaft alignment between

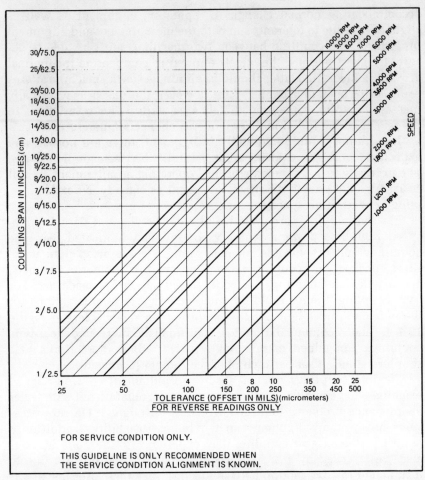

13–1—Alignment tolerance chart.

shutdown machinery. In the face and rim method, a face (axial) measurement (figure 13-2) and a rim (radial) measurement (figure 13-3) determine the angle and position, respectively, of one shaft relative to another. The reverse indicator method uses two rim measurements, one from each coupling, to locate one shaft centerline relative to the other.

Both face and rim measurements are normally made with a dial indicator. As illustrated in figure 13-2, a face measurement, expressed as the difference between opposite sides of a coupling hub measured from a line perpendicular to the shaft centerline from which the mea-

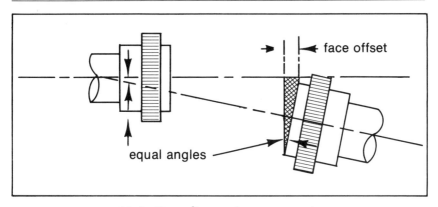

13–2—Face alignment measurement.

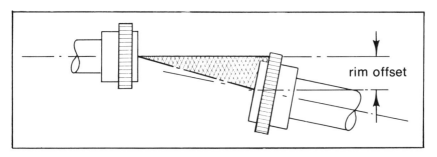

13–3—Rim alignment measurement.

surement is being made, is actually a method of determining the angle. between the two shaft centerlines.

In a rim measurement, a dial indicator is used to measure the radial difference between opposite sides of a coupling hub from the adjacent shaft centerline. As illustrated in figure 13-3, the offset from one shaft centerline extended to the other centerline at its coupling hub is one-half the value measured with a dial indicator.

Although there are many variations—depending on the distance between coupling faces, the diameter of the coupling hub, and the offsets involved—a rim measurement is usually larger in magnitude, easier to read, and much more accurate than a face reading. In addition, rim readings are not affected by shifts in a rotor's axial position which require special precautions when making face readings.

In general, a rim reading is more accurate and easier to make than a face reading whenever the distance between coupling hubs is larger than the hub diameter. Since this is generally the case in high-speed machinery where alignment is most critical, the reverse dial indicator method has gained widespread acceptance.

DIAL INDICATOR

A dial indicator (figure 13-4) consists of a spring-loaded plunger mechanically linked to a needle which rotates within a circular dial. In the English system, the dial is conventionally graduated in 0.001-in. increments numbered every 0.010 in.

The dial indicator is constructed such that a deflection of the plunger is read directly in engineering units on the dial. When the plunger is compressed or moved toward the dial (figure 13-5a) the needle moves clockwise. Conversely, when the plunger moves away from the dial it produces a counterclockwise rotation (figure 13-5b).

13–4—*Dial indicator.*

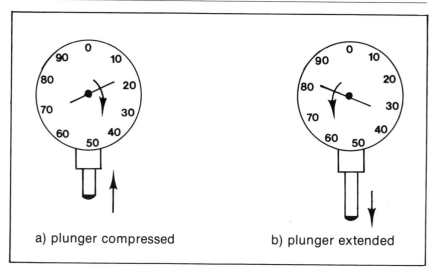

a) plunger compressed   b) plunger extended

13–5—Dial indicator movement.

In addition to needle movement corresponding to plunger movement, the graduated face of a dial indicator can be rotated manually through 360° by simply turning an external ring attached to the dial. This feature allows the indicator to be zeroed with the plunger in any position.

Note that clockwise deflection of the needle from zero (plunger movement toward the dial) is designated plus (+) while counterclockwise rotation of the needle from zero (plunger movement away from the dial) is designated minus (−) (figure 13-6). This convention is extremely important in plotting reverse indicator measurements.

CHECKS PRIOR TO ALIGNMENT

Before beginning any alignment procedure, one must first check the machine and certify everything is ready for alignment. It is extremely frustrating to spend hours or days trying to attain a satisfactory alignment only to find that some problem or condition that should have been anticipated prevents continued progress.

Before beginning any alignment procedure, first ensure that the machines being aligned are not affected by outside forces transmitted through the piping. The safest way to align is with all piping detached, including smaller-diameter lubricating and seal piping. Piping is re-attached only after the alignment has been completed and with dial indicators in place and being observed to ensure the newly aligned

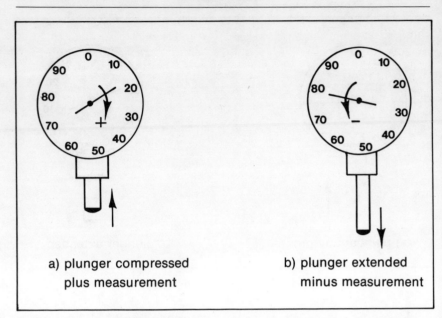

a) plunger compressed
plus measurement

b) plunger extended
minus measurement

13–6—Dial indicator sign convention.

machines are not moved as the piping is bolted in place. The piping must be fitted, aligned, and supported so that it is properly aligned, unattached, and thermal changes from ambient to operating conditions do not impose excessive forces on the machines which will force them out of line.

Proper piping support is always a controversial subject. On machinery subject to a change in temperature from ambient to operating conditions, the piping must be supported and/or offset to accommodate dimensional changes. In a properly designed system, spring hangers and supports, pipe stops, and expansion loops must be provided so that nozzle stresses and moments will be well within the machine manufacturer's allowable limits under all ambient and operating conditions.

The shim packs themselves are the next to be checked. Shims should be fabricated from stainless steel to preclude corrosion and trimmed carefully to eliminate any raised edges. A total shim thickness of approximately 0.125 in. (3.0 mm) is recommended as a beginning to ensure that there will be some room to lower a machine if necessary. There is nothing more frustrating than reaching the last case in a five-case string and find it must be lowered 0.070 in. then discover there is only a 0.040-in. shim remaining.

A good shim pack should have no more than two or three thick shims to make up the bulk of the height and two or three thinner shims for fine adjustment. A large number of thin shims will be springy, making it difficult to achieve consistent results.

Finally, the shim area on both the support structure and machine mount must be clean, free of debris, and preferably stoned to a smooth finish. Here again dirt or corrosion products between the shim pack and machine will produce inconsistent results and greatly prolong the alignment process.

With proper shim packs installed, check for a soft foot. Defined as a variation in elevation between the mounting feet, a soft foot places strain on a machine casing, can produce internal misalignment, and makes alignment very difficult as indicator readings will change as the mounting bolts are tightened.

To check for a soft foot, mounting bolts should be loosened then tightened one at a time. Any significant change in alignment as read on a dial indicator measuring to the shaft on an adjacent machine indicates a soft foot. A soft foot is corrected by adding or subtracting shims from one or more supports until all the mounting bolts can be tightened with a negligible effect on alignment.

While in the area of the mounting bolts, check that each has sufficient radial clearance to permit moving the machine horizontally. If a mounting bolt(s) is hard against one side of its hole, one can be absolutely certain which way he will have to move the machine.

Each mounting foot should be equipped with jacking bolts (figure 13-7). The jacking bolts must control movement in the horizontal and axial planes and lift the machine vertically to change shims.

As a final check prior to beginning actual alignment, the face-to-face distance between each coupling should be checked against a manufacturer's drawing to ensure the coupling spool piece will fit with the proper clearance. This check is particularly important on flexible diaphragm couplings which must be axially offset to compensate for thermal growth in order to minimize the axial deflection of the flexible member at operating conditions.

TAKING AND RECORDING DIAL INDICATOR MEASUREMENTS

In addition to a dial indicator, a rigid indicator mount for spanning the coupling is needed (figure 13-8). Indicator mounts are best fabricated from steel tubing with triangular braces to ensure rigidity. If space is available behind the coupling hub, it is sometimes possible to fabricate a clamp so the machines can remain coupled with the bar in

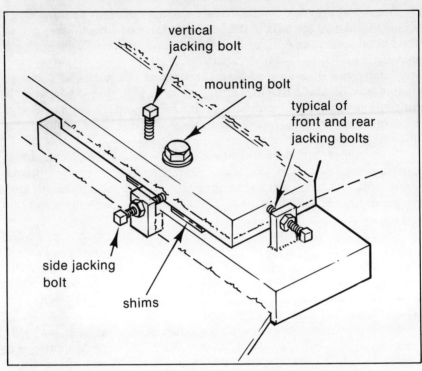

13–7—*Typical mounting foot jacking bolt installation.*

place. Aligning coupled has two major advantages. First, both shafts turn together so measurements will not be affected by any coupling hub runout. Second, much time can be saved if two bars are installed and both sets of reverse measurements are taken at the same time.

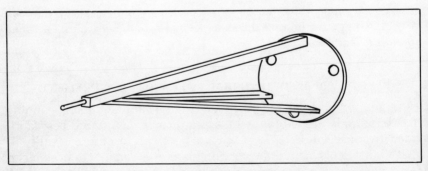

13–8—*Dial indicator mount.*

Although properly designed and fabricated indicator bars should be quite rigid, the weight of the bar and indicator may produce some deflection or sag, particularly on long bars designed for small-diameter coupling hubs (figure 13-9). Sag can be measured by installing the bar and indicator(s) exactly as they will be used on the machine on a rigid fixture such as a length of heavy wall pipe. The indicator deflection is observed as the fixture is rolled 180° from a position with the bar on top. As shown in figure 13-10, the change in indicator reading is a measurement of the bar's deflection both toward and away from the fixture and is thus twice the sag referenced to a true horizontal. With the bar in a horizontal position (figure 13-11), the effect of sag lowers the indicator and results in a measurement point which is slightly below the true horizontal. Although this has a negligible effect, a horizontal reading contains bar sag due to the offset applied when the indicator was zeroed on top. As a result, horizontal indicator readings must be corrected by subtracting bar sag from the value read on the indicator face. Figure 13-12 contains two examples of indicator readings corrected for a bar sag of 3 and 5 mils, respectively. The horizontal offsets are not affected; however, the vertical measurements are in error by the amount of bar sag which, if not corrected, will result in a corresponding error in alignment.

Several precautions and conventions should be followed before measuring with dial indicators:

- Inspect and clean the surface on the coupling hubs on which the indicator will travel. In addition to being clean and free of debris, the surface must be free of scratches or other imperfections which would influence the indicator reading.

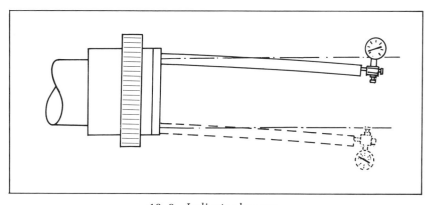

13–9—Indicator bar sag.

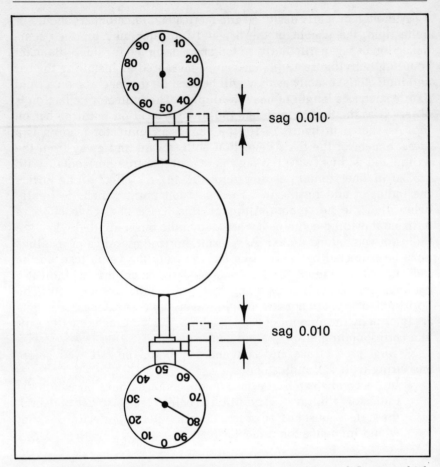

13–10—*Sag measured top and bottom results in an indicator deflection which is twice sag.*

- Make certain the indicator mechanism works freely.
- Check the indicator mounted square to the surface being indicated.
- Check coupling hubs for runout by turning the hub being indicated with the indicator held stationary.

Following convention, the dial indicator will always be set to read zero on top of the shaft. The shaft should be rotated in one direction only with measurements taken exactly 90° apart. A circular pipefitter's level with graduations every 90° and attached magnetically is a great help in achieving consistent readings—especially when offsets are

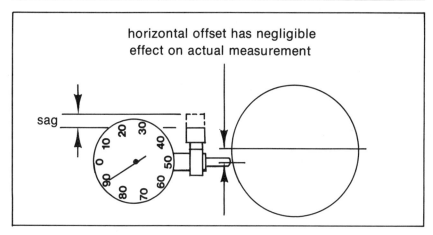

13–11—Zeroing the indicator at the top produces a deflection in the horizontal plane equal to bar sag.

large—for in this situation a small increment of rotation has a large effect on the measurement.

As a precautionary measure, the circular level should not be attached to the surface observed by a proximity probe, for any residual magnetism left in the shaft by the magnet will affect the probe reading.

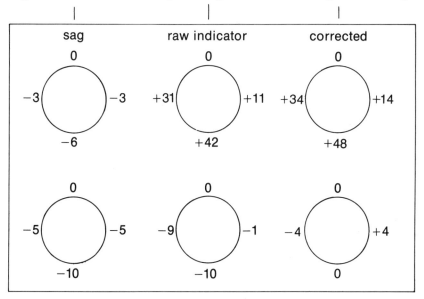

13–12—Raw indicator readings and measurements corrected for bar sag.

Horizontal measurements must be labelled in some perfectly clear way such as east and west so the direction of measurement can never be in doubt.

If measurements are accurate, the algebraic sum of the vertical measurements must equal the algebraic sum of the horizontal measurements.

As has been stated earlier, the difference between two dial indicator measurements taken 180° apart is twice the centerline offset (figure 13-13). Raw dial indicator readings, called total indicator readings (TIR) must be divided by 2 before used in an alignment procedure.

Dial indicators are normally mounted to indicate the outside diameter (OD) of a shaft (figure 13-13). There may, however, be occasions

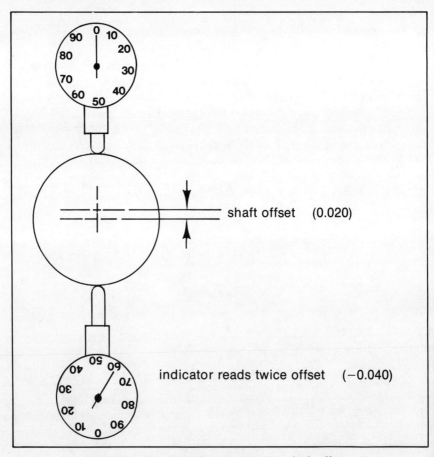

shaft offset   (0.020)

indicator reads twice offset   (−0.040)

13–13—*Indicator deflection is twice shaft offset.*

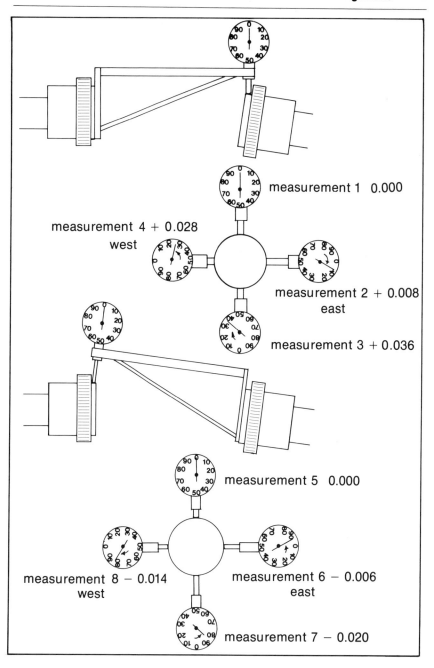

measurement 1   0.000

measurement 4 + 0.028
west

measurement 2 + 0.008
east

measurement 3 + 0.036

measurement 5   0.000

measurement 8 − 0.014
west

measurement 6 − 0.006
east

measurement 7 − 0.020

13–14—Reverse dial indicator measurements.

when it is necessary to indicate an inside diameter (ID). All the examples in this chapter assume OD indication; if an ID indication must be used, the sign convention must be reversed.

Figure 13-14 illustrates the procedure for taking reverse dial indicator measurements. Although eight steps are shown, they can be cut in half by using two indicators and two extension bars and taking simultaneous measurements on each coupling. If the single indicator eight-step procedure is used, either turn both shafts together or confirm that the hub being indicated has negligible runout by turning its shaft and observing that the indicator needle does not move.

Although not specifically illustrated in figure 13-14, a set of dial indicator measurements is not complete until the indicator is returned to the top and the zero initial measurement is repeated. Before accepting a set of dial indicator measurements, they should be taken at least twice and observed to repeat within a reasonable tolerance. These measurements appear valid, as the algebraic sum of the horizontal and vertical dial indicator readings agree within 0.001 in.

PLOTTING DIAL INDICATOR READINGS

Although the same tasks can be performed mathematically, a graphic demonstration of the use of reverse dial indicator readings is much easier to follow. In either method one must first measure the distance from a convenient reference at either end of a machine string to each coupling and to the centerline of each shim pack. These measurements are then transferred to graph paper at some convenient horizontal scale such as 1 in. = 1 ft (1 mm = 10 cm) as shown in figure 13-15. Once a suitable vertical scale is selected—1 in. = 0.010 in. (1 mm = 10 μm) is commonly used—the measurements in figure 13-14 can be plotted.

In plotting reverse dial indicator measurements, only three simple rules must be remembered.

- Measurements are TIR or twice offset.
- The offset being measured is from one shaft centerline extended to the other shaft centerline at the coupling hub on which the indicator is reading (figure 13-16).
- If the shaft indicated is below the extended centerline of the shaft on which the indicator is mounted, the reading at the bottom will be plus. Conversely, if the shaft indicated is above the extended centerline of the shaft on which the indicator is mounted, the reading at the bottom will be minus.

These rules can be applied to plot one shaft's position relative to the

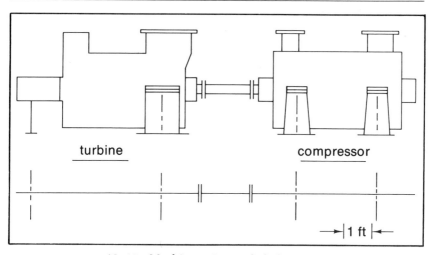

13–15—*Machine string scaled elevation.*

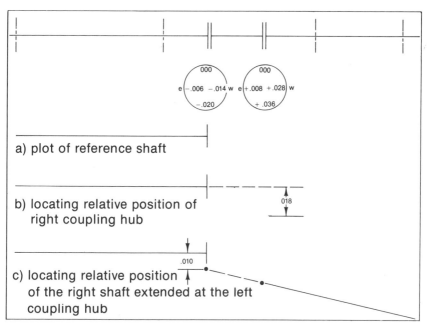

13–16—*Plot of vertical reverse indicator measurements.*

other. As a slight digression, a plot of reverse dial indicator readings will always be relative; there is no way of actually locating either shaft's true position in space with this method alone. For the purposes of illustration, assume the shaft on the left is the reference shaft, shown as a horizontal line (figure 13-16a).

Recognizing that the bottom indicator readings of −20 and +36 represent vertical offsets of minus 10 and plus 18, respectively, the only task remaining is to determine which direction. Going back to the rules for plotting reverse dial indicator readings, a plus offset means that the shaft being indicated is below the centerline extended of the shaft on which the indicator is attached. In this example, the centerline of the right-hand shaft at its coupling hub (where the measurement was taken) is below the centerline extended of the left shaft by 0.018 (figure 13-16b).

The bottom reading at the other coupling, −20, is the distance between the right-hand shaft centerline extended and the centerline of the left, reference, shaft at its coupling hub. Since the measurement is minus, the right shaft centerline extended must be below the left shaft centerline at the left shaft's coupling hub. With both direction and offset known, a second dot is marked (figure 13-16c). Since both dots must lie on the right shaft centerline extended, connect the two and continue the line to show the vertical position of the right-hand shaft relative to the left.

Thus far, the discussion has been limited to vertical measurements because the zero on top convention makes the offset much easier to visualize. Although horizontal offsets may be a bit more difficult than vertical offsets, one additional step will create an artificial zero in the horizontal plane. Then, one can proceed exactly as with the vertical offsets. The easiest way to handle the horizontal readings from figure 13-14 is to select a value which, when subtracted from both horizontal readings taken at one coupling hub, will reduce one reading to zero. Although it will work either way, it is probably best to pick values which will place the zero readings on the same side of the shafts.

Subtract −14 and +28 from the left and right shaft horizontal dial indicator readings, respectively (figure 13-17b). To plot these readings, refer to the direction in which the readings were taken. If the zeros are west, a plus reading indicates that the shaft centerline on which the measurement was taken was to the east of the shaft centerline extended on which the indicator was mounted. Conversely, if the east reading were minus, the indicated shaft centerline was to the west of the shaft centerline extended on which the indicator was mounted. In figure 13-17c, these rules are applied to locate the right shaft in its proper horizontal position relative to the left shaft.

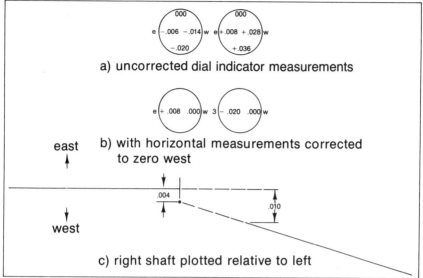

a) uncorrected dial indicator measurements

b) with horizontal measurements corrected
to zero west

east

west

c) right shaft plotted relative to left

13–17—Procedure for correcting and plotting horizontal indicator measurements.

DETERMINING SHIM CHANGES FOR A DESIRED ALIGNMENT OFFSET

Now, the procedure must be taken one step further before it is really useful. Once one shaft is located relative to another, the shim changes necessary to bring it to a desired offset must be accurately determined. The second half of this chapter is devoted to methods for determining an alignment offset; however, for now assume the offset has been determined and plotted as shown in figure 13-18a. If the measurements obtained in figure 13-14 represent the initial alignment, some changes will have to be made.

The shim changes necessary to achieve the desired offset may be determined from the scaled graph. As shown in figure 13-18c, the distance between the actual and desired shaft positions at the centerline of each shim pack is measured to determine the appropriate thickness of shims which must be added or removed to achieve the exact position desired. In the horizontal plane, apply the same principle by attaching dial indicators at each foot, then move the machine with the jacking bolts the required amount.

Where the machine's final vertical position is tilted to the plane of the supports to compensate for differences in thermal growth, the effect of the length of the support must be considered in making a shim change. In severe cases it may be necessary to grind a tapered shim to obtain the proper contact along the length of the support.

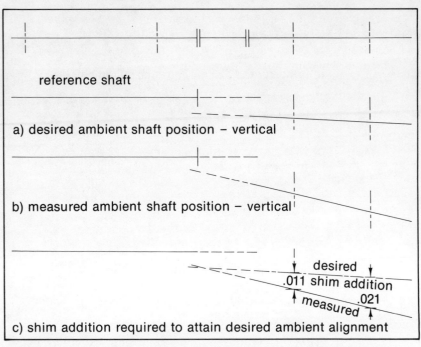

reference shaft

a) desired ambient shaft position – vertical

b) measured ambient shaft position – vertical

desired

.011 shim addition

.021

measured

c) shim addition required to attain desired ambient alignment

13–18—Graphical method to determine the shim changes needed to attain a desired ambient shaft alignment.

HELPFUL HINTS FOR SHUTDOWN ALIGNMENT

These additional hints may be of help:

- To determine which machine(s) to move in a string, consider the type of machine and how it is mounted. Gears are often shimmed unevenly to obtain optimum tooth contact and once set should not be moved unless absolutely necessary. If it is necessary to move a gear, the tooth contact must be checked after the movement has been completed.
- Once set, steam turbines are generally not moved.
- Centerline-mounted machines where the shim packs are readily assessible are the easiest to move and should be moved before foot-mounted machines.
- When aligning, rough align in the horizontal plane, then bring the machines into their final vertical position. When the vertical alignment is perfected, use the horizontal jack bolts to bring the horizontal alignment into its final exact position.

- When aligning a string of machines, plot the desired shaft positions on graph paper and the existing positions on a movable transparency. With this arrangement the existing alignment can be moved around until the easiest move or combination of moves are found. Sometimes Murphy takes a holiday and one simple move will place a multicase machine string in perfect alignment.
- After machines are finally aligned, most large critical machines will be doweled in place. Manufacturer's instructions will generally specify dowel size and location; however, the latter should be reviewed to ensure its effect on thermal growth is understood.

DETERMINING ALIGNMENT OFFSETS

The change in alignment from shutdown ambient to operating conditions can be estimated by calculation or measured using one or a combination of several methods. Although calculations can provide an estimate, they are often in error due to unexpected thermal gradients, radiant heat from piping, and foundation distortion. As a result, calculations should never be trusted for an accurate measure of thermal growth.

For years, a hot alignment check meant shutting down a machine which had been allowed to stabilize at temperature, installing dial indicators, and taking measurements. While this procedure may work reasonably well on pumps where the coupling is readily accessible and indicators may be installed in a matter of minutes, it does not work well on high-speed machinery where it may take several hours to gain access to a single coupling and install indicators during which time the machine is cooling and changing alignment. As a result, methods had to be developed for directly measuring alignment changes on large high-speed machinery.

Essinger method

The first method was developed by Jack Essinger of Shell. It is relatively simple, does not require a large investment in equipment, and provides excellent results if set up properly with attention to detail. In the Essinger method, three or four tooling balls are installed at each bearing (figure 13-19a). One or two tooling balls are attached to the bearing housing, while the other two are attached to a stable part of the machine base. Stable in this system means thermally and mechanically stable, preferably concrete and definitely not a metal baseplate, pipe support, or some other structural fitting which is likely to move. A clear line for measurement from center to center of the tooling balls is necessary.

To use the system, the distance between pairs of tooling balls, labeled A and B in figure 13-19a, is measured accurately with a preci-

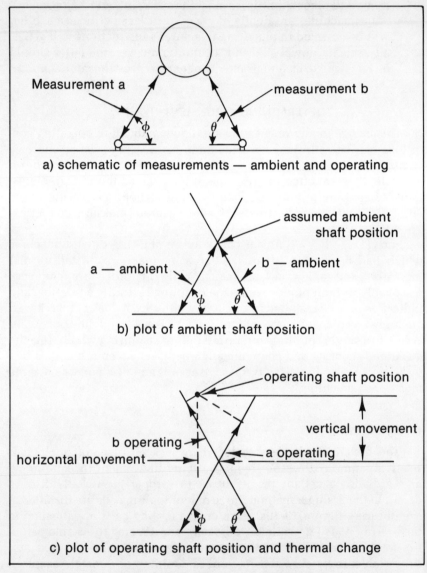

a) schematic of measurements — ambient and operating

b) plot of ambient shaft position

c) plot of operating shaft position and thermal change

13–19—Essinger alignment system.

sion extension bar and a dial indicator. The two angles, designated θ and ϕ, are likewise measured with a machinist's level. With this information, a scaled plot is constructed (figure 13-19b). The intersection created by the two measurements plotted at their respective angles is the presumed ambient position of the shaft. The machine is next brought to operating temperature and the measurements are repeated at each bearing. Operating measurements are plotted as shown in figure 13-19c along the original ambient measurement lines. At the end of each operating measurement, a perpendicular is drawn with the operating shaft position occurring at the intersection of the two perpendiculars. The difference between ambient and operating conditions is resolved into vertical and horizontal components, providing an accurate measure of the thermal change in alignment which took place at that particular bearing.

PROXIMITY PROBE

Cold stand (Jackson) method

Noncontact displacement pickups are used in two methods for measuring alignment changes. The first, the cold stand method originated by Charles Jackson of Monsanto, places water-cooled pipe stands at each corner of each machine in a string. Two noncontact proximity probes are attached to each stand, observing targets rigidly attached to the machine in both the horizontal and vertical directions (figure 13-20). DC gap voltages, recorded with the machine at ambient conditions and as it reaches operating conditions, are a direct measure of the change in alignment occurring at each point. Although it is generally impossible to take measurements directly at the couplings, it is a simple task to transpose the changes observed at the measurement points to changes in alignment at the coupling faces.

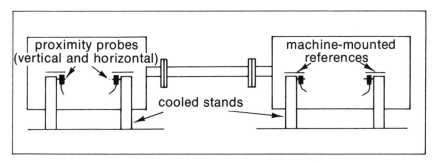

13-20—Jackson (cold stand) method.

The cold stand method has two principal advantages. First, once set up, measurements are easily obtained and can be recorded on a chart recorder if desired for a continuous record of the change in alignment from ambient to operating conditions. Second, the cold stand method measures alignment changes relative to the machine foundation, which makes problems such as pipe strain much easier to identify.

Problems with the cold stand method include the difficulty of finding clear space and a stable location on the machine foundation on which to mount the stand, the added complexity of supplying cooling water to stabilize the stand thermally, the potential for error due to uneven thermal growth between the shaft and the targets on the machine, and the ever-present possibility of someone bumping the stand and altering its position.

Relative (Dodd bar) method

A second method using noncontact proximity probes to measure changes in alignment was invented by V. R. Dodd of Chevron. In this method, an extension bar, fabricated from three aircraft steel tubes welded in a triangular configuration for rigidity, is attached to each machine spanning its coupling (figure 13-21). Two proximity probes oriented in the horizontal and vertical planes are mounted on one bar observing a target mounted on the adjacent bar. So the measurements can be directly translated to alignment changes, the probes are located in line with the coupling hubs.

The bars are identical in function to the reverse indicator system. As in the cold stand method, gap voltages are recorded at ambient conditions. As the machine assumes operating temperature, the change in voltage—translated to a distance—is a very accurate measure of the

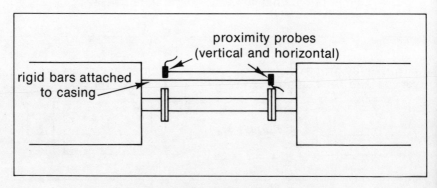

13–21—Dodd (relative) bar method.

change in alignment. Here again, once set up the measurement is easy to make, may be continuously recorded for a permanent record, and can be left in place. Like the cold stand method, the validity of the measurements may be jeopardized if the bars are hit during use.

On the negative side, the Dodd bar method measures changes in alignment of one machine relative to another, which sometimes makes localizing a pipe-strain problem to a single machine difficult. Additionally, if the points at which the bars are mounted to the machine distort due to thermal gradients or the bars themselves are exposed to uneven heating, the voltage changes obtained from the bars may not represent the changes in alignment (figure 13-22).

OPTICAL MEASUREMENTS

Optical measurements used in machinery alignment are an adaptation of the optical tooling equipment and techniques developed and refined by the aircraft and aerospace industries. In principle, optical tooling is relatively simple to understand. A high-powered precision telescope establishes a known line of sight from which very accurate measurements can be made. Fitting the telescope with axles and adding a level permits the telescope to be referenced to gravity and turned at will in two directions. Thus, the telescopic line of sight becomes either a horizontal or vertical plane of sight.

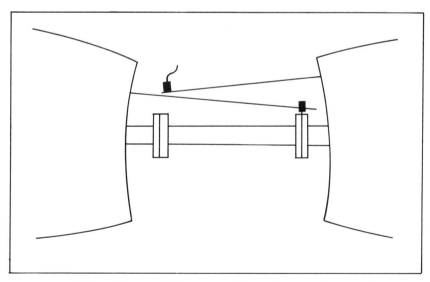

13–22—Effect of thermal distortion of the casing on alignment bars.

An optical tooling jig transit is shown in figure 13-23. The telescope is free to turn in both azimuth and elevation around two mutually perpendicular axles; one located in the base and the second where the

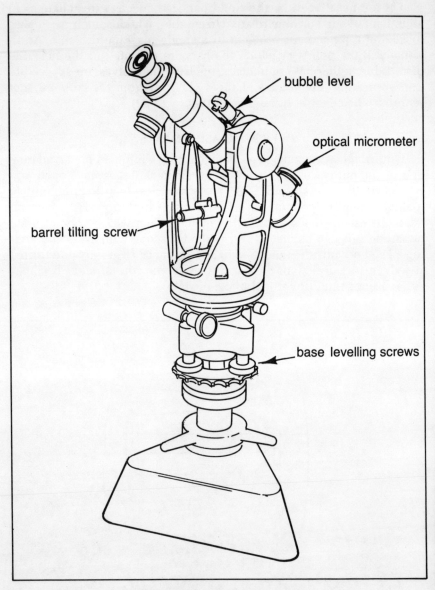

bubble level

optical micrometer

barrel tilting screw

base levelling screws

13–23—*Optical tooling jig transit.*

telescope is mounted to the yoke. As with any optical tooling instrument, the axles and bearings must be manufactured and aligned to extremely close tolerances.

A precision bubble level is attached to the barrel of the telescope and aligned parallel to the telescopic line of sight. The level provides a gravity reference which is utilized to plumb the transit and position the two axes in vertical and horizontal planes, respectively. The transit is plumbed by clamping the barrel to its tilting screw and alternately adjusting the barrel tilting screw and the base leveling screws. When the barrel is level and can be rotated through 360° in azimuth without further adjustment, the telescopic line of sight lies in a level, horizontal plane regardless of its position in azimuth. Unlocking the horizontal axle, locking the vertical axle, and turning the transit in elevation about the horizontal axis causes the telescopic line of sight to define a vertical plane.

An optical micrometer (figure 13-24) is attached to the objective end of the telescope. The micrometer consists of a drum graduated in 0.001-in. increments which is connected through a gear to a flat glass. As the micrometer drum is turned, the glass tilts in the line of sight, refracting and displacing the line of sight parallel to the telescope axis. The micrometer may be rotated so that the displacement occurs in either the horizontal or vertical plane.

The telescope mount must be solid and unaffected by vibration and other outside influences. An optical tooling tripod is generally adequate if it can be supported directly on the concrete foundation. If,

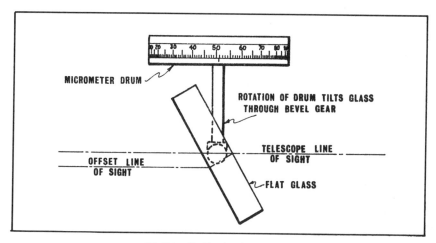

13–24—Optical micrometer.

however, a solid support is not readily available in the area in which the telescope must be located, it often becomes necessary to fabricate special stands which extend down to grade from a mezzanine-mounted machine or attach to the side of an elevated concrete structure. A telescope stand should not be supported on deck grating or steel walking deck, for deflection caused by factors as slight as the telescope operator shifting his weight as he rotates the telescope will throw it out of precise level needed for accurate measurements.

To obtain alignment measurements on a machine, external reference points, usually tooling balls or ground pins, are attached as closely to each bearing as possible. The reference points should be located so they will not be removed or disturbed during maintenance and overhaul. Additionally, reference points should be located so their movement with respect to the shaft from ambient to operating temperature is minimal. Thus, reference points should generally be mounted on the lower half of bearing housings with those used for horizontal measurements located as close to the vertical centerline as possible and those used for vertical measurements located as close to the horizontal centerline as possible. When reference points must be located off the centerlines, a temperature correction must be applied (coefficient of expansion × temperature difference × distance from the centerline) to each measurement. A second temperature correction may be required to compensate for differences in thermal growth of the scales if the temperature to which they are exposed varies significantly along a machine string.

The reference points, including those attached to the foundation to establish a vertical reference plane of sight, must be permanently and solidly fixed to the machine or foundation as appropriate and protected. With this precaution, the system can be dismantled and reassembled at a later date with confidence that measurements will accurately represent machine movement.

As has been discussed, the telescope establishes a level horizontal plane of sight from which vertical measurements will be made to the reference points installed on the machine casing. To take a measurement, a spherical scale level is attached to an optical scale; the scale is placed on a reference point and moved until the level bubble is centered (figure 13-26). This action places the scale in a true gravity-referenced vertical. The transit operator checks the telescope level and adjusts the optical micrometer to place the crosshair on the next lowest tenth-inch graduation on the scale. Inches and tenths are read directly from the scale (figure 13-25) to which are added thousandths from the optical micrometer reading. The total reading is an accurate vertical measurement of the distance from the plane of sight to the reference point h.

If true motion in space is desired, a stable reference point must be established and its distance (H) measured from the horizontal plane of sight at the same time measurements are being made from the machine. Subtracting the two measurements (H−h) provides an accurate distance between stable reference and the reference point on the machine.

Using a stable reference has a number of advantages. Motion of the baseplate and foundation induced by temperature gradients or outside forces and affecting alignment can be measured and are more readily recognized.

A simpler procedure is to assume that one reference point on the machine does not move and calculate all the differential heights using this point as a reference. If all points on the machine change position an equal amount with this procedure, the calculated Δh would indicate zero growth.

Horizontal measurements are essentially the same as vertical measurements except that two stable reference points must be used to establish, in azimuth, a line or plane from which all measurements will

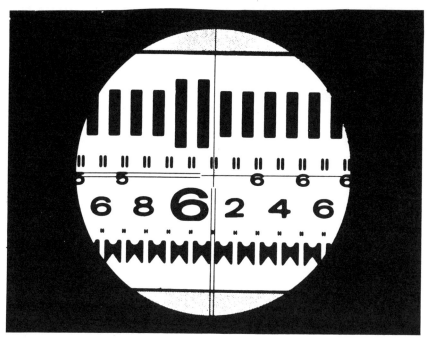

13–25—Viewed through an optical alignment telescope.

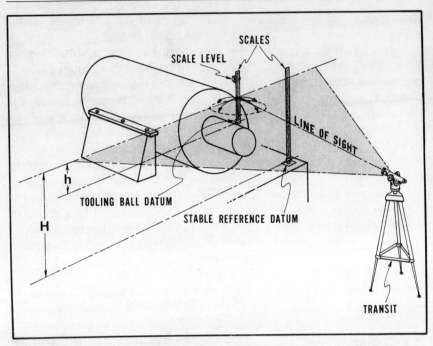

13–26—*Optical vertical measurements.*

originate. If the horizontal measurements and stable reference points are at different elevations—almost always the case in machinery alignment—it will be necessary to establish a gravity-referenced vertical plane through the stable reference points from which to make the measurements (figure 13-27). To establish a vertical reference plane, the alignment instrument, a jig transit, must first be plumbed by clamping its vertical axis and placing the telescopic line of sight in a level horizontal plane using the same procedure described for vertical measurements. With this accomplished, the geometry of the jig transit is such that its vertical and horizontal axes will be in gravity referenced true horizontal and vertical planes respectively. After the transit has been plumbed, the vertical axis clamp is released freeing the telescope to rotate in elevation in what is now a true vertical plane.

Once the telescope is plumbed and its vertical axis unclamped, it is bucked in to the reference plane. Bucking in is accomplished by alternately rotating the transit in azimuth and moving the plane of sight horizontally using a precision cross slide similar to the cross feed used on a lathe. Once the transit line of sight is in the reference plane, or parallel to it, at a known horizontal distance, a scale is placed on a reference point and leveled (figure 13-27). Unfortunately, this action alone does not locate the scale perpendicular to the line of sight as it did for vertical measurements. To achieve the perpendicular relationship between scale and line of sight needed for accurate, repeatable measurements, the leveled scale is swept slowly back and forth in the horizontal plane until a minimum measurement indicates the scale is perpendicular to the plane of sight. The minimum measurement is then recorded as the distance from the plane of sight to the reference point on the machine.

It should now be obvious that the type of reference points, their location, and the method of attachment are extremely important to system accuracy and repeatability. The necessity of applying a temperature correction to the measurement to compensate for thermal growth between the shaft centerline and the reference point and the desireability of locating reference points as close as possible to the machine centerline to minimize the differential between shaft and reference point have already been mentioned. Also, the reference points must be solidly attached and protected from damage. Finally, the type of reference itself has a significant impact on system accuracy. Pin or dowel references have a serious flaw; it is impossible to field drill holes to receive the dowels which are perfectly level and perpendicular to the reference plane of sight used for horizontal measurements. As a result,

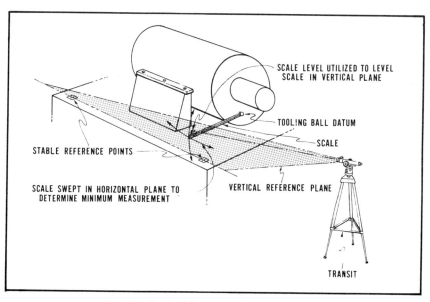

13–27—Optical horizontal measurements.

scales, placed in holders on the pins, can be leveled in one plane but are generally tilted to the line of sight in the other, producing an error in measurement which may or may not be constant. A much more accurate method is to use tooling ball references with the scales either held or clamped in contact with the crown of the ball. The precision spherical surface of the tooling ball allows the scale to be positioned accurately in any plane, independent of the tooling ball's orientation to the optical system.

On most machines, scales and telescope can't be located so that all measurements can be taken from a single location. When this occurs (most of the time), a stable reference must be selected which can be observed from all telescope positions or some other means of relating all the measurements on a machine to one another must be established. Often one or more scales can be viewed from all telescope locations and these measurements can be used to relate all the remaining measurements to one another. When this technique will not work, a scale or reference point may be placed at some arbitrary location which can be viewed from all telescope positions. Subsequent measurements are taken from the plane of sight to this turning point and are then used to relate all the measurements made on the machine to one another.

In use, a set of optical measurements are made with the machine at either ambient or operating temperature then repeated under the opposite conditions. The difference between the two is an accurate measure of the change in position at each reference point.

Optical system accuracy under ideal conditions is approximately ± 0.001 in ($\pm$ 25 μm) at a distance of 10 ft (3 m) between scale and telescope. Above 10 ft, accuracy decreases linearly at a rate of about 0.001 in. (25 μm) per each additional 10 ft (3 m) out to 50 to 60 ft (150–180 m). For optimum results, every effort should be made to take measurements as close to the scales as possible, for under actual conditions there are always problems with less-than-optimum lighting, vibration, heat waves, steam and oil vapors which act to reduce system accuracy.

Optical measurements are accurate, and once the system is established it can be completely disassembled and reassembled at any time over an extended period and the measurements repeated within close tolerances. It is thus very good for studying long-term changes caused by foundation settlement. When referenced to a single point, optical measurements can provide an excellent means of sorting out complex pipe strain problems. The optical equipment itself is not overly expensive; however, measurements require time and there is a great deal of skill and technique required to obtain accuracy as well as recognize and correct potential problems.

Converting Measured Alignment Changes to Alignment Offsets

To transfer alignment changes to a plot and determine alignment offsets, begin with a scaled plot with all shafts in line, their desired operating condition (figure 13-28a). Thermal changes measured at each point on the machine are inverted and applied to the shaft's collinear operating position (figure 13-28b). Lines drawn through pairs of points on each machine become the ambient shaft positions desired to achieve collinear shafts at operating conditions (figure 13-28c). Comparing the plot developed in figure 13-28c with figure 13-18 shows a way of obtaining alignment offsets. If desired, the plotted ambient shaft positions can be converted to dial indicator readings.

In closing, one point should be emphasized. No matter what procedure is used, taking time to make certain the system is set up correctly, exercising care in taking measurements, and approaching each move slowly and methodically always results in better final results in minimum time. Alignment is always the last major task to be accomplished at both installation and maintenance and as such is often subject to the pressures of time. Nevertheless, the pressures of time must be resisted and the alignment completed properly if the machine is going to enjoy an extended, problem-free lifetime.

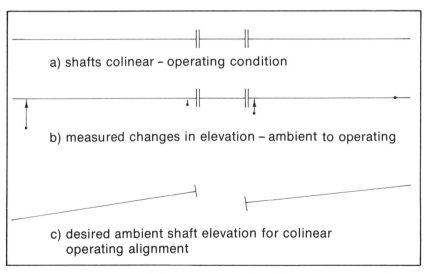

a) shafts colinear – operating condition

b) measured changes in elevation – ambient to operating

c) desired ambient shaft elevation for colinear operating alignment

13–28—Development of shaft elevation offsets for optimum operating alignment.

14

Machinery Analysis Case Histories

The following descriptions of actual machinery problems are not intended as typical, for most problems encountered are unique. Rather, they are presented to illustrate symptoms, information available, and the thought process and conclusions reached under a particular set of circumstances.

SUBSYNCHRONOUS INSTABILITY

Maximum operating speed of a large centrifugal compressor limited by subsynchronous amplitude.

The subsynchronous instability illustrated in figure 14–1 occurred on a high-speed (11,500-rpm) vertically split centrifugal compressor which had suffered from this problem since installation.

The presentation in figure 14–1 contains a series of spectra taken at approximately 50-rpm increments and rotated about 35° so the subsynchronous response will be in the plane of the paper to facilitate study. Each spectrum is the average output from a shaft displacement pickup at the speed listed on the horizontal axis. The measured phase lag between the component at running speed and a fixed phase reference is shown at the end of each frequency spectrum.

In this example, the instability excited the first critical speed and remained at a relatively constant amplitude to approximately 10,900 rpm. Above 10,900 rpm, the instability increased rapidly until at 11,100 rpm the instability component dominated the spectrum at an amplitude approximately twice that of the running frequency compo-

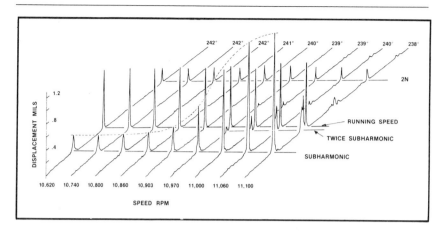

14–1—*Centrifugal compressor instability.*

nent. Note that throughout this range the amplitudes at running speed and twice running speed (2N) remained essentially constant. Also note that, as the subsynchronous component grew in size, it generated a harmonic string of its own, probably due to nonlinear effects in the bearing. Since the second harmonic of instability, if present, will usually be quite close to running speed, it often causes puzzlement; however, in the spectrum presentation it is easily recognized and identified.

On this compressor equipped with tilting pad bearings and low profile seals, when the data displayed in figure 14–1 were recorded, changes were attempted to eliminate or even reduce the instability. The tilt pad bearings were rotated to place a gap between pads at the bottom, the pad curvature was altered to form a stiffer oil wedge, and the pivot point on the pads was moved—all to no effect. The final solution was to shorten and stiffen the shaft, a modification which required major modifications to the bearing and seal area.

This example is admittedly an extreme case which resisted the corrective methods that are normally successful in eliminating instability. Generally, a change to a stiffer bearing will eliminate instability. As a temporary measure to permit continued operation, machines have been deliberately misaligned to apply more downward preload on the unstable bearing and, in several cases, the misalignment was accomplished with the machine in operation using steam and water to heat and cool support structure. Temporary measures such as this are messy but worthwhile if they allow continued operation and production.

IMBALANCE

**Operating speed of a centrifugal compressor limited by
excessive vibration amplitude**

Figure 14–2 contains a series of signatures showing a compressor's imbalance response as speed is increased through the operating range. The peak in amplitude indicates the possibility of a critical speed close to the desired operating speed of 5,700 rpm. Although the compressor had operated for over 25 years, no one suspected a peak in amplitude in the operating speed range until the unit was subjected to detailed analysis including an examination of vibration characteristics during a speed change.

Note a dip in the running speed amplitude envelope at 5,600 rpm. The dip in the vertical amplitude displayed in figure 14–2 coincided with a peak in the horizontal amplitude as the unit passed through horizontal resonance at a slightly lower speed due to lower stiffness.

The presence of harmonics in the signatures suggests looseness and, in fact, there were several mils' clearance between the bearing shell and cap.

With the problem defined as a change in the amplitude at running frequency through the operating speed range, the next question is what corrective action can be implemented. Although this specific problem was a combination of system dynamics and imbalance, time limitations precluded addressing the question of dynamics. As a result, it was decided to lower the exciting force by balancing the rotor to vastly reduced tolerances. The dotted line in figure 14–2 shows the machine's response at the same transducer location after the rotor had been rebal-

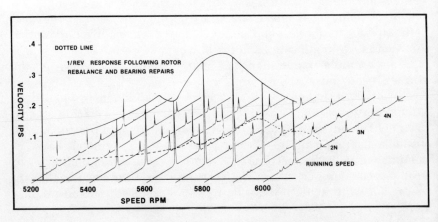

14–2—Centrifugal compressor imbalance response.

anced. Note that the amplitude peak is still present and shifted upward in frequency by restoring the proper bearing clearances. The success of balancing in at least reducing symptoms can be noted by comparing peak amplitudes before and after balancing. In this case, although the peak remained, its value had been reduced to a level which has been easily tolerated in continuous operation.

As an interesting aspect of this problem, the machine had been operated to a limiting vibration amplitude for several months before it was finally shut down for repairs. This requirement forced a gradual decrease in speed to remain below limits. In retrospect, the slow increase in vibration was caused by operating the unit below the resonant peak where the constant exposure to excessive vibration increased bearing clearances which in turn decreased stiffness. As stiffness decreased, the resonant peak moved lower and closer to the operating speed, causing an increase in vibration which aggravated the situation. The problem thus fed on itself. Had this relationship been recognized by an early detailed analysis, the machine could have been operated at a speed above the peak where any reduction in stiffness would have worked to decrease vibration by moving the peak away from operating speed.

Variation in amplitude with time on an electric power generator

Figure 14–3 illustrates an unusual problem of changing amplitude with time which occurred on an electric power generator. In this particular problem, vibration amplitude measured on the generator would begin to change rapidly with time shortly after load was applied. If the generator were balanced after some time at load, then vibration amplitude was excessive at start. If the generator was balanced at start, then vibration at load was excessive. Since it was to be used as a standby power source, neither alternate was acceptable. The time history displayed in figure 14–3 represents a compromise which was unsuccessfully attempted to split the difference in imbalance.

A time history such as that illustrated generally suggests misalignment; however, alignment had been checked and was within tolerance. An examination of vibration signatures recorded on the generator disclosed that nearly all the excitation, as well as the changes in excitation, occurred at running frequency, indicating a change in rotor balance. Perhaps most important the condition could be temporarily balanced out, an impossibility had the problem been alignment.

In this case, phase lag was the key parameter which led to an understanding of the mechanism involved. Phase lag, the top trace in

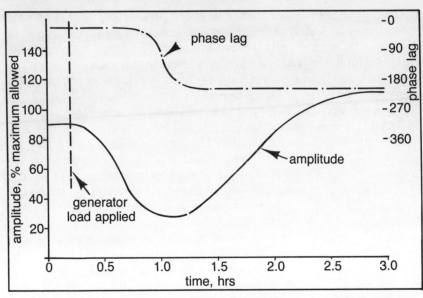

14–3—*Variations in vibration amplitude and phase lag with time recorded on an electric power generator at constant load and speed.*

figure 14–3, remained relatively steady for a period of time, changed rapidly through approximately 180°, then stabilized again. When the two changes, amplitude and phase, were plotted together as they are in figure 14–3, the situation became obvious.

The initial amplitude generated by the rotor was due solely to mechanical imbalance. As the generator was loaded, the rotor heated up, but the heating was asymmetrical causing the rotor to bow. Naturally, the bow affected balance and the amplitude began to change. As the thermal bow cancelled out mechanical imbalance, the overall amplitude decreased and phase began to change, slowly at first, then very rapidly as amplitude went through a minimum. The thermal bow continued as the generator heated up until, at equilibrium conditions, the final amplitude was the vector sum of mechanical imbalance and imbalance caused by the thermal bow.

To test the theory, the generator was allowed to stabilize at temperature then unloaded and allowed to cool at operating speed. As was expected, the vibration followed the curve backward as the rotor cooled and the thermal bow came out.

With the problem identified, several solutions, including redistributing the flow of cooling air through the rotor, could be devised.

High-amplitude vibration at startup following overhaul

Another case of imbalance illustrates the necessity of exercising caution prior to making major changes in the balance of a rotor.

A steam turbine which had been operating at very low levels of vibration for several years was opened for a routine visual inspection and overhaul. During the course of the overhaul, the rotor was removed, cleaned, and rebalanced. When the turbine was reassembled and started, vibration amplitudes were very high, all at running speed, indicating imbalance. A review of the balance report revealed that a large weight change had been necessary to achieve a satisfactory balance. After a great deal of discussion and analysis to rule out other potential sources such as misalignment, it was finally decided to disassemble the turbine and check balance the rotor a second time. As suspected, the rotor was badly out of balance. The balance was corrected, and the turbine ran successfully with low levels of vibration.

No one will ever know whether a mistake was made when the rotor was rebalanced, or if perhaps the rotor was bowed when it was removed, and then balanced with the bow in place. The important lesson to be learned, however, is to have a good idea of what balance corrections might be necessary, based on a machine's vibration characteristics at shutdown. If a large balance correction is required on a machine that was running well prior to shutdown, one must determine why before allowing the weight change to be made. To this end, rotors being balanced would be followed closely and the balance order should specify that balance corrections will not be made without approval.

Satisfactory low-speed balance does not necessarily guarantee performance at operating speed

Before leaving balancing problems, it should be mentioned that a low-speed balance is often useless on a high-speed rotor. In this situation the only way to achieve a satisfactory balance is by balancing at speed, either in place or on a high-speed balancing machine operating in a vacuum. Two examples, both steam turbines, illustrate the point. The first rotor had been high-speed balanced by the manufacturer, then crated and shipped as a spare to the plant site. A minor failure to the operating rotor necessitated installation of the spare which was cleaned and, as a precaution, checked on a balance machine prior to installation. The low-speed balance indicated the rotor was out of balance and would require correction; however, because it had been high-speed balanced and runouts were unchanged from those taken at final inspection, it was decided to install the rotor without a balance change. It ran flawlessly at operating speed with extremely low vibration amplitudes.

A second steam turbine exhibited very high levels of vibration on its initial in-place uncoupled test run. The rotor was removed, checked on a low-speed balance machine, and found to be badly out of balance. A balance was achieved and the rotor reinstalled, but vibration at speed was worse than before. An attempt was made to balance in place with the coupling sleeves held with balanced spin plates; this too was unsuccessful. Finally, the rotor was balanced in place at speed with the coupling hubs removed and half keys held with thin shrunk-on sleeves. The couplings were reinstalled, the turbine was coupled to the driven equipment, and it ran successfully.

In the second case, a low-speed balance was totally unsuccessful as a means to achieve acceptable operation at speed. In addition, the rotor appeared to have been so sensitive to overhung weight that high-speed, in-place balancing could only be accomplished with the coupling hubs removed.

The potential need for high-speed balancing to achieve satisfactory performance at operating speed is much greater on machines such as steam turbines where most of the rotor weight is concentrated in a single piece. With this type rotor, it is very difficult to eliminate the dynamic couples which can produce excessive imbalance at speed with conventional low-speed balancing techniques. On the other hand, proper stack balancing procedures used with built-up rotors will minimize dynamic couples and reduce the need for high-speed balancing.

ROTOR DYNAMICS

Centrifugal compressor could not be successfully restarted following overhaul

A high-speed (9,500-rpm) steam turbine-driven centrifugal compressor in ammonia refrigeration service failed catastrophically at startup following overhaul. Three successive attempts to overhaul and restart the machine over an 18-month period similarly ended in failure. Each failure was the same: the minimum governing speed, approximately 8,200 rpm, vibration amplitude would increase over approximately 50 seconds until a rub occurred, destroying the rotor and internal seals.

The compressor had a low first critical speed, approximately 3,000 rpm, suggesting a very flexible rotor and the probability of a second critical close to operating speed. It had been in operation about 18 years, following a very difficult commissioning period spanning approximately 18 months. Records indicated the problem had been high, uncontrollable vibration which was partially corrected through a series of trial and error changes. Although the problem had been reduced to a point where it could be tolerated, it was certainly not corrected, as the compressor had suffered bearing or seal failures about every six months since commissioning.

In one final desperate attempt to restart the compressor, it was overhauled as closely as possible to manufacturer's tolerances by the best available craftsmen and supervisors. The rotor was carefully stack balanced and tilt pad bearings were installed, replacing the cylindrical bearings previously used. Noncontact shaft displacement pickups, installed during a previous attempt to start the compressor, were augmented such that each bearing had two X-Y probes outboard of each bearing spaced 90° apart and a single probe on the inboard side of the bearing closest to the seal in the Y plane.

When the compressor was started, its first critical speed was observed at 3,200 rpm. At minimum governing speed, amplitude increased over approximately 50 seconds at constant speed until at 12 mils (300 μm) it seemed wise to shut down to avert almost certain damage. Vibration signals obtained from the four positions along the shaft were predominantly at running frequency, as shown in figure 14–4a. Note that the amplitudes are approximately equal across each bearing but the signals are 180° out of phase. Note also that there is a 180° phase difference from the seal (inboard) end of one bearing to the seal (inboard) end of the opposite bearing. Figure 14–4b shows the mode in which the rotor must be operating to produce the observed vibration characteristics.

From the foregoing observations, one can quickly conclude that the rotor is operating at or very close to its second critical speed and the bearings are located at shaft nodes where they are unable to apply much restraining force. From these rather bleak observations only two choices were left: balance the rotor at operating speed to reduce the force developed to a level which can be contained by the bearings, or move the bearings inboard where they can apply more restraining force to the shaft. The latter, although addressing the problem directly, was intolerable from the standpoint of time. In-place balancing was attempted and quickly abandoned due to the very limited location at which weights could be applied. The rotor was then removed and shipped to a facility capable of balancing the rotor at maximum speed in a vacuum chamber. Rectangular Bode plots of amplitude before and after high-speed balancing are shown in figure 14–5. Note the extreme sensitivity to imbalance at the second critical.

Following high-speed balancing, a very tedious task requiring the best part of two 24-hour days and 50 runs, the rotor was shipped back to

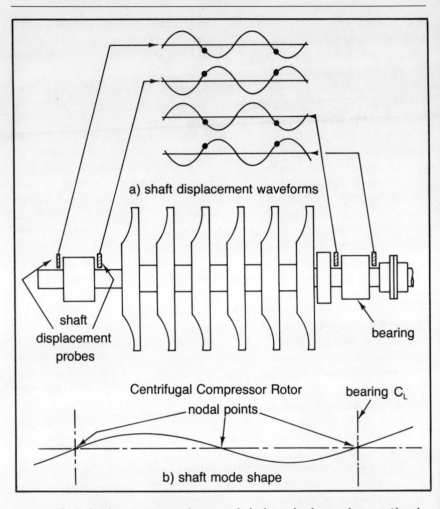

a) shaft displacement waveforms

shaft displacement probes

bearing

Centrifugal Compressor Rotor

nodal points

bearing C_L

b) shaft mode shape

14–4—*Shaft displacement waveforms and shaft mode shape of a centrifugal compressor operating just below its second critical speed.*

the plant and reinstalled. Following some anxious moments on starting, probably caused by stresses applied during shipment, the rotor ran successfully.

As a postscript to this problem, the balanced rotor ran without difficulty, including several short shutdowns for approximately six months after the successful startup, at which time some minor seal repairs became necessary. When the bearings were opened for access to the seals, the outboard bearing was found completely destroyed, appar-

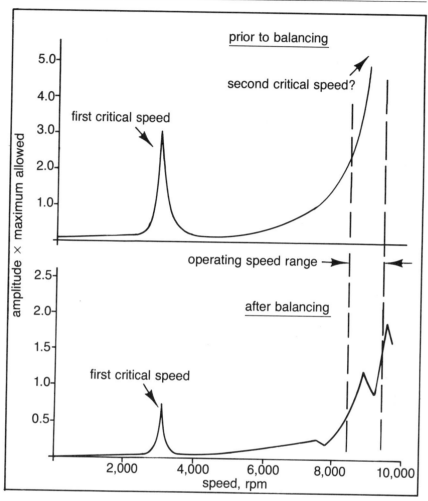

14–5—*Plots of amplitude vs. speed before and after balancing, centrifugal compressor rotor.*

ently from loss of lube oil and overheating. The failure appeared to have occurred several months earlier, and there were clear signs the rotor had been riding on the outboard seal as a bearing. At restart, following repairs to the shaft journal, the original problem, rapidly increasing vibration at minimum governing speed, reoccurred; however, an in-place balance correction successfully reduced vibration to a tolerable operating amplitude.

Reduced bearing and seal lifetime due to excessive vibration

This problem is very similar in many aspects to the previous problem. A motor-driven centrifugal compressor which had operated successfully for about 20 years was uprated from approximately 8,500 rpm to 11,250 rpm by changing gear elements. In the uprated condition, bearing and seal lifetime were reduced significantly—a matter of weeks on occasion. Operating vibration signatures and vibration response on coastdown were recorded to gain insight into the problem. Shown in figure 14–6, the operating signatures contained several subsynchronous components of which the component at 4,500 rpm was judged to be the fundamental. The components at 6,660 rpm and 15,840 rpm were believed to be lower and upper sidebands of a 4,560-rpm modulation of running frequency. Rundown response, shown in figure 14–7, was inconclusive.

Based on the information recorded on the machine, the problem was diagnosed as a combination of imbalance and instability. Since the compressor was equipped with cylindrical bearings and long oil bushing seals, there were several relatively easily implemented modifications proposed to correct the problem.

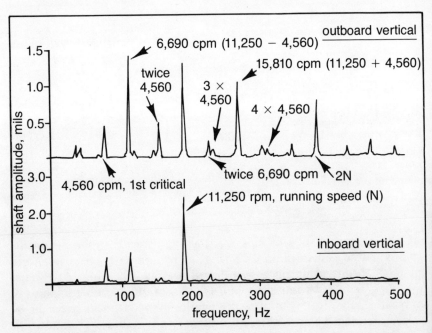

14–6—*Centrifugal compressor operating shaft spectra with cylindrical bearing.*

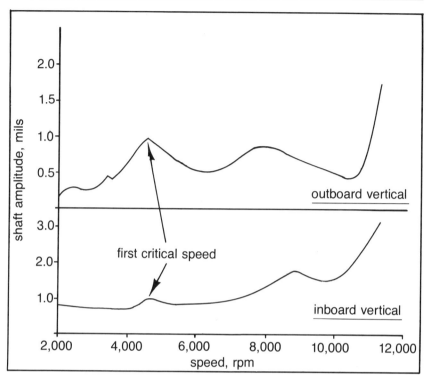

14–7—*Centrifugal compressor shaft amplitude response vs. speed on coastdown—before modifications.*

At the same time, it was feared that an effort to address one problem without the other might result in a worse situation. As a result and even though one would never know what actually solved the problem, simultaneous corrective action of improved bearings, preferably tilt pads, modified seals to reduce force applied to the shaft, and the potential of chatter due to a lower than design differential pressure and high-speed rotor balance were recommended.

Since interchangeable pressure dam bearings were readily available, they were installed as an interim measure to see if bearing lifetime couldn't be improved while the permanent modifications were being engineered. Figure 14–8 shows vibration characteristics with cylindrical and pressure dam bearings. Note that the pressure dam bearings improved rotor stability; however, the running speed component increased.

Following this interim change, the compressor was completely disassembled, the rotor balanced in a vacuum chamber at full operating

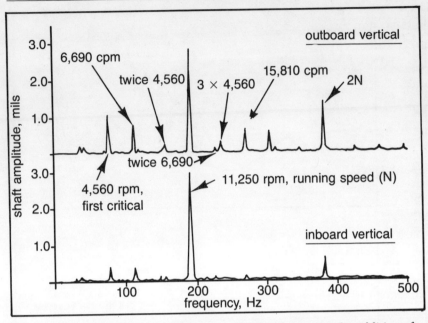

14-8—*Centrifugal compressor operating shaft spectra after the addition of pressure dam bearings.*

speed, and the machine reassembled with tilt pad bearings and shorter bushing seals. Figure 14-9 shows the rotor response in the balancing machine both before and after balancing. Note the coincidence of the first critical speed with the subsynchronous frequency observed in the operating spectrum (figure 14-6). Note also that just like the previous example the compressor operating speed coincides with the second bare rotor critical, a factor not recognized in the operating data. Since the amplitude response recorded with the rotor in the case (figure 14-7) had a much lower peak than the amplitude recorded in the balance machine, the original seals probably exerted a considerable amount of restraint on the shaft.

Figure 14-10 is a shaft signature recorded from the same location as figures 14-6 and 14-8 after the compressor had been in operation for approximately 24 hours following high-speed balancing and installation of tilt pad bearings and modified shaft seals. Note that running speed is now the dominant component in the signature.

Figure 14-11 is the amplitude response recorded at the same location as the compressor was tripped and restarted as a comprision with figures 14-7 and 14-9.

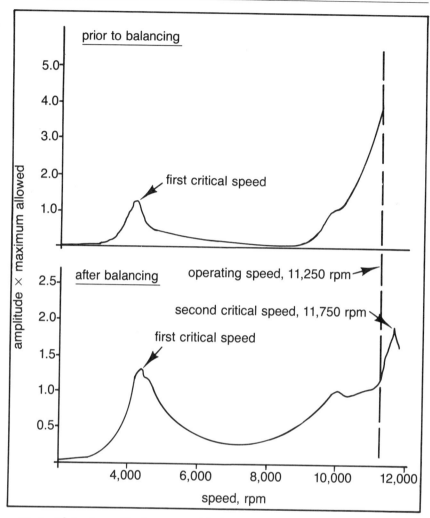

14–9—*Plots of amplitude vs. speed before and after balancing, centrifugal compressor rotor.*

Motor-driven centrifugal compressor totally destroyed on several occasions during startup at the first critical speed

Like the two previous examples, this compressor was a 20-year-old machine which, for a variety of reasons, had been modified over the years. Operating at 11,800 rpm, the compressor was driven at one end by a 1,200-rpm synchronous motor through a speed-increasing gear and by a direct coupled hot gas expander at the other end.

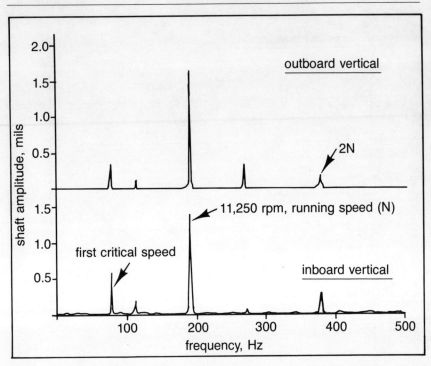

14–10—*Centrifugal compressor operating shaft signatures following high-speed balancing; change to tilt pad bearings and seal modifications.*

On several occasions the compressor suffered catastrophic failures during startup at the critical speed. In each failure the sequence of events was identical: everything appeared satisfactory until the compressor reached the critical speed. At the critical speed, vibration amplitude at running speed instantaneously increased to a level which destroyed all the internal seals and heavily rubbed both the shaft and impellers.

Attributed to a loss of damping, a slight modification to the pressure dam bearings eliminated the problem. Interestingly enough, a second identical machine installed about 10 feet (3.3 m) away, feeding into the same discharge and with the same modifications, never suffered a similar failure.

MISALIGNMENT

High vibration on a steam turbine-driven centrifugal compressor corrected without interrupting operation

Misalignment can generally be recognized by the presence of a

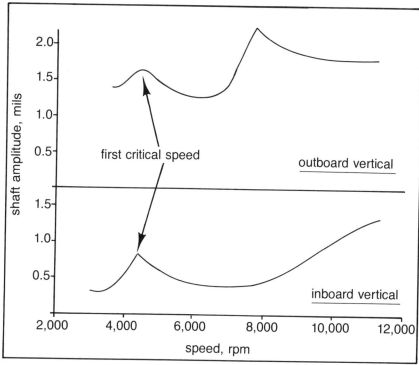

14–11—*Centrifugal compressor shaft amplitude response vs. speed on coastdown, after modifications (not corrected for shaft runout).*

prominent component at twice running frequency; however, this may not always be the case.

A relatively slow-speed centrifugal compressor was operating with excessive vibration levels, all at running speed, at its outboard bearing. Vibration amplitudes at the compressor and turbine bearings adjacent to the coupling were moderate but not particularly of concern. Some symptoms of misalignment were present in the coupling end signatures of both machines, but they did not appear of a magnitude for concern.

In an effort to learn more about the behavior of the problem, an air blower was directed at each outboard support on the compressor. Vibration levels immediately dropped. Cold water was substituted for air and the levels dropped even more. Finally, alignment shims were removed from the outboard end of the compressor with the unit in full operation to make the changes achieved with air and water permanent. Vibration levels were reduced to a point where operation could continue indefinitely.

Although it was never learned if the problem in this particular case was one of misalignment, a change in alignment successfully reduced the symptoms to a point where operation could continue. Changing alignment with a machine in operation is at best a very risky undertaking that should only be attempted as a last resort and with a great deal of caution. In order to avoid creating a larger problem, one must have some positive means of holding the machine in place and preventing unwanted movement while the changes are being made. Finally, have some accurate method such as optics or proximity probes to determine exactly what changes are being made.

High vibration on a motor expander-driven centrifugal compressor

This problem actually began as imbalance with the presence of misalignment recognized only after rotor balance had been improved. Figure 14–12 shows the initial casing signatures recorded on the compressor. Note the extremely high amplitude at running frequency on the inlet, outboard end. Diagnosing the problem as imbalance, the rotor was removed from the case, disassembled, and stack balanced as it was reassembled. Signatures recorded following rebalancing (figure 14–13) revealed that although amplitudes were greatly reduced, the compressor was likely misaligned. Optical measurements shown in figure 14–14 confirmed the presence of severe misalignment and provided the information needed to realign the compressor.

THRUST BEARING PROBLEMS

Identical thrust bearing failures suffered shortly after startup on two identical centrifugal air compressors operating in parallel

Both compressors had been operating for over 15 years without any thrust bearing problems. In an effort to increase capacity, a small blower was installed in the common inlet as a supercharger. Along with checking to make certain power was available, the effect of supercharging the inlet on thrust load had been calculated and found well within safe limits. Despite these precautions, the thrust bearings on both compressors failed shortly after startup.

Following repairs, both thrust bearings were instrumented with thermocouples imbedded in the pads, and pressure gauges were installed at the discharge from each stage. When the compressor was started and discharge pressure increased, thrust temperature began to climb almost immediately. Had temperature not been monitored, a second thrust failure would have unquestionably been suffered by each

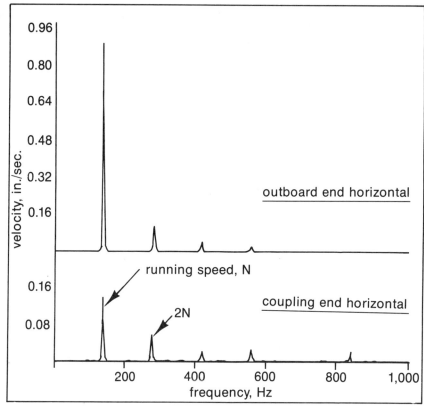

14–12—*Centrifugal compressor radial casing vibration signatures prior to balancing.*

machine. However, with temperature monitoring discharge pressure could be adjusted to keep thrust temperature within safe limits.

In this particular compressor the combined thrust force developed by the first, low-pressure impellers was balanced by reversing the direction of the last three impellers. A balance drum was not provided. An examination of the stage pressures recorded at startup revealed that the addition of supercharging had resulted in a slight increase at the discharge of each impeller. As a result of the pressure increases, the last impeller, which normally provided about one-third of the thrust balance, operated at a negative or zero differential through most of the startup procedure and therefore could not contribute to balancing the thrust developed by the low-pressure impellers. Thus, operating the compressor supercharged at startup, while the process unit was

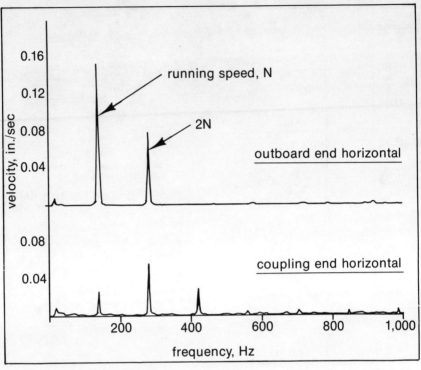

14–13—*Centrifugal compressor radial casing vibration signatures following low-speed stack balancing.*

being pressurized and heated, resulted in a partial loss of thrust balance which in turn overloaded the thrust bearing. As the process unit approached full operation, differential pressure across the final impeller increased to its normal value, thrust balance was restored, and thrust bearing load, observed as bearing temperature, decreased to a value well below limits for reliable continuous operation.

With the nature of the problem understood, it was easily resolved by changing the unit startup procedure to prohibit use of the supercharger until the plant was at full operating pressure.

This problem is cited to emphasize the necessity of considering startup and partial load operation on machine and component performance. All too often a machine, its components, and external piping are engineered for full-load continuous operation with little regard for how it will reach full load or the possibility of extended operation at partial load.

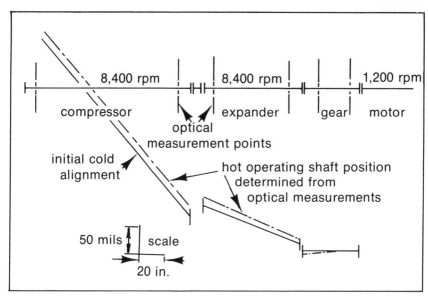

14–14—*Vertical alignment plot. Motor/expander-driven centrifugal compressor, initial cold-shaft alignment and operating position determined from optical measurements.*

Thrust bearing failures suffered on a motor-driven, speed-increasing gearbox

High and increasing vibration, particularly in the axial direction, on a motor-driven, speed-increasing gearbox was viewed with great concern. Initial vibration signatures, the top signatures in figure 14–15, were inconclusive except for the presence of an unusual frequency component at 120 Hz corresponding to four times the motor/low-speed gear running frequency and twice line frequency.

Vibration, monitored with apprehension, increased over a two-month period. In November, detailed vibration spectra showed that a dramatic increase had occurred at 120 Hz. Based on an analysis of the signatures, it was concluded that the high vibration at 120 Hz was being generated by an electromagnetic anomoly in the motor even though the highest amplitudes were recorded on the gear. The plant reached the opposite conclusion and decided to open the gear for inspection. The thrust bearing was found in a failed condition.

The gear was repaired and restarted in early December. A subsequent signature analysis revealed that the 120-Hz component was still present but at a reduced amplitude. Everyone breathed easier.

By January, the vibration had increased to its previous high amplitude and the gear became noticeably noisier. A shutdown and

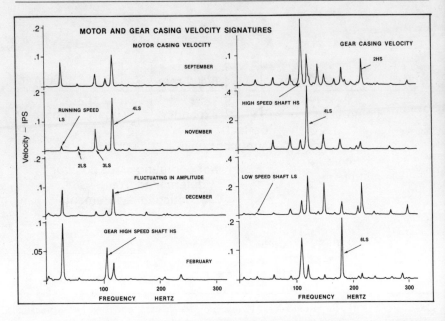

14–15—*Motor and gear casing velocity signatures.*

inspection disclosed a second thrust bearing failure and a large crack in the low-speed gear. Based on the conclusions reached at the earlier analysis, the motor rotor was also removed and carefully inspected. Over half of the rotor bars were found cracked where they attach to the shorting rings. Repairs were made to the motor rotor, the gear elements were replaced, and the unit was returned to service in late January.

Vibration signatures recorded in early February contained a 120-Hz component at a normal amplitude. Note that balance of the replacement high-speed pinion is considerably worse than the original pinion. The origin of the high-amplitude component at 6 times the low-speed shaft running frequency could not be explained; however, the unit operated successfully without further difficulty, demonstrating that the basic problem was solved.

NONSYNCHRONOUS COMPONENTS

A strong nonsynchronous component present in the frequency spectrum recorded on a centrifugal compressor could not be related to a mechanical event

The casing signature shown in figure 14–16 is dominated by a very unusual nonsynchronous component between the third and fourth harmonics of running speed. The component is also in the shaft signature at a much lower level. Although it is not unusual to observe the

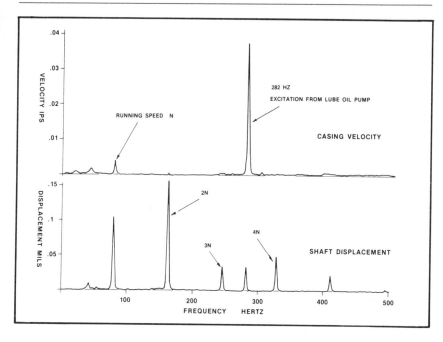

14–16—*Centrifugal compressor shaft and casing signatures containing a prominent nonsynchronous component.*

running frequencies of adjacent machines in a vibration signature, it is very unusual to observe a nonsynchronous component of this magnitude at this point in the spectrum. Such an anomaly calls for a thorough investigation to determine its origin.

In this particular case, the nonsynchronous component was traced to a lube oil pump which, despite warnings that something was wrong, failed shortly after the signatures were collected.

MECHANICAL LOOSENESS

Vibration signatures recorded over a period of approximately one month on a high-speed steam turbine contained erratic harmonics

Figure 14–17 contains a series of casing vibration signatures recorded on a high-speed steam turbine over a period of approximately one month. The number and strength of the harmonics of running speed were immediately recognized as an abnormality even though shaft signatures recorded at the same time appeared normal. Subsequent analyses revealed the harmonics were irregular, sometimes present and sometimes not.

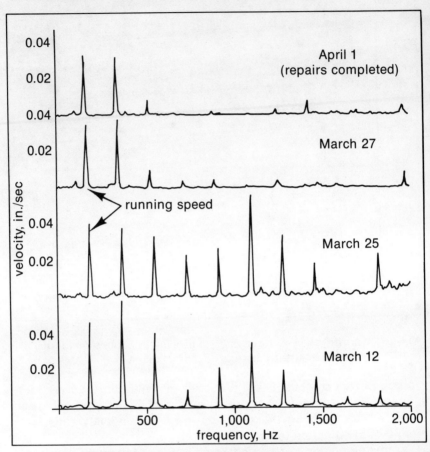

14–17—*Steam turbine exhaust bearing horizontal casing vibration signatures showing the effects of cracked axial struts.*

In the belief that the harmonics were produced by a cracked or loose component, the bearing bracket was closely inspected. Three struts, installed between the bearing bracket and turbine casing, were found cracked. Temporary weld repairs restored the signatures to normal without interrupting operation.

RESONANCE

High vibration on the gear casing of a gas turbine-driven electric power generator

The amplitude response plots shown in figure 14–18 were collected from a group of identical gear-driven electric power generators. In each

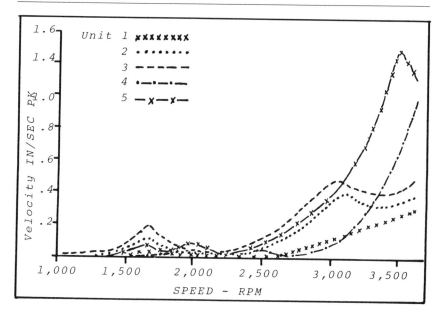

14–18—Gas turbine generator gearbox amplitude response.

case, note an amplitude peak at or near synchronous frequency. Although the units pictured in figure 14–18 form but a small sample, many other users had reported excessive levels of vibration and extreme difficulty in balancing due to inconsistent and erratic phase angles. All these characteristics point to a resonance as the cause.

Even though all the units studied were supposedly identical, clear differences can be observed in the position of the resonant peak as well as the amplification. The former is mainly associated with stiffness, while the latter depends on damping. Although this problem was never really solved, the vibration on some machines could be reduced by tightening bolts, on others by stiffening the baseplate and adding vertical support, while some wouldn't respond to any changes that were made. In all cases it appeared that the basic problem was a structural resonance which would likely require major design changes to eliminate.

Figure 14–19 shows the mode of baseplate vibration. Obtained by plotting phase and amplitude measured with a tracking analyzer triggered by a phase reference at the dominant frequency of vibration, such a mode shape is easily obtained and provides valuable guidance to the location of stiffening for maximum effect.

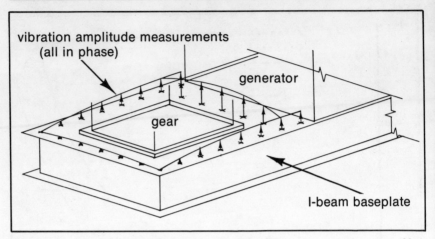

14–19—*Gear-driven generator showing baseplate vibration mode determined by vibration and phase measurements taken at regular intervals on the baseplate.*

Failure of a high-pressure pump seal equalizing line

The second resonance problem involved a high-pressure water pump which, after several years of successful operation, suddenly began suffering failures to the seal equalizing lines where they threaded into the pump casing. Pump vibration was checked and found to be very low; however, the seal line itself was vibrating heavily. A check of the frequency of vibration proved it was at pump running frequency. The pump was shut down, an accelerometer was attached, and the line was struck with a block of wood. Again the line vibrated at a frequency equal to the running speed of the pump, indicating a resonant condition with excitation present. The solution of course was simple: the pipe could be either shortened, lengthened, or stiffened with braces to tune it away from pump running frequency where it wouldn't be excited.

A question still remained: why did the pipe suddenly begin breaking after years of operation? An investigation disclosed the original seal balance line had been routed such that it pressed heavily on and interfered with the pump casing. When the pump was overhauled, someone decided to "improve" the situation by rerouting the line to minimize interference. This modification tuned the line to running frequency, precipitating the failures.

High vibration on a shipboard condensate pump

Both vertical main condensate pumps onboard a tanker were ob-

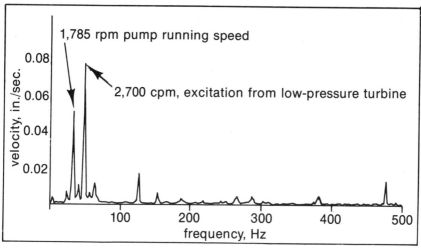

14–20—*Casing velocity signature recorded underway on a shipboard vertical main condensate pump.*

served vibrating heavily. Vibration signatures (figure 14–20), disclosed the dominant frequency on the pumps was the running frequency of the main engine low-pressure turbine. As a result of this excitation, unfiltered vibration measurements taken underway as part of a planned maintenance program were not at all indicative of the condition of the pump. Measurements either had to be filtered to eliminate the excitation from the low-pressure turbine or unfiltered measurements taken in port when the main engine was secured.

Conflicting information

Conflicting information which leads to different conclusions, depending on which is used, often creates problems of its own in machinery analysis. As a frequently encountered example, what conclusion should be reached when casing vibration is well outside limits yet shaft vibration indicates normal condition? Generalities are dangerous, for each specific situation will have its own set of conditions. Thus, when faced with conflicting data the analyst must make every effort to determine the reasons for the conflict, especially if some abnormality(s) is being discounted to permit continued operation.

High shaft vibration on a high-speed centrifugal compressor forces reduced production to remain within limits

Figure 14–21 shows vibration signatures and the amplitude re-

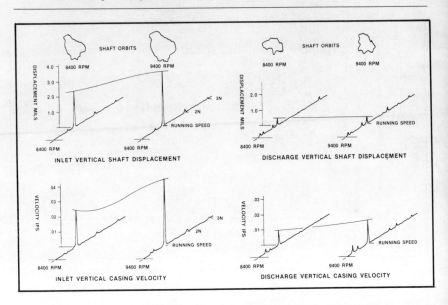

14-21—*Centrifugal compressor shaft and casing amplitude response.*

sponse recorded on a high-speed centrifugal compressor during a speed increase. Within the speed range shown, the increase in shaft vibration at the inlet end resulted in a total amplitude which was considered unacceptable for continuous operation, thereby placing restrictions on production. Casing amplitude likewise increased but was considered well within safe limits for the specific type of machine.

Based on a careful analysis of the apparently conflicting data, as well as the work accomplished during the shutdown just prior to the appearance of the high shaft vibration, it was concluded that the high, speed-dependent shaft vibration was due to imbalance in the inlet end coupling amplified by shaft probes located a significant axial distance away from the bearing. This theory fit well with all the symptoms, including the observation that repositioning the coupling spoolpiece axially during a short shutdown had a large effect on vibration amplitude.

Ignoring high casing vibration amplitudes because of a low or moderate shaft amplitude led to shaft failure

Unfortunately, failures of this type have occurred on several occasions and in each case have been catastrophic and expensive.

In one such case a clearly abnormal casing amplitude on a large high-speed steam turbine, sufficient to damage pressure gauges and crack lube oil piping, was discounted because shaft amplitude was at a normal level and not changing. Failure to heed clear and obvious symptoms ended in a catastrophic shaft fracture.

In a second similar case, the plant had been tracking casing vibration along with shaft vibration. Casing vibration had been trending steadily upward and was approaching dangerous levels with high-frequency harmonics also present in the signature. Shaft amplitudes were in a range considered acceptable for continued operation and while trending up were doing so at a much lower rate. Here again, discounting some clearly abnormal information in favor of data which allowed continued operation resulted in a catastrophic shaft fracture.

Failure to heed the warning provided by changing gap voltage ended in a bearing failure

Gap voltage, obtained from a radial shaft displacement probe installed on a large steam turbine, increased over a several-month period. Although calculations indicated the shaft had dropped enough to rub the seals and was nearly through the babbit bearing liner, there was no appreciable change in shaft vibration. Believing that the change in voltage was somehow caused by the probe and did not accurately reflect conditions within the machine, the decision was made to continue operation. Finally, the turbine shut itself down when the shaft had dropped enough to contact the overspeed trip latch. Fortunately, the only damage sustained was to the bearing itself and the seals which in fact had rubbed.

BLADING

The final three examples illustrate problems with blading. The first was a serendipitous discovery based only on the knowledge of what a typical high-frequency signature should look like, while the second was a more systematic test procedure designed to determine if blade defects would produce a deviation from a statistical baseline. The third illustrates a situation where a problem, disclosed by spectrum analysis, led to the design of a monitoring system which later provided warning of a repetition.

An abnormal vibration signature led to the discovery of cracked blades on a high-speed steam turbine

This example (figure 14–22) began at the first analysis of a high-speed condensing steam turbine, accomplished about one month prior

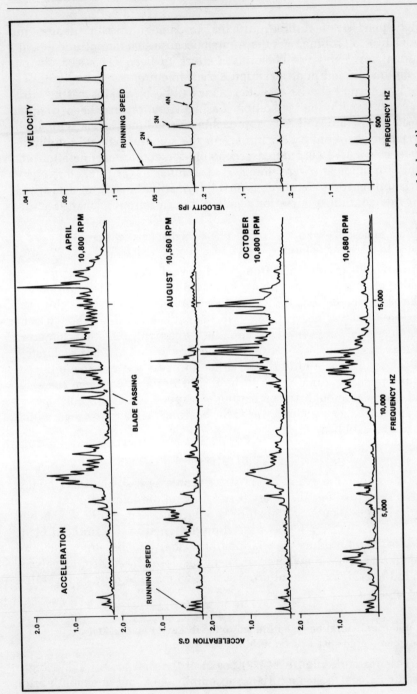

14–22—Steam turbine casing acceleration signatures recorded during a blade failure.

to a scheduled plant turnaround. Although the turbine had never been subjected to detailed analysis before and therefore historical data were not available for comparison, the initial acceleration signature was clearly abnormal due to the large number of harmonics between approximately 12 and 18 kHz. Additionally, the harmonic pattern in the velocity signature recorded at the same location was unusual and had been cited as a potential cause of blading failures aboard the *Queen Elizabeth II* during her shakedown voyage.

Based solely on this information, it was felt that a turbine blade problem of some sort was highly likely and a visual inspection was strongly suggested. After a great deal of discussion, for the turbine had not been scheduled for work during the maintenance period and therefore represented a significant increase in the work load, the casing was lifted and the rotor removed. Six cracked blades were found in the next-to-the-last stage.

The turbine manufacturer, upon being advised of the problem, specified that the diaphragm be moved upstream slightly to reduce the impulse on the blades. This was accomplished; the turbine was reassembled with the spare rotor and returned to operation. The second signature from the top in figure 14–22 was obtained following the modification with the turbine at speed. Note clear differences between the two; the lower is considered normal.

The turbine was operated for approximately five months and the third set of signatures shown in figure 14–22 was obtained. The similarity between the third and the first signature suggested the reoccurrence of cracked blades, so the turbine was disassembled for the second time and the rotor was removed. This time no external evidence of cracking could be found visually or with dye penetrant and magnetic particle inspections. Fortunately the original rotor, which by this time had the affected blade row replaced, was installed in the turbine, for when it was finally decided to remove blades from the rotor that had operated for five months, numerous cracks were found propagating from the inside out in the upper section of the root.

This time a design problem was clearly recognized and the diaphragm was redesigned with approximately 50% more openings. The modified diaphragm was installed and the turbine has operated satisfactorily for approximately six years. The bottom signature in figure 14–22 shows a signature obtained after approximately three years' operation following the diaphragm change. Some of the activity viewed as suspicious in the original signature is still present, although the turbine has demonstrated by successful operation that the problem has been corrected.

This problem emphasizes several points. First, the turbine had operated successfully for about five years prior to this episode without any blade problems, yet cracking developed in only five months' operation with the replacement rotor. Why? It turned out that the plant had been heat-sink limited during the first five years of operation, a condition that limited turbine speed which was corrected during the turnaround where the first cracks were discovered. After the heat-sink problem was corrected, it was possible to operate the turbine continuously at high speeds it had only attained for brief periods prior to the modification. The problem was thus present all along, but the lower speed separated the excitation produced by the diaphragm sufficiently from the blade resonance such that the blades were overstressed only during the brief periods the turbine could be operated at high speed.

Second, why were the original signatures picked as being abnormal? That is a very difficult question to answer; it is obvious that the characteristics were more qualitative than quantitative. Acceleration amplitudes certainly aren't excessive and, while the velocity signature appears abnormal, it is not known how either contributed to or represented the problem. The conclusion was intuitive; it could not have been accomplished mechanically. A great deal more work is required before this type of failure can be detected and predicted with any degree of certainty.

Efforts to learn if known blade damage could be recognized in a vibration signature

The next case involves some work that was done in an attempt to learn if blade damage could be detected from external vibration signatures. If blade-passing frequencies were generated by turbulent wakes, would the amplitude at the blade-passing frequency increase on blades operating with known damage and would the change be sufficient to predict damage?

The lower signature in figure 14–23 is a representative baseline constructed from the turbine signatures of five identical gas turbines operating at or close to full load. The upper signature was recorded on the same type turbine, operating with badly eroded first stage blading. Although the upper signature contains large amplitude sidebands below the first stage blade-passing frequency, the amplitude at blade-passing frequency is comparable to the amplitude of the same component in the baseline signature. This discovery destroyed the original hypothesis that damage would increase turbulence and hence amplitude at blade-passing frequency, until it was realized that the defective turbine was limited by exhaust temperature to approximately 60% load. Follow-

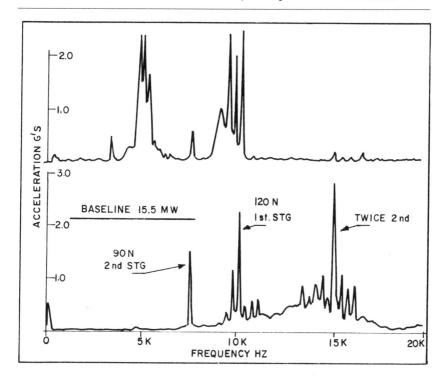

14–23—*Gas turbine exhaust casing acceleration signatures showing turbine blade pass frequencies.*

ing this line of reasoning, it appeared logical that observing normal full load amplitudes at blade-passing frequency at 60% load might be quite abnormal. As a test, one of the units used to construct the baseline was run up to full load to make certain it fit the baseline, then it was dropped back to 60% and a signature recorded. When this signature was compared to the signature obtained at the same load from the turbine with the known defects, there were clear differences which would have hopefully led to the correct conclusion.

There were of course several other significant differences between the two signatures. The presence of sidebands in the signature recorded on the turbine with the known damage is one major difference which might have led to the correct conclusion had the type, extent, and severity of the damage been unknown.

Although this was a limited test, it emphasizes that data must be taken under equal conditions if a comparison has any meaning. At the low frequencies around running speed, the changes may not be so large; however, at high frequencies very large variations may occur normally.

High and varying amplitudes noted at the blade-passing frequency of an axial flow air compressor

Figure 14–24 contains the acceleration signature recorded on the casing of an axial air compressor equipped with variable angle stator blades in the first four rows. A comparison of several signatures recorded in the early morning, at midday, and in the late afternoon revealed a large fluctuation in the amplitude at rotor blade-passing frequency. Based on the observation, a prediction was made that one or perhaps several blades had become detached and assumed an angle of attack different from the remaining blades in the row. When the compressor was shut down and disassembled, several first section stator blades were found corroded in place with the pins which transmit motion from the external linkage sheared.

Based on this experience, a monitoring system was engineered and installed on a similar compressor. Following several years of successful operation during which time the measured amplitude remained essentially constant, an amplitude increase was noted. Recalling the reason for installing the system, the blading was carefully examined during a shutdown. Several moveable stator blades were found frozen in place.

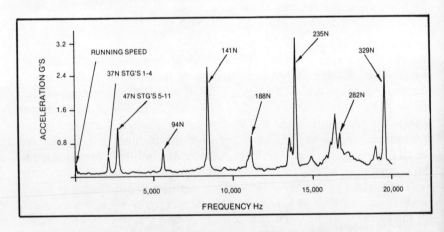

14–24—*Axial flow compressor acceleration signature.*

15
Establishing a Program of Machinery Predictive Analysis

Predictive analysis can describe a variety of programs from simple to complex. At one end of the scale are programs where raw vibration amplitudes are taken at periodic intervals on selected equipment and recorded. At the opposite extreme, many organizations employ continuous monitoring augmented with detailed spectrum analysis at frequent regular intervals. Which is best depends largely on the particular situation, the type of equipment, its past operating history, the probability and financial impact of an unexpected failure, and of course requirements which may be imposed by others such as an insurance carrier. For example, if one is responsible for older, relatively slow-speed equipment which has enjoyed a largely trouble-free operating history, a few vibration readings every 2–3 months will undoubtedly provide adequate protection. On the other hand, a much more rigorous program including continuous monitoring of several condition-related parameters combined with periodic spectrum analysis is easily justified on new, high-powered or high-speed equipment in critical service operating on the fringes of design limits and possibly subject to potentially damaging operating upsets.

WHY ESTABLISH A PROGRAM OF PREDICTIVE ANALYSIS?

The incentive for establishing a program of machinery predictive analysis is generally based on the need for an accurate method to assess and trend the condition of operating equipment in order to minimize the risks and economic impact of an unexpected shutdown or failure. Predictive anlysis has repeatedly proven its value when used on unspared critical equipment whose loss would stop production and is rapidly being extended to smaller equipment. Other areas in which the accurate respresentation of machinery condition provided by predictive analysis can be very useful are:

- Safely extend the interval between overhauls.
- Minimize the number of "open, inspect and repair if necessary" overhaul routines.
- Improve maintenance efficiency by directing repair and overhaul actions at specific known deficiencies.
- Aid overhaul planning in the areas of manpower and spare parts requirements.

To gain some idea of the return on investment attainable through predictive analysis, a net reduction in maintenance costs of 30% or more compared to the costs before the program was implemented are typical and have been reported by numerous organizations. In many organizations the largest percentage of this savings comes from the identification and resolution of chronic repetitive problems among small noncritical equipment which are identified for the first time by a disciplined program of predictive analysis.

In addition to improved availability and reduced maintenance costs attainable with a program of predictive analysis, the instrumentation and awareness of machinery condition promoted by predictive analysis greatly facilitates the diagnosis of identified problems. In fact, the two go hand in hand: the knowledge gained in problem analysis provides the data base by which to judge new machinery, verify its performance, establish compliance with specifications, and identify potential long-range problems. It is important to note that the return on predictive analysis may be difficult to justify initially; however, don't despair, for most programs of this type start small with relatively modest objectives then grow as the benefits become increasingly apparent.

PERIODIC MEASUREMENT OF VIBRATION AMPLITUDES

By far the simplest type of predictive analysis program involves recording periodic vibration amplitudes at specific points on the casing of selected equipment at regular intervals. The measurements can be tabulated or graphed. The latter is recommended (figure 15–1), for trends will be visible much sooner than if the same information is displayed in tabular form. Preprinted forms (figure 15–2) are available from numerous sources for recording measurements as well as data on the machine itself. Most organizations with this type of program utilize

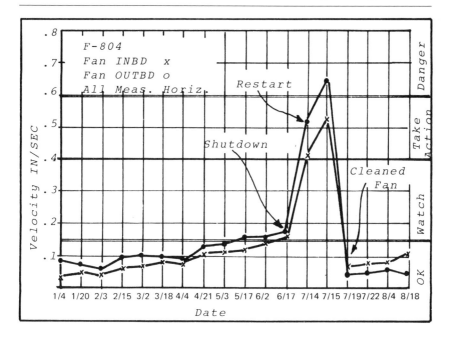

15–1—*Graphical method of displaying vibration measurements.*

operators or technicians to take and record the measurements at regular 30 to 60-day intervals with 30 days being the most common. To save time, some organizations require only one measurement in the plane of highest amplitude, generally horizontal, as long as it remains below a specified value determined by experience. If the single-plane measurement is above the threshold value, measurements in all three orthogonal planes will be required. Other organizations will require measurements in all three planes regardless of amplitude.

As another way to save time and improve the effectiveness of recording periodic vibration measurements, at least one organization has printed a predetermined route to be followed and has equipped the technician taking the measurements with a battery-powered tape recorder and throat microphone. Instead of writing the measurements directly on a log sheet, the technician speaks the equipment identification number and vibration measurement into the microphone, then transcribes all the values onto their respective log sheets in the quiet of an office where out-of-limit measurements and trends are recognized more easily. As another perhaps more exotic means to the same end, the use of a small hand-held terminal such as that used to inventory the

MECHANALYSIS PMP DATA SHEET

MACHINE : Condensate Pump

LOCATION : Lower Level-FWD

OPERATING CONDITIONS : _____

PERIODIC CHECK : Monthly

INITIAL CHECK VIB. LEVELS : IN/SEC. PK.

	A	B	C	D	E	F	G	H
ATHWTSHP*	.22	.16	.10	.08				
VERTICAL*								
FORE/AFT*	.35	.20	.10	.05				

VIBRATION TREND CHART — (IN/SEC. PK.)

0 0.1 0.2 0.3 0.4 0.5 0.6 0.7 0.8 0.9 1.0

D-C-B—A

D-C —— B —— A

PERIODIC CHECK VIB. LEVELS : IN/SEC. PK.

DATE	BY	A*(F)	B*(F)	C*(A)	D*(A)	E*( )	F*( )	G*( )	H*( )
3/15	PLC	.25	.20	.11	.04				
4/22	PLC	.23	.19	.10	.05				
5/15	JSH	.27	.24	.12	.04				
6/25	JSH	.25	.22	.10	.04				
7/14	JSH	.31	.25	.11	.05				
8/22	JSH	.33	.27	.12	.06				
9/31	LPC	.29	.24	.10	.04				
10/15	LPC	.30	.25	.10	.05				
11/10	LPC	.33	.28	.13	.05				
12/20	JSH	.34	.30	.12	.04				
1/5	JSH	.31	.29	.14	.05				
2/15	PLM	.29	.29	.13	.05				
3/22	JSM	.32	.31	.15	.04				
4/10	LPC	.34	.30	.14	.04				
5/20	LPC	.32	.33	.13	.04				
6/15	LPC	.33	.32	.14	.05				

VIBRATION TREND CHART — (IN/SEC. PK.)

0 0.1 0.2 0.3 0.4 0.5 0.6 0.7 0.8 0.9 1.0

15–2—Typical predictive maintenance data sheet.

shelves of grocery stores has been proposed by Exxon Research and Engineering Co. In this system the technician would record the measurement along with the equipment identification number on a keyboard. After a sequence of measurements had been completed, the portable terminal would be connected to a computer and its record transferred for a determination of out-of-limit conditions, trending, and storage.

If instrumentation is available, a detailed vibration signature should be obtained from each machine, preferably in three orthogonal planes at each bearing at the beginning of the program and following any major maintenance or repairs. This baseline signature documents machine condition at one point in time and is extremely useful for comparative purposes if a problem develops later.

There are several reasons to measure casing vibration in terms of velocity. Shaft vibration is conventionally measured and recorded in terms of displacement. In either case, a wideband or filter-out reading generally provides sufficient information and is much less prone to error. In some instances, particularly casing measurements made on machines such as gears, the filter-out measurement may be high yet represents normal condition. This condition is usually caused by an abundance of harmonic orders and may be handled in several ways. First, simply set a higher limit for that particular machine. Second, record its vibration in terms of displacement, which attenuates the higher order harmonics. Third, in addition to a wideband reading, record filtered measurements at shaft speed. Finally, record both broadband velocity and displacement.

Setting a higher limit is the simplest method, but it can cause confusion unless people are reminded constantly that the higher limit only applies to a specific machine(s). Recording casing vibration in terms of displacement while ignoring velocity has ended with some spectacular and very costly fatigue failures where the principal symptoms were at higher frequencies. Filtered measurements take time and are prone to error but also provide the most information when accomplished correctly. A filtered measurement of the amplitude of the largest component, usually running frequency, combined with an unfiltered measurement defines a given situation about as well as any two measurements. Where a filter is unavailable, simultaneous measurements of unfiltered velocity and displacement can be used to derive a quick estimate of frequency content from the following equation relating displacement and velocity:

$$\text{Velocity in./sec or mm/sec} = 0.052 \times \text{rpm} \times \text{DA}$$

Rpm is assumed to be shaft speed and DA is peak-to-peak displacement in inches or millimeters, respectively. To perform the estimate, which can also be accomplished on a slide rule available from many vibration instrument suppliers, a velocity is calculated using the measured displacement and machine speed. The calculated velocity is then compared with measured velocity. If the measured velocity is larger than the calculated velocity, a significant portion of the overall vibration exists above rotational speed such as might occur with misalignment or a prominent pump vane-passing frequency. If the reverse is true (calculated velocity greater than measured velocity), a significant excitation is present below rotational frequency, a primary symptom of instability. This can significantly enhance the usefulness of easily made measurements, for information is available to estimate frequency content as well as detect changes in frequency content without adding the complexity of filtered measurements.

Comparable instruments (figure 15–3) are available for measuring the condition of rolling element bearings. Generally using acceleration or acoustic emission energy at high frequencies, 35 kHz and above, these measurements detect and measure the severity of defects which produce impacts as they contact or are contacted by a moving part of the bearing before they would be observed as low-frequency vibration. The measurements are expressed numerically, though often on an arbitrary unitless scale, and may be trended for early detection of deteriorating condition in the same way as vibration measurements. Many instruments designed to examine the characteristics of rolling element bearings will also include provisions for measuring vibration at the lower frequencies around rotating speed. With this combination, two measurements, obtained with a single instrument, will provide a very accurate picture of the overall condition of machinery with rolling element bearings.

Regardless of what information is measured and recorded, fixed limits should be established in terms of absolute levels and change since the last measurement. Many organizations use 0.3 in./sec (8 mm/sec) overall and 0.1 in./sec (2.5 mm/sec) change from the last measurements as casing velocity limits which require additional analysis and evaluation if exceeded with 0.4 in./sec (10 mm/sec) as an overall level requiring corrective action. The limits should be prominently displayed on the sheet on which the measurements are recorded. For maximum effectiveness, an out-of-limit measurement should automatically flag that piece of equipment for closer surveillance and more detailed analysis. One way to accomplish this is to have the person making the measurements place a small red tab on one corner of the page containing the out-of-limit measurement so the person reviewing

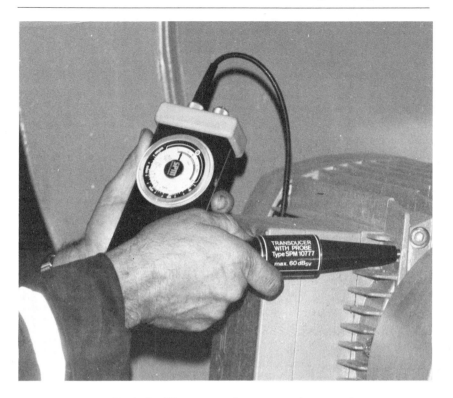

15–3   *Typical rolling contact bearing condition analyzer*
(courtesy Testing Machines Inc.)

the measurements can quickly identify and turn to those pages requiring additional attention.

Remember that, for maximum effectiveness, a predictive analysis program constructed around vibration amplitude measurement should be designed so that operators and/or craftsmen who may be unfamiliar with all the details of vibration analysis can quickly and accurately screen a large number of operating machines with a minimum chance for error. Each machine should have a separate page on which several years of measurements recorded at approximately monthly intervals can be recorded. A graphical presentation of raw or unfiltered velocity is recommended for early detection of trends with consideration given to recording raw displacement as well so that an analyst can estimate frequency content. Absolute and rate of change limits (0.3 IPS (8 mm/ sec) absolute and 0.1 IPS (2.5 mm/sec) change are recommended) should be set and displayed prominently on the page where measurements are recorded. The measurements should be reviewed by a skilled analyst as soon as possible after they are made. The review should be concentrated on machines where out-of-limit conditions have been identified and will probably include more detailed signature analysis to discover the exact nature of the problem and vibration surveys at closer intervals to spot further changes before damage can result. Organizations with this type program in effect usually have a status board on which a prioritized listing of out-of-limit equipment is maintained, the date it was last examined, the date it is to be next examined, and any comments.

This type of program can be very effective: it best uses people with varying levels of skill in machinery analysis, promotes awareness of machinery condition, and ensures most problems will be identified in time to avoid outright failure.

PREDICTIVE ANALYSIS ON MACHINERY EQUIPPED WITH CONTINUOUS-MONITORING SYSTEMS

If machinery monitors are simply installed, commissioned, and promptly forgotten until an alarm is received, potentially valuable information is being neglected. To maximize the usefulness of an installed continuous monitoring system, its levels should be recorded and observed exactly as described in the section on manual periodic monitoring using portable equipment.

Along with shaft vibration, the gap voltage from all radial displacement pickups should be recorded and trended in any comprehensive program of predictive analysis. Frequently this information will reveal bearing deterioration due to electric discharge etching or lube oil contamination long before any recognizable change in vibration has occurred.

By establishing some formal method of charting measurements from a continuous monitoring system, the chance of identifying a trend before it reaches the alarm stage is greatly improved. This type program seems to work best when shift operators record measurements once each shift in a graphical format capable of accommodating several months' measurements (figure 15–4). Here again, the objective is to establish a disciplined method for tracking regular measurements which does not require much time yet will increase awareness of machinery condition and detect trends early. Many organizations with larger systems and a computer perform the logging and trending automatically with a computer program designed to recognize out-of-limit conditions as well as short and long-term trends.

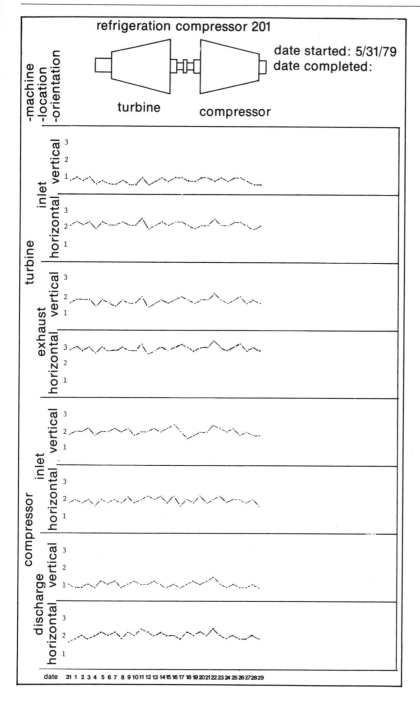

15–4—Typical vibration monitor log.

PREDICTIVE SPECTRUM ANALYSIS

Most organizations undertake predictive spectrum or signature analysis as a logical extension or refinement of an ongoing program such as periodic trending. Other organizations evolve into predictive signature analysis from continuous monitoring in an effort to gain more insight into machine condition so they can anticipate rather than react to problems. Still others find periodic predictive signature analysis the most cost effective means to monitor the condition of critical smaller equipment where installed sensors, hardwired into a central monitoring system, may be prohibitively expensive.

Once a decision has been made to investigate the feasibility of a predictive signature analysis program, several preliminary steps must be taken in order to ensure success. First, develop a long-range plan of attack containing all the pertinent data such as the investment required for equipment, the number and type of people needed to implement the plan, and the expected savings if the plan is adopted. The latter should account for maintenance expenditures, the expected savings if potential failures are caught earlier in their development, and the current fatality rate of equipment. Attendance at seminars, discussions with experienced specialists, reviewing the latest technology through instrument manufacturers' descriptive and application literature, and reading the technical papers on the subject are all ways in which a newcomer to signature analysis can educate himself in the technology. Remember that management doesn't like to hear about problems but will always consider a planned and documented solution to a problem. The more information you have to demonstrate the success of signature analysis solving your type problem, the greater the chance your proposed program will be accepted.

Several areas must be noted once a decision has been made to embark on a program of signature analysis in order to maximize the chances for future success. First, select and purchase good instrumentation. Remember, the program won't be much better than the tools, so talk to others, learn what they are using and why, what changes they would make if they had to begin again, and what instrumentation they would purchase initially. It is sometimes difficult for a person beginning a program of signature analysis to judge between the relative merits of accessories to an instrument which refines a task or permit greater resolution and a basic instrument which performs an entirely different task.

Next, select good, enthusiastic, open-minded, motivated people. In a signature analysis program, enthusiasm, motivation, and the willingness to learn are far more important than formal education. Maintenance experience with machinery can be a big advantage; for much of what is observed makes logical sense to one who has worked with bearings, seals, etc.

Third, use all the skills you have at your disposal; work with and help people, don't fight them. For example, most good mechanics are skilled at listening to machinery and can tell about a machine's internal condition by its sound. Use the ability to present what he hears in a measurable form; make every effort to work with him and benefit from his experience. In this way most skilled mechanics will become interested in the program, and you'll be surprised how helpful they can be. The same philosophy applies to management. Keep them informed of progress and, while you should certainly advertise your successes, don't attempt to hide failures; use your failures as a learning experience for the next problem.

Don't shy away from tough problems. You have powerful instrumentation at your disposal which can often provide the key insight needed to solve a problem. Once you have achieved the reputation of being able to solve problems where your results can be measured in dollar earnings through increased production, you'll be surprised at how easy it is to justify an expansion of the program. In fact, you may even be pushed to expand faster than you would like as production superintendents recognize and want the benefits of predictive signature analysis.

Finally, be patient. Although many have been lucky and have experienced success relatively soon, plan on at least a year to see concrete results from a predictive signature analysis program. At all times in a signature analysis program, but especially during the first year or two, keep meticulous records of predictions, what was found, and an estimate of the savings. This type of documentation is always appreciated: it provides the financial justification for your program and it can be used by management as a positive demonstration of their stewardship, performance, and insight for the idea of a predictive analysis program.

There are two basic methods available for accomplishing signature analysis on operating equipment. Some organizations favor recording vibration data on magnetic tape for later analysis in a laboratory. Others house the analysis equipment in a trailer or van which can be brought on site for direct reduction and analysis. In the latter method, a multiconductor extension cable for reaching the farthest machine is generally used to connect the sensor(s) into the analysis equipment. The cable is stored on a reel when not in use.

In many situations such as mezzanine-mounted machinery, it may be highly desirable to install an extension cable permanently from the machine deck to grade in order to eliminate the necessity of dragging a portable cable up several flights of stairs. The cable is terminated in watertight boxes at both ends with the box on the machine level fitted with connectors to mate with vibration sensor extension cables and the box at grade fitted with a connector to mate with a cable from the van or trailer.

A two-way communication channel should be included in the extension cable. This way, two people can coordinate their activities very effectively: one at the machine equipped with a headset to move sensors, check oil levels, and general condition, and the other in the trailer or van performing the analysis.

Although the van or trailer approach is more expensive, it has several advantages when used in a plant. It minimizes the time necessary to set up instrumentation and thereby enables an extremely quick response to problems. The analysis equipment is out of the weather and in a controlled environment; yet it is readily accessible and can easily be used for extended periods in the field for continuous monitoring of critical problems. Finally, there is no need to carry heavy equipment into a unit and up several flights of stairs to a machine.

The interval between periodic predictive signature analysis can vary greatly depending on the requirements of the specific organization. Some organizations will survey equipment monthly, while others will survey quarterly. To a large degree the interval is best determined by the type of equipment, its past history, and whether or not it is protected by a continuous monitoring system or included in a program of periodic vibration measurement. As a starting point, consider analyzing critical equipment with a good operating history not equipped with continuous monitoring at two-month intervals and critical equipment equipped with continuous monitoring systems and noncritical equipment at three-month intervals. Naturally, the intervals are shortened for machinery experiencing difficulties or machinery where significant changes or trends are noted since the previous analysis.

Detailed analyses should definitely be conducted immediately prior to an overhaul as a planning measure and immediately following an overhaul as soon as steady-state operating conditions have been established to assess the effectiveness of the overhaul and to provide beginning of run baselines.

Invariably included in the electronic equipment required for programs will be a real-time spectrum analyzer, an oscilloscope to view the spectral output, and an X–Y plotter to produce hard copies. If many machines are to be analyzed, a computer, bulk storage, and software to perform the comparison should be considered. Although not required for a program of signature analysis, an XYY' recorder is a good investment if one contemplates constructing Bode plots of amplitude and phase versus speed during startup and shutdown.

A multichannel instrumentation-grade magnetic tape recorder for recording and reproducing in both FM and direct is nearly always included as part of signature analysis instrumentation. The recorder collects and stores dynamic data for later detailed analysis without the need to expose expensive analysis equipment to a field environment. Although trailer or van-mounted instrumentation eliminates some of the need for a tape recorder, it is still recommended as a means to collect and store data received from multiple transducers too rapidly for individual detailed analysis during transients such as startup and shutdown. In addition, magnetic tape is an easily understood, practical method to store steady-state dynamic data.

Periodic predictive signature analysis can and should utilize the signals from a variety of sources. The signals from permanently installed transducers should always be included. Where permanent transducers are not installed, portable transducers can be used effectively if they are solidly attached to the machine casing at specific, well-defined, repeatable locations. Of the portable vibration transducers in common use, velocity pickups are probably the most popular. However, accelerometers have advantages in terms of frequency response and insensitivity to electrical fields and are therefore rapidly gaining acceptance, particularly in applications on gearing, turbines, and rolling element bearings. When accelerometers are used, the signal may be viewed, analyzed, and plotted in acceleration units or integrated to velocity. The former tends to emphasize the high frequencies, whereas the latter is a better indicator of overall condition.

In operation, the predictive signature analysis program is performed in a similar manner to the periodic measurement program. Vibration spectra are obtained from specific locations on the equipment included in the program. Generally, each location has a separate page on which successive spectra are stacked, one on top of the other, using the same amplitude and frequency scale. In this fashion the person plotting the data can quickly recognize changes which are then flagged for more detailed study (figure 15–5). So that numerical values are available for comparison, record the overall amplitude somewhere adjacent to the signature as well as a gap voltage when applicable. When the machine has other monitored variables such as speed, temperature, and position, these should be recorded in some convenient form along with vibration.

There is a great deal of interest in automated signature analysis incorporating a computer as a method of saving manpower. In this scheme the computer accomplishes the comparison with previous data and prints out deviations outside a predetermined normal envelope. This approach frees people from the tedious and not particularly in-

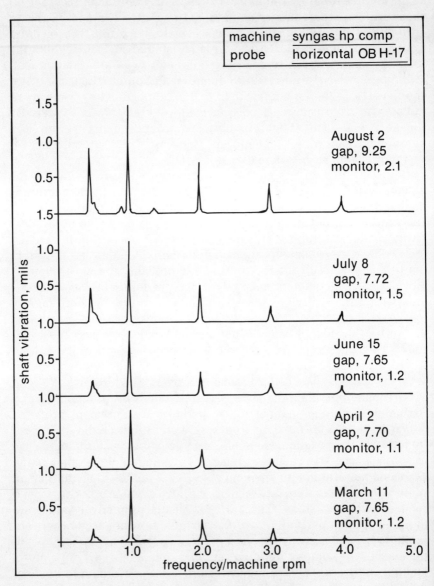

15–5—*Typical vibration monitor signature record.*

teresting task of comparing data so they will have more time to concentrate on analyzing problems. Unfortunately, it is not uncommon for a vibration signature recorded on equipment in stable satisfactory condition to change in response to variations in operating conditions. While an experienced analyst familiar with the machine can read through the changes to reach a valid determination of machinery condition, it is difficult to program a computer to that level of sophistication.

Although these two types of predictive analysis have been presented separately, the best and most comprehensive programs of predictive analysis will contain the elements of both. The mixture and emphasis, how much and which type will be applied to specific machines, is a decision only you can make.

SUGGESTED PROGRAM OF PREDICTIVE ANALYSIS

Since nearly all programs of predictive analysis are limited by manpower, money, or both, it is well to examine some compromises that can be made to maximize the effectiveness of a program.

Most will agree that it is not an efficient use of time to expend a great deal of effort performing detailed analyses on equipment in good condition. It is far better to devise some method to screen equipment than subject only that portion in questionable or deteriorating condition to more detailed analysis. In one type of program, equipment is divided in categories by the potential and impact of failures and service. Generally, most equipment can be classified in one of the following four categories:

- Critical unspared machines where an unexpected shutdown or failure is quickly compounded by significant production loss.
- Critical or possible failure-prone spared machinery in arduous service where an unexpected failure to one will jeopardize but not interrupt production.
- Critical spared machinery in light-duty service.
- Noncritical spared machinery.

The category, modified by factors such as operating experience and degree of manning, will generally dictate the scope and extent of machinery protection, monitoring, and analysis. For new machinery in the first category with little or no operating history, the consequences of an unscheduled outage will easily justify a comprehensive continuous monitoring and protection system along with periodic detailed analyses to detect long-term trends. Although the interval between detailed signature analyses varies greatly between organizations, many consider monthly intervals necessary on critical machinery.

In the second group, the extent of monitoring and/or periodic analyses depends on the specific installation. Periodic measurements of overall vibration and bearing condition where applicable, taken at monthly intervals augmented with detailed signatures every six months to a year, are considered adequate protection for machines in the second group by most organizations.

The scope of a monitoring and/or analysis program for machines in the third and fourth groups depends on a number of factors, not the least of which is the manpower required to operate a program compared to the cost of a failure. Many organizations consider quarterly checks of overall vibration and bearing condition an acceptable compromise for machinery in groups three and four.

External influences may change the category. For example, it is generally possible to lose one fan in a multicell cooling tower during cold weather without affecting production, whereas its loss during hot weather may force an immediate curtailment.

The extent of a monitoring and analysis program depends on a number of factors which are specific to the installation. Generally, what is to be done on critical equipment is self-evident; determining what and how much coverage will be expended on smaller less critical equipment is much more difficult.

The program diagrammed in figure 15–6 was designed to provide a method for quickly and accurately screening equipment so that detailed analysis efforts can be concentrated on equipment in questionable or deteriorating condition. The program consists of four parts, beginning with a detailed signature analysis on each piece of equipment to establish baseline conditions. At this stage, some machines will probably be found in marginal condition requiring close surveillance, monitoring, or perhaps outright repairs.

Apart from defining initial conditions, the baseline also provides a good idea of how representative overall vibration meter readings will be of mechanical condition. If the signature contains only components generated by the specific machine, an overall vibration level is a fast, reasonably accurate method to estimate condition. Conversely, if the signature contains prominent components originated by adjacent equipment, an overall vibration level may not be at all representative of condition.

Assuming that the baseline signatures indicate that an overall level is a reasonably accurate measure of mechanical condition, unfiltered vibration readings recorded periodically from monitors or portable instruments can be used to screen a large population of machinery inexpensively. During the screening process (figure 15–1), most equip-

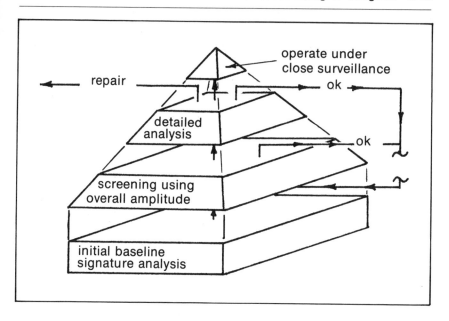

15–6—Typical predictive analysis program.

ment will be acceptable and will continue on the program of overall measurements while others will be in changing or questionable condition. This latter category is subjected to detailed analysis with the baselines recorded earlier used as a reference. Following analysis, some of the questionable machines will be judged acceptable and returned to the screening program, while closer, perhaps more detailed surveillance or even immediate repairs may be recommended for others.

It is no coincidence that figure 15–6 is drawn as a pyramid. The program is designed to use the simplest means possible to separate questionable from good machinery, thus reserving the more costly detailed analysis for machinery actually requiring more study.

Before leaving the subject of predictive analysis a number of areas just as important to eventual success as the procedure, type of instruments, and interval between analyses should be mentioned.

First, know as much as possible about the machinery being analyzed. Records should be kept for each major rotor, listing critical speeds, numbers of impellers, vanes, blades, and teeth as applicable as well as any peculiarities such as runout patterns or tendency toward instability and any repairs such as metal sprayed journals. The analysis team must know which rotor is installed at all times.

Second, a record of equipment failures should be maintained regardless of whether predictions and/or recommendations were or were not made. An equipment failure is bad enough; not learning anything from it to prevent the next one is even worse.

Third, every prediction should be followed up by the person who made it. When a machine is opened, the person predicting its internal condition should be there as an observer. If the actual conditions do not agree with the prediction, try to find out why so the next prediction will be more accurate.

Finally, predictive analysis is concerned with total machine health. Vibration is only one criterion. Select the variables most descriptive of a machine's health, whether they are vibration, position, temperature, pressure, flow, or some combination, then set up the program accordingly.

ASSEMBLING THE SYSTEM

In the next sections are some recommendations for the sequence in which instruments might be purchased most effectively as a program of machinery analysis is developed. Suggestions for calibration and data taking are offered.

Priority for purchasing instrumentation

Any sequence or priority for purchasing instruments is very much personal opinion and is highly dependent on the objectives of the specific program. What follows is an attempt to suggest a sequence of instrument purchases which will develop a program of machinery analysis in progressive, manageable steps or stages.

Stage 1. Obtain broadband vibration measurements; establish a program of routine surveillance.
Portable vibration meter
Stage 2. Add capability for vibration analysis and field balancing.
Manually tuned vibration analyzer with strobe
Note: Stage 3 is designed for locations with continuous shaft displacement monitoring systems in service. If such systems are not installed, the equipment in Stage 3, although highly desirable, can be deferred for purchase in Stage 6.
Stage 3. Add the instrumentation necessary for viewing and analyzing shaft vibration signals in the time domain. Establish a program of regular, periodic analysis of shaft signals. Photograph signals for comparison over time.
Laboratory-type oscilloscope with Polaroid camera

Stage 4. Add capability for real-time frequency analysis
   Real time analyzer with built-in oscilloscope
Stage 5. Procure test and calibration equipment
   Test equipment: audio signal generator and digital multimeter
   Calibration system for displacement probes if applicable
Stage 6. Add magnetic recording capability, establish a program of detailed periodic signature analysis.
   Portable FM magnetic tape recorder
   Preamplifiers
   Portable oscilloscope
   XY or XYY__ plotter
   High-fidelity amplifier and speaker to enable listening to signals as they are reproduced
   Velocity pickups, cables, and connectors necessary for patching pickups into the recorder.
Stage 7. Expand analysis frequency range
   Accelerometers and, if required, a means to convert a charge signal to a voltage signal
Stage 8. Complete calibration system
   Small dynamic shaker capable of exciting the pickups supplied with the analyzers purchased in stages 1 and 2 and the pickups purchased in stages 6 and 7
Stage 9. Add an automatic tracking filter for the analysis of start-up response and for dynamic balancing.
   Tracking analyzer
Stage 10. Add to recording capacity for startup or transient analysis
   7 or 14-channel magnetic tape recorder
   Additional preamplifiers and transducers as required
Stage 11. Refine analysis instrumentation
   Frequency translator (depending on the RTA purchase in stage 4, this and item B may be built in)
   Order normalizing adapter
   Cascade spectrum adapter

Typically, one or more stages such as 4 and 5 or 5 and 6 may be procured at one time; however, if the equipment is obtained in the general order listed, one instrument naturally leads into another as learning and experience progress. The biggest mistake one can make is attempting to do too much too quickly. The old adage "you must walk before you can attempt to fly" certainly applies to machinery instrumentation.

Method for data acquisition and analysis

This section describes one method for acquiring vibration data, recording it on magnetic tape, and finally reducing it into a frequency spectrum and waveform if desired for detailed analysis. So that the description is as general as possible assume acceleration, velocity, and displacement transducers will be used and include a tape recording step in a typical system (figure 15–7).

For a total view of mechanical condition, the vibration characteristics of an operating machine should be collected at each bearing using casing transducers, velocity pickups, and/or accelerometers and noncontact shaft displacement transducers whenever they are installed. Selecting the appropriate transducer or transducers for a specific application is governed by the type of machine.

Low-frequency velocity measurements from approximately 10 to 1,000 Hz should be made in three orthogonal planes at each bearing. High-frequency acceleration measurements are generally made in a single plane, usually vertical, at each bearing. Magnetic mounts can

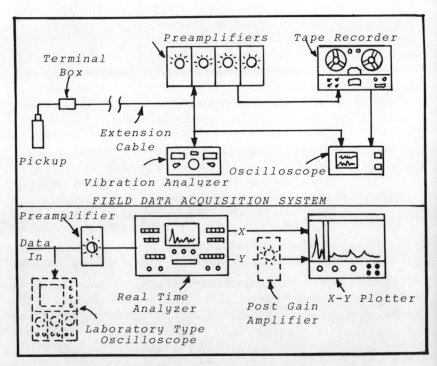

15–7—*Typical machinery analysis recording and analysis system.*

attach the velocity pickups to the machine casing; however, adapters, either glued to the casing with epoxy or threaded into the casing, are mandatory to obtain good acceleration data at high frequencies.

Transducer positions at each bearing are selected to be representative of machine condition. Radial pickups used to obtain velocity measurements should be positioned at the approximate longitudinal centerline of each bearing and moved parallel to the shaft centerline to determine if the bearing is vibrating in a rocking mode where amplitude is sensitive to position. Although this is not a common occurrence, it does happen and should be checked. When vibration amplitude varies greatly with transducer position, a location should be chosen which is somewhere between the maximum and minimum amplitudes present. It should be clearly marked so that a transducer can be removed and then replaced in the same exact position. Under the conditions described, very small differences in transducer location can cause large differences in amplitude which in turn will obscure or invalidate trend measurements. In any case, the final location of each pickup must be marked so that all subsequent data will be collected at the same exact positions on the machine.

As stated, high-frequency acceleration measurements may be made in a single plane or in all three planes, depending on the purpose and depth of the analysis. Generally, a single radial measurement, usually made in the vertical plane, is adequate for routine mechanical analyses; however, a second radial and an axial measurement may be advisable on equipment such as gears where the high frequencies contain proportionally more condition-related information. Again, while magnetic mounts or even hand-held probes are adequate for low-frequency velocity measurements, a fixed, rigidly attached mounting, either glued or screwed to the machine casing, must be used if valid high-frequency acceleration data are to be obtained. As discussed in chapter 5, the locations chosen for attaching accelerometers must be rigid, preferably braced in some fashion, and free from high amplification resonances within the frequency range under study. A vertical mounting along the horizontal centerline is generally adequate; mounting an accelerometer on an unsupported section of the bearing cap or casing should be avoided.

The output from an accelerometer should be converted to a low impedance voltage signal as close to the accelerometer as possible to minimize the effects of cable noise. Once converted, the acceleration signal along with the outputs from velocity pickups or a displacement measuring system can be transmitted over multiconductor shielded pair extension cable to the recording preamplifiers. The preamplifier gain is adjusted to give the proper recording level and the signal is recorded on magnetic tape.

As discussed earlier, recording vibration signals for later detailed analysis in a room, office, trailer, or van where the analytical equipment can be set up permanently and the environment controlled will generally produce better results than if the analysis is performed in the field with portable instrumentation. Additionally, the time required to collect the data is much less than the time required for analysis, thus reducing the chances of an operational change midway through an analysis which could affect mechanical characteristics.

Vibration data should be recorded with a machine operating at normal conditions of load and speed unless the objective of the test is to determine variations in mechanical characteristics corresponding to variations in operating parameters. In either case, operating variables—load, speed, pressures, and temperatures—should be recorded as the data are collected so that subsequent analyses can be performed under the same conditions. Low-frequency displacement and velocity signals are best recorded in FM, while acceleration signals are usually recorded in direct.

During the recording process, the transducer and recorder outputs should be observed simultaneously on a two-channel oscilloscope to ensure the preamplifier and tape recorder are producing a faithful, undistorted reproduction of the input signal. Additionally, and as a check on the recording process, it is a good idea to measure the amplitude of one component, generally running frequency, in the signal from the transducer with a portable vibration analyzer. This value, along with the preamplifier gain, should be recorded on a tape log for future reference. In addition to assisting in the recording process, these two steps provide the opportunity for a preliminary assessment of machine condition which, if anomalies are observed, might warrant the collection of additional data.

As an aid in the recording process, it is advisable to develop an abbreviated method to designate the measurement location along the length of a machine string as well as the transducer orientation and type. Designating measurement location with a letter sequence (A,B,C, etc.) normally beginning at the outboard drive end of a machine string (figure 15–8) is simple yet effective. A second letter can be used to designate the pickup orientation while a third letter designates type of pickup. Thus, the notation AHV might indicate a horizontal measurement made with a velocity pickup on the outboard bearing of the driver.

An accurate tape log is vital to the recording process. It should

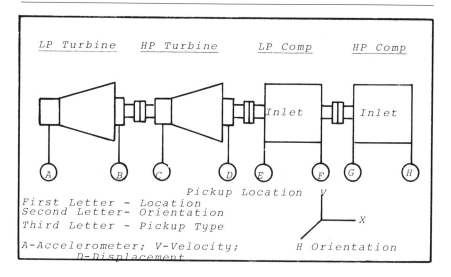

15-8—Shorthand method of designating transducer location and orientation
on a typical machine string.

contain the location at which the measurement is obtained, pickup
orientation, type of pickup, preamplifier gain, the footage at the start
and end of the recording, and a direct measurement of the amplitude of
at least one component in a spectrum. When a recording is being made
during transient conditions, such as startup or shutdown, the tape log
should be annotated with any significant events to ease locating the
appropriate sections of tape.

Once the data have been recorded on magnetic tape, the next step is
to reproduce them with the desired analysis equipment in order to
reduce the complex signal into some meaningful format for interpretation. An amplitude-versus-frequency spectrum using a real-time
analyzer is particularly effective.

Since the input gain on a real-time analyzer is graduated in decibels, there are advantages placing linear gain step preamplifiers between the tape recorder output and input to the real time analyzer, as
well as between the real-time analyzer output and plotter (figure 15–7).
With this arrangement, gains may be adjusted to an optimum value for
analysis and plotting then easily divided out of the plot vertical coordinate to regain the original recorded amplitude.

Each signal is reproduced into the real-time analyzer, observed for
dynamic characteristics such as amplitude fluctuations or beats, and
committed to a hard-copy amplitude versus frequency spectrum with

an X–Y plotter. The waveform and orbital presentation may be photographed and added to the spectrum plot. For statistical accuracy, spectrum plots are generally made with averaged data; however, on occasion it may be necessary or beneficial to display a single spectrum captured manually or a peak spectrum in order to preserve vital information.

Once a spectrum has been obtained, the running frequency is identified and prominent harmonic orders are located. Often a harmonic order such as a blade pass or gear mesh frequency can be related directly to a mechanical component; others may simply be harmonic orders of running frequency or some other fundamental. Another characteristic to look for is regularly spaced sidebands around a major component. The sidebands are produced by a modulation process, and their frequency spacing provides a clue to the generating mechanism.

Once all the prominent components have been identified, the spectrum is analyzed for unusual amplitudes or harmonic patterns. From this evaluation an overall assessment of machinery condition can be formed.

In addition to providing information to evaluate mechanical condition at one point in time, a series of signatures taken on an individual machine constitutes its baseline performance and can be used for subsequent comparison.

Recording and calibration

Assume that the sensitivity of all the transducers being used is known, that the gain steps on the preamplifiers have been checked with a voltage source and in fact produce the specified multiplications, and that the tape recorder has been calibrated and set for unity gain. This is easily accomplished by feeding a signal to the tape recorder at its rated input, adjusting the input gain if provided to produce the proper deflection on the input meter, then adjusting the output gain to produce an output at the same amplitude as the input. The procedure may vary from recorder to recorder; however, the objective is the same: to obtain an output voltage which is equal to the input. On both FM and direct recorders, but particularly the latter, vary the frequency of the input across the range of interest to make certain the recorder is as close as possible to unity gain for all frequencies.

Once this has been accomplished, make an end-to-end check of the data acquisition system. Assuming the tape recorder was set for a 1 VRMS input, apply a 0.1 VRMS signal at the transducer input, set the preamplifier gains for 10, and, if everything was done correctly, observe a 1 VRMS output from the tape recorder. This calibration signal should be recorded for a short distance on the tape as a reference.

Although everything has been checked and is presumably working, repeat the end-to-end test when the data acquisition system is set up in the field and prior to recording data. Small battery-powered signal generators are available to facilitate this task.

To record machinery data on magnetic tape, simply set the pre-amplifier gain to obtain the proper input level, record the preamplifier setting on the tape log, and start the recorder.

With the data acquired and collected on magnetic tape, the next task is to calibrate the analysis system and analyze the signals. Since most spectrum analyzers have input and output gains calibrated in decibels, add an instrument amplifier with linear gain steps ahead and behind the spectrum analyzer to facilitate any gain changes which might be necessary during the course of the analysis. Since the output of the spectrum analyzer is DC, the output amplifier must of course be able to amplify a DC signal.

Assuming the input preamplifier does not have an attenuator, that is gain steps of less than 1, its gain should be set at 10 to allow some attenuation if necessary. Next, the tape is reproduced through the amplifier and into the analyzer and an analyzer input gain selected that is close to overload on most signals.

With this accomplished, a calibration voltage is calculated for the transducer. Using a 200 mv-pp/mil-pp (8 mv/μm) displacement transducer as an example, 200 mv-pp = 70.7 mv-RMS, the value which will be read on a meter. Thus, a 70.7 mv-RMS signal at the input of the preamplifier is equivalent to a vibration amplitude of 1 mil (25.4 μm) peak to peak. With preamplifier still set on 10, there are 0.707 volts or 10 mils (254 μm) peak to peak at the input of the analyzer.

Next, the frequency markers in the analyzer are tuned on and an 8 or 16 average is taken of the combined input and frequency marker signals. The calibration signal must not overload the analyzer. With the calibration signal averaged, the plotter connected to the analyzer, and both the analyzer and the external output amplifier set for unity gain, calibrate the plotter.

The first step in calibrating the plotter is to set the zero and full-scale frequency points at the proper location on the selected graph paper. As a suggestion, use graph paper with squares in multiples of ten across the frequency axis to facilitate measuring frequency.

With the plotter frequency axis calibrated, the last item remaining is to calibrate the amplitude axis. Depending on the size of the paper, the amplitude of the vibration recorded, and how high one wishes the peak amplitudes to reach, one might choose ten vertical squares to equal 4 mils (120 μm) peak to peak. Recalling that the signal represents 1 mil (25.4 μm) at the input to the preamplifier, adjust the vertical gain on the plotter until the amplitude from the analyzer equals 2½ squares English units (2.1 squares metric) in height and the system is calibrated so 1 vertical square equals 0.4 mil (12 μm) peak to peak with an amplification of 10.

In this system, amplification/attenuation can be inserted at three states: prior to the tape recorder, prior to the analyzer, and following the analyzer. Multiples of four were picked for a particular reason. Table 15.1 lists the total amplification through the system that is the product of the three amplifier settings against the displacement value per square in the example.

TABLE 15–1
Total Gain Versus Calibrated Amplitude Per Square

Total gain	Displacement amplitude per square (10 square height)	
	Mils pp	Micrometers pp
1	4	120
2	2	60
4	1	30
5	0.8	24
8	0.5	15
10	0.4	12
20	0.2	6
40	0.10	3
50	0.08	2.4

Note that utilizing multiples of four results in values per square that are easy to handle for every possible gain combination.

With the analysis system calibrated, check the calibration signal recorded on tape to ensure the tape recorder calibration has not changed and analyze.

The illustrate how the procedure works, assume a signal is reproduced into the analyzer and an analyzer input amplification of 5 and output amplification of 2 are necessary to achieve the desired signal height on the graph paper. The signal was originally recorded with an amplification of 2. Multiplying three amplifications together, a total amplification of 20 is obtained. With an amplification of 20, each square equals 0.2 mil or 6 μm, depending on the units, and the plot is labeled.

This all may seem quite complicated, but it really isn't. Admittedly, one may be able to use a much simpler procedure for displacement signals; however, with velocity and certainly acceleration signals, the flexibility to adjust gain quickly without the need for recalibration is absolutely necessary. In the case of velocity and acceleration setting, 0.4 in./sec peak or 12 mm/sec peak and 4 Gs peak, respectively, equal to ten vertical squares allows using the same gain table with only a leftward shift of one decimal place required for velocity. Notice also that the calibration is end to end, the most effective method to prevent error.

So there it is, a brief summary of how other organizations have established programs of machinery analysis, a recommended priority for instrument purchases, along with methods of data-taking and calibration which have proven successful over the years. However, there is a great deal more to establishing an effective program of machinery analysis than the mechanics of purchasing and using instruments. The way the instruments are assembled and packaged, details such as interconnecting cables, adapter boxes wired to facilitate specific tasks, methods of storing extension cables when not in use, and certainly most important of all the people to establish and carry out the program are all as vital as the instruments themselves.

BIBLIOGRAPHY

PUBLICATIONS/PAPERS FOR ADDITIONAL INFORMATION

General

Jackson, Charles, "The Practical Vibration Primer," Gulf Publishing Company, 1979.

Alignment/Couplings

Campbell, A.J., et al., "Tutorium on Alignment Techniques and Practices," Proceedings of 9th Turbomachinery Symposium, Texas A&M, December, 1980.

Dodd, V.R., "Total Alignment," PennWell Books, 1975.

Dreymala, James, "Factors Affecting & Procedures of Shaft Alignment," Published, 1974 by James Dreymala.

Gibbons, Charles B. "The Use of Diaphragm Couplings in Turbomachinery" Proceedings Machinery Vibration Monitoring and Analysis Seminar, April, 1980, Vibration Institute.

Gibbons, C. B., "Coupling Misalignment Forces," Proceedings, 5th Turbomachinery Symposium, Texas A&M University, October, 1976.

Mitchell, John W., "What is Optical Alignment?" Proceedings, 3rd Turbomachinery Symposium, Texas A&M University, October, 1974.

Balancing

Bulanowski, Edward A., "Practical Considerations For a Rated Speed Shop Balance," Proceedings, 7th Turbomachinery Symposium, Texas A&M University, December, 1978.

Carlson, Paul, O. L., "Four Run Balancing Without Phase," Proceedings, Machinery Vibration Monitoring and Analysis Seminar, April, 1979, Vibration Institute.

Fox, R., et al., "Tutorium on Balancing Principles with Application," Proceedings of 9th Turbomachinery Symposium, Texas A&M, December, 1980.

Gunter, E. J., Editor, "Selected Papers on Field Balancing of Turbomachinery—Advanced Theory and Techniques," Vibration Institute, March 1978.

IRD Mechanalysis, "Dynamic Balancing," Application Report No. 111.

Langlois, Armond B. and Rosecky, Edward J., "Field Balancing," Allis-Chalmers Corporation, 1968.

Nicholas, J. C., Gunter, E. J., and Allaire, P. E., "Effect of Residual Shaft Bow on Unbalance Response and Balancing of a Single Mass Rotor," ASME papers, 75 GT 48 and 75 GT 49.

Rieger, Neville F., "Balancing of Rigid and Flexible Rotors," Shock and Vibration Information Center, Naval Research Laboratory, 1981.

Wilson, D. S. and Others, "Rotor Bearing Dynamics Technology Design Guide, Part VII—Balancing," Technical Report AFAPL-TR-78-6 Part VII Air Force Aero Propulsion Laboratory, Wright Patterson Air Force Base, Dayton, Ohio.

Electromagnetic Discharge

Sohre, J. S., Nippes, P. I., "Electromagnetic Shaft Currents and Demagnetization on Rotors of Turbines and Compressors," Proceedings, 7th Turbomachinery Symposium, Texas A&M University, December, 1978.

Electrical Runout

Beebe, Dale W., "New Techniques in Overcoming Electrical Runout," Hydrocarbon Processing, August, 1976.

Bently Nevada Corporation, "Glitch Definition and Methods for Correction, Including Shaft Burnishing to Remove Electrical Runout," Applications note, August, 1978.

Biggs, David H., "Electrical Runout & Eddy Current Displacement Proximity Transducers," ASME Paper September, 1975.

Schanzenbach, G. P., "Reduction of Electrical Runout to Improve the Accuracy of Eddy Current Probe Sensing of Turbomachinery Vibration," ASME Paper, 72, Lub R.

Van den Bergh, Mathiew, "Runout Subtraction for Improved Resolution and Accuracy in Shaft Vibration Monitoring," Dymac Division of Spectral Dynamics Corporation Application Note, October, 1977

Gearing–Dynamics and Analysis

Chang, Chung-tong, "Multistage Planetary Gear Trains (arrangement, ratios, characteristics)," Design News, June, 1965.

Dambly, B. W., Lawler, E. D., "Investigation of Centrifugal Compressor Gear Noise Influenced by Gear Geometry," ASME Paper, November, 1969, Winter Annual Meeting.

Drosjack, M. J., Houser, D. R., Tinney, A. C., "Investigation of Gear Dynamics Signature Analysis," USSAAMRDL-TR-75-1, Ohio State University Research Foundation.

Dudley, Darle, W., "Gear Handbook," McGraw Hill, 1962

Gu, A. L., Badgley, R. H., "Prediction of Vibration Sidebands in Gear Meshes," ASME Paper October, 1974, Design Engineering Technical Conference.

Mark, William, D., "Analysis of the Vibratory Excitation of Gear Systems: I Basic Theory, II Tooth Error Representations, Approximations and Application," Journal of Acoustic Society, May, 1978, December, 1979.

Randall, R. B., "Gearbox Fault Diagnosis Using Cepstrum Analysis," Institution of Mechanical Engineers (UK), 1975

Seager, D. L., "Dynamic Behavior of Helical Gears," ASME Paper, March, 1969, Vibration Conference

Taylor, James, I., "Identification of Gear Defects by Vibration Analysis," Seventh Technology Interchange, Vibration Institute.

Thompson, R. A., Weichbrodt, Bjorn, "Gear Diagnostics and Wear Detection," ASME Paper, 69-VIBR-10, March 1969.

Thompson, R. A., McCullough, J. R., "The Detection of Wear in Gears," ASME Paper 72-PTG-24, October, 1972.

Welbourn, D. B., "Gear Noise Spectra—A Rational Explanation," ASME Paper 77-DET-38, September, 1977

Welbourn, D. B. "Gear Errors and Their Resultant Noise Spectra," Institution of Mechanical Engineers (UK), Gearing in 1970 Conference Proceedings.

Machinery Instrumentation

Bently Nevada Corporation, "Proximity Probes and Related Accessories: A General Guideline for Installation Considerations and Practices," Application Note, December, 1978.

Capitao, John W., "Thrust Bearing Design Criteria," paper from, "A Legacy of Leadership", published by General Electric Corporation

B & K Instruments Inc., "Measuring Vibration," Booklet published 1979.

Erskine, J. B., "Condition Monitoring in the Heavy Chemical Industry Using Noise and Vibration Measurements," Proceedings, Machinery Vibration Monitoring and Analysis Seminar and Meeting, April, 1980, Vibration Institute.

Frarey, J. L., "Concepts and Use of the Real Time Analyzer," Proceedings, Machinery Vibration Monitoring and Analysis Seminar, April, 1980, Vibration Institute.

Schanzenbach, G. P., "The Installation and Application of Sensors for Turbomachinery Monitoring," Proceedings, 3rd Turbomachinery Symposium, Texas A&M University, December, 1978.

Machinery Analysis

Piety, K. R., Mayette, T. E., "Statistical Techniques for Automating the Detection of Anomalous Performance in Rotating Machinery," Proceedings, Machinery Vibration Monitoring and Analysis Seminar, April, 1979, Vibration Institute
Sohre, J. S. "Operating Problems with High Speed Turbomachinery, Causes and Corrections," Sawyers Turbomachinery Maintenance Handbook, Vol. II, Turbomachinery Publications, Norwalk, CT.

Rolling Element Bearing Analysis

Barthel, Karl, "The Shock Pulse Method for Determining the Condition of Anti-Friction Bearings," Proceedings, Machinery Vibration Monitoring and Analysis Seminar and Meeting, April, 1979, Published by the Vibration Institute.
Block, Heinz P., "Predict Problems with Acoustic Incipient Failure Detection Systems," Hydrocarbon Processing, October, 1977.
Burchell, R. F., Frarey, J. L., Wilson, D. S., "New Machinery Health Diagnostic Technique Using High-Frequency Vibration," Shaker Research Corporation, Application Note.
Darlow, M. S., Badgley, R. H., "Applications for Early Detection of Rolling Element Bearing Failures Using the High Frequency Resonance Technique," ASME Paper 75-DET-46.
Smith, K. A., "Mechanical Signature Analysis of Rotating Machinery," Presented at the 1st Signature Analysis Conference, July, 1977.
Taylor, James I., "Determination of Anti Friction Bearing Condition by Spectral Analysis," Vibration Institute, February, 1978.

Rotor Dynamics

Bently, D. E., "Forward Subrotative Speed Resonance Action of Rotating Machinery," Proceedings, 4th Turbomachinery Symposium, Texas A&M University, October, 1975.
Ehrich, F. E., "Identification and Avoidance of Instabilities and Self Excited Vibrations in Rotating Machinery," Proceedings, Machinery Vibrations III, Sept. 1979, Vibration Institute.
Jackson, Charles, Leader, Malcom E., "Rotor Critical Speed and Response Studies for Equipment Selection," Proceedings Machinery Vibration Monitoring and Analysis Seminar, April, 1979, Vibration Institute.
Ronde, S. M., Allaire, P. E., Maday, C. J., Editors, "Topics in Fluid Film Bearing and Rotor System Design," American Society of Mechanical Engineers, 1978.
Rieger, Neville F., Crofoot, James F., "Vibrations of Rotating Machinery, Part I—Rotor Bearing Dynamics", Vibration Institute, November 1977.

Torsional Vibration

Eshleman, R. L., "Torsional Vibration of Machine Systems," Proceedings of the 6th Turbomachinery Symposium, Texas A&M University, December 1977.

APPENDIX

By far the best work published on turbomachinery problems was authored by John Sohre. Entitled "Operating Problems with High-Speed Turbomachinery Causes and Correction," the paper was originally presented at the September 1968 ASME Petroleum Mechanical Engineering Conference and has since been reprinted in several languages. In addition to being a clear and concise description of typical machinery problems, this outstanding paper contains four charts relating symptoms to probable cause which are reprinted with the kind permission of the author, John Sohre.

359

SYMPTOMS AND DISTRESS MANIFESTATIONS

These charts are reproduced with the permission of Turbomachinery International Publications, Division of Business Journals, Inc., 22 South Smith Street, Norwalk, Connecticut, U.S.A. 06855, and may not be reproduced without its prior written permission.

CHART NO. 1 ◄──────── VIBRATION ANALYSIS ────────

CAUSES OF VIBRATION	Rotor or Stator resonant frequencies	Oil whirl frequency	40-50% ⅔s	50-100% ⅔s	1x running frequ.	2x RF	Higher multiples	1/2 RF	1/4 RF	Lower multiples	Odd frequ.	Very high frequ.	Line frequ.	Multiples of L.F.	Slip frequ.	Vert.	Horiz.	Axial	Shaft	Brgs.	Casing	Foundation	Piping	Coupling
initial unbalance	5				90	5	5									40	50	10	90	10				
permanent bow or lost rotor parts (vanes)	30				90	5	5																	
Temporary Rotor bow	20				90	5	5																	
Casing distortion Temp.		←10→			60	20	10									▼	▼							
Casing distortion Perm.		←10→			60	20	10									▼	▼							
Foundation distortion	20				40	30					10					▼	▼	▼	30	40			10	
Seal rub	10	10	10		20	10	10			10	10	10				30	40	30	60	20	10			10
Rotor rub. axial		←20→			30	10	10			10	10	10				30	40	30	70	10	20			
Misalignment	5	10			30	60	10					10				20	30	50	30	10	10			50
Piping forces	5	10			30	60	10					10				20	30	50	10	10	10			50
Journal & bearing eccentricity	60				40	60										40	50	10	90	10				
Bearing damage	20→				40	20						20				30	40	30	70	20	10			
Bearg. & Support excited vibration (oil whirls. etc.)	20	60						10	10							40	50	10	50	20	20	10		
Unequal bearing stiffness. horizontal vs. vertical	80					80	20									40	50	10	40	30	30			
Thrust brg. damage	90→											10				20	30	50	30	20	20			30
Insufficient tightness in assy. of:	PREDOMINANT FREQUENCY WILL SHOW AT LOWEST CRITICAL, OR RESONANT FREQUENCY																							
Rotor (shrink-fits)	40	40	10		10	10	10				10					60	20	10						10
Brg. liner	90→										10					40	50	10	70	10	10			10
Brg. case	90→				30						10					40	50	10	40	20	10			30
Casing & support	50→				30						50					40	50	10	30	20	30			20
Gear inaccuracy or damage						20		Gear-mesh freq. →20→60								20	20	60	20	20	30			30
Coupling inaccuracy or damage	10	20	10		20	30	10	Gear mesh freq. →80								30	40	30	70	20				30
Aerodynamic excitation	60	20			20						10	10				30	40	30	40	20	20	10	10	
Rotor & brg. system critical	100				100											40	50	10	70	30				
Coupling critical	100				100	ALSO MAKE SURE TOOTH FIT IS TIGHT!										20	40	40	10	10				80
Overhang critical	100				100											40	50	10	70	10				20
Structural resonance of: Casing	100	10			70	10		10					30	30	30	40	50	10		40	40	10	10	
Supports	100	10			70	10		10					30	30	30	40	50	10	20	50	20	10		
Foundation	100	20			60	10		10					30	30	30	30	40	30	10	40	40	10		
Pressure pulsations	80	MOST TROUBLESOME IF COMBINED WITH RESONANCES														30	40	30	CAN EXCITE WHIRLS OR RESONANCE 30	30	40			
Electrically excited vibrations	80												←100→			30	40	30		40	40	20		
Vibration transmission	30	30									40					30	40	30		40	40	20		
Oil-Seal-induced vibr.	30	70														50	50		100 Very severe					
NAME OF PROBLEM	THE SECTION BELOW IS MEANT TO IDENTIFY BASIC MECHANISMS												POSSIBLY ELECTRIC ORIGIN											
Sub-harmonic resonance	100							←100→					ORIGIN			30	30	40	IF BRG. EXCIT 20	20	20	20	20	
Harmonic resonance	100				←100→								100			40	40	20	20	10	10	30	30	
Friction induced whirl	100	30	10													40	50	10	80 Very severe	20				
Critical speed	100				100											40	50	10	60	40				
Resonant vibration	100	20			60	20	5	10	5							40	40	20	20	10	20	30	20	
Oil whirl		80			WATCH FOR AERODYNAMIC ROTOR-LIFT (PARTIAL ADMISSION ETC.)											40	50	10	80	20				
Resonant whirl	100	100														40	50	10	20	20	20	20	20	
Dry whirl	100											100				30	40	30	40	20	20	10		10
Clearance induced vibrations	50	50			20	30	10									DEPENDS ON NATURE & LOCATION OF GAP								
Torsional resonance	100	10			40	20	20				Gear speeds. Mesh-frequ. ←100→		IF ELECTRICALLY EXCITED ←100→			TORSIONAL 40	40	NAL LATERAL AMPLITUDE						10
Transient torsional	100				50							50				▼	NAL MOTION 100	40	40					10

Numbers indicate % of cases showing above symptoms for causes listed in vertical column at left.

(Sawyer's Turbomachinery Maintenance Handbook 1980 Edition)

VIBRATION ANALYSIS										OPERATIONAL EVIDENCE																	
Amplitude Response to Speed Variation during vibration-test runs										Effect of Operating Conditions										Effect of Oil p & t and Flow							
Speeding up					Slowing down					No effect	Full load		No load		Part load		Start up only or surge	After load dump	When other machine starts or shuts down	Increase p		Decrease p		Increase t		Decrease t	
Increases	Decreases	Peaks	Comes out suddenly	Drops out suddenly	Stays same	Increases	Decreases	Comes out suddenly	Drops out suddenly		in	out	in	out	in	out				better	worse	better	worse	better	worse	better	worse
100	PEAK AT						100			100										90	10	10	90	10	90	90	10
100							100			100										Slight changes only, due to variation of oil-film damping							
60	5		5		30	5	50	5	10		10	20	20	10			20	20									
50	5		5	10	30	5	50	5	10		10	20	20	10			20	20									
60					40		60			40	10	10	10	10			10	10									
80					20		80			40	10	10	10	10			10	10									
70			10	10	10		70	10	10	10	10	10	5	10			20	20	5								
40	10		20	20	10		50	20	20	5	30	10	5	10			10	30									
30	10		20	20	20		40	20	20	10	30	10	5	5	5	5	20	10									
40			20	20	20		40	20	20	10	20	10					20	20	20								
50	10				40	10	50			100																	
50	10		20	10	10	10	50	10	20	90																	
10			90				10		90	30	5	5	5	5	20	20	MOSTLY MULTI-BEARING SOLID COUPLED							90	10	10	90
40		50	10				40		10	100																	
50	10		10	10	20	10	50	10	10	30	5	5	30				30										
			90	10				10	90	30	30	5	5	10			30	10	20								
			90	10				10	90	90							10										
			90	10				10	90	90							10										
			90	10				10	90	10	5	5	5	5	30	30	10										
20	20	20	10	10	20	20	20	10	10	30	10	10	20	10	10	10											
20			40	10	10		20	10	40	LOOSE SLEEVE, FRICTION, OR DIRT IN TEETH / (80% IF TOOTH FRICTION OR DIRT IN TEETH)	10	10	30	10	10	10	10	20									
20	20		30	10	20	20	20	10	30	0	60	40	20	80	80	20	50	30	20								
20		80					20			90																	
20		80	←LOOSENESS→				20	50% IF LOOSE		90	IF LOOSE	IF LOOSE					IF LOOSE	IF LOOSE									
30		70					30			90																	
20		80					20			90										NO EFFECT							
20		80					20			90																	
20		80					20			90																	
← 10% DEPENDING ON ORIGIN OF DISTURBANCE →			90	10						20	5	5	5	5	20	20			20								
			90							50	40								10								
			90							50									50								
30	0	0	70			0	50		50	80	0	0	20				30			PRESSURE-DROP ACROSS SEAL HAS PRONOUNCED EFFECT							
20	20	30	30		20	30	30	40			20	20					20										
20	60		20		20	20		80	10								10										
		90	10		10	90	40	20	40	60			10	30						90	10	10	90	90	10	10	90
20	80					20			100											SMALL DAMPING EFFECTS ONLY				10		10	10
20	80					20			100																	
		100					100	60			20	20								90	10	10	90	90	10	10	90
		80	20		20	80	50	50 ────→									50			90	10	10	90	90	10	10	90
		80	20	80			20	90	10								10			90						50	50
		80	20	20		20	60	40			20	20								SMALL DAMPING EFFECTS ONLY							
20	30	30	20	20		20	30	30	50		10	10															
		50	30	20			30	20		100																	

1968 John S. Sohre, Turbomachinery
Consultant. Revised June 1980.
One Lakeview Circle
Ware, MA 01082 USA

SYMPTOMS AND DISTRESS MANIFESTATIONS, CONTINUED

These charts are reproduced with the permission of Turbomachinery International Publications, Division of Business Journals, Inc., 22 South Smith Street, Norwalk, Connecticut, U.S.A. 06855, and may not be reproduced without its prior written permission.

CHART NO. 2 — CAUSES OF VIBRATION	Lo frequ. "Rumble"	Loud "Roar"	"Hum"	Comes and goes periodically ("beat")	High pitched "whine"	Very high loud "scream"	Very high "squeal"	Ultrasonic (measure w. sound analyzer)	Initial startup	1st year	1-10 years	Over 10 years	Seals rubbed	Shaft bent	Thrust Bearing damage
Initial unbalance		80	20						✓✓				10		
Permanent bow or lost rotor parts (vanes)		80	20						✓		✓	✓	50	+	
Temporary Rotor bow	10	70	10	10					✓✓	✓			90	10	
Casing distortion	10	70	10	10							✓	✓	90	10	
Foundation distortion	10	50	30	10					✓	✓	✓	✓✓	90	10	
Seal rub	20	40		10		10	10	10	✓	✓	✓	✓	+	15	
Rotor rub axial	30	40		20				10	✓✓	✓			90	30	30
Misalignment		40	40	20					✓	✓	✓	✓	50	10	30
Piping forces	30	40	30						✓✓	✓	✓	✓✓	50	10	
Journal & bearing eccentricity		10	90						✓✓						
Bearing damage	20	40	10		10	10	10		✓	✓	✓	✓	90	10	
Bearg. & Support excited vibration (oil whirls. etc.)	60	10		30					✓✓				90	10	
Unequal bearing stiffness horizontal—vertical		10	60	20	10				✓✓				10		
Thrust brg. damage	80	10	10						✓✓	✓	✓	✓	90	20	+
Insufficient tightness in assy. of:															
Rotor (shrink-fits)	60	20		20					✓	✓✓	✓	✓	90	10	
Brg. liner	60	20		20					✓✓	✓			90	10	
Brg. case	60	10		30					✓✓	✓			50	5	
Casing support	60	20		20					✓✓	✓	✓	✓	20		
Gear inaccuracy or damage	20	10	10	20	20	10		10	✓✓						40
Coupling inaccuracy or damage	10			40	10	40	ALSO "METALLIC" SOUND		✓✓	✓			20		60
Aerodynamic excitation	60			60					✓✓		✓	✓✓	10		50
Rotor & brg. system critical		50	30	20					✓✓	✓			50	10	
Coupling critical			20	40	20	20			✓✓	✓			30	10	
Overhang critical		50	40	10					✓✓	✓			50	20	
Structural resonance of:															
Casing	20			20	60				✓✓	✓			20		
Supports	20			20	60				✓✓	✓	✓		20		
Foundation			10	80	10				✓	✓	✓		20		
Pressure pulsations	40	20		40					✓	✓✓	✓	✓	30		30
Electrically excited vibrations		10	80	10					✓✓	✓			20		
Vibration transmission	20		20	60					✓	✓			20		
Oil-Seal-induced vibr.	90 (if whirl)	40								✓	✓✓	✓✓	90	50	
NAME OF PROBLEM															
Sub-harmonic resonance	80			20					✓✓	✓	✓		10		
Harmonic resonance			40	20	40				✓✓	✓			10		
Friction induced whirl	60	20		20					✓✓	✓✓	✓		90	10	
Critical speed		50	30	20					✓✓				50	10	
Resonant vibration	40		30	30					✓✓	✓			20		
Oil whirl	60	10		30					✓✓	✓	✓		60	10	
Resonant whirl	60	20		20					✓✓	✓	✓		80	15	
Dry whirl							20	80	✓	✓	✓	✓	80	10	
Clearance induced vibrations	60	20		20					✓✓	✓			90	10	
Torsional resonance	10	20	20	30	10	10			✓✓	✓			5		
Transient torsional				60 (cough)		20	20		✓✓	✓			5		

Figures indicate the likelihood in % that the symptoms (top. horizontal) will occur where causes (left. vertical) are involved.

(Sawyer's Turbomachinery Maintenance Handbook 1980 Edition)

OPERATIONAL EVIDENCE, CONT'D

Damage or Distress Signal

Wiped	Fatigued	Babbitt squeezed out	Case distorted or cracked	Out of alignment	Coupling burned or pitted	Gear teeth broken or pitted	Gear teeth marked on back side	Shaft cracked or broken	Galling or fretting marks under disks or hubs	Coupling bolts loose	Foundat. settled or cracked	Soleplates loose or rusted	Sliding surfaces binding	Thermal expansion restriced	Fluid marks on internals	Rotor components eroded	solids accumulated on vanes & rotor	Salt deposits on internals	Main flanges leaking	Seals leaking
10	10																20	20		
30	10	10													20	20	60	60		10
50		20			20	20	20	5		5										20
50	10	10	+	10	20								30	30					50	20
50	30			50	30						+	30	10						20	10
15	10	10	10	20	10					10	10	10	10	10			10	10		50
50					20		10			10			20	40						50
10	20		20	+	40					10	50	50	10	50						10
10	20		40	40	40					10		10	20	50					50	10
30	60																			
	+		10	40	20	20	10	10	20	20	20	20	20	20	40	10	10	10	10	10
80	60	30			20	20	10	10	10											10
40	40																			
50		30						10		10					60	30	60	60		50
60	60	40			80	40	40	20	50	10					40	10				30
30	30	40			80	20	20	10	5	10										30
20	20	30			20	20	20	10	5	10										10
40	60	10			20															10
20	20					40	20	10												
20	20				40															10
20	30				30	20	20	5	20	10	10	30				40	40	20		20
50	50				30	20	10	5												20
50	50				30															
60	60	10			40			5												25
20	20																			10
20	20				20						30	20	10							10
20	20			30	30						30	10	10	20						10
30	30			20	30						30	20								15
20	20				30	10	10	5		5										
20	20			30	30															10
90	10	20			50			10		20	40	40								90
20	10				10	30	10	5		5	10	10								
20	20				20	30	10	5		5	10	10								
60	60	40			80	40	40	20	50	10					40	10				
50	50				30	20	10	5												
20	20				20						30	10	10	20						
80	60	30			20	20	10	10	10											
90	80	40			40	30	20	20	20	10	10									
90	20	40			10	5	5	30	5	70										
30	30	20			80	20	20	10	5	10										
5	20				40	80	80	40	5	40										
5	5				30	80	80	50	10	50										

Note (row 2): LOOK FOR LOST BLADES & CRACKED DISKS. ETC. — DUE TO CORROSION FATIGUE OR STRESS CORROSION

1968 John S. Sohre, Turbomachinery Consultant. Revised June 1980.
One Lakeview Circle
Ware, MA 01082 USA

POSSIBLE CAUSES OF DIFFICULTY

These charts are reproduced with the permission of Turbomachinery International Publications, Division of Business Journals, Inc., 22 South Smith Street, Norwalk, Connecticut, U.S.A. 06855, and may not be reproduced without its prior written permission.

CHART NO. 3

CONDITIONS LIKELY TO BE RESPONSIBLE FOR DIFFICULTIES — OPERATION

CAUSES OF VIBRATION	Started too quickly	Loaded too quickly	Sudden temp. variation (6°F/min. = max.)	Sudden press. variation	Fluid slugging	Carry over	Boiler priming	Chemicals in steam	Case filled with fluid	Fluid sucking up from drains	Trapped fluid flashing up	Dirt in oil	Drains not closed after warmup	Drains closed too early	Sealing steam left on standg. rotor	Purge gas left on standg. rotor	Hot leakage getting on standing rotor	Cooling air on hot standing rotor
Unbalance	✓	✓	✓	✓	✓	✓	✓	✓	✓									
Permanent bow or lost rotor parts (vanes) *(LOOK FOR LOST BLADES, ETC. — DUE TO CORROSION FATIGUE OR STRESS CORROSION)*	✓	✓	✓		✓	✓✓	✓✓	✓✓	✓	✓	✓				✓	✓	✓	✓
Temporary Rotor bow	✓	✓✓	✓✓	✓	✓✓	✓	✓		✓✓	✓✓	✓✓	✓			✓	✓✓	✓✓	✓✓
Casing distortion	✓✓	✓✓	✓✓	✓	✓✓	✓	✓		✓✓	✓	✓		✓	✓				
Foundation distortion																		
Seal rub	✓	✓✓	✓✓	✓	✓✓	✓	✓		✓	✓✓	✓	✓	✓	✓	✓	✓	✓	✓
Rotor rub. axial	✓	✓✓	✓✓	✓	✓✓													
Misalignment	✓	✓	✓	✓	✓					✓✓								
Piping forces				✓														
Journal & bearing eccentricity																		
Bearing damage	✓✓	✓✓	✓✓	✓	✓✓							✓✓						
Bearg. & Support excited vibration (oil whirls. etc.)	✓	✓	✓	✓	✓													
Unequal bearing stiffness. horizontal—vertical																		
Thrust brg. damage	✓	✓		✓✓	✓✓								✓	✓✓				
Insufficient tightness in assy. of:																		
Rotor (shrink-fits)	✓	✓	✓✓	✓✓	✓✓	✓✓	✓		✓✓	✓	✓✓				✓			✓
Brg. liner																		
Brg. case																		
Casing & support	✓	✓	✓		✓	✓												
Gear inaccuracy or damage					✓								✓✓					
Coupling inaccuracy or damage					✓✓	✓✓							✓✓		✓			
Aerodynamic excitation															✓	✓		
Rotor & brg. system critical																		
Coupling critical																		
Overhang critical																		
Structural resonance																		
Casing																		
Supports																		
Foundation																		
Pressure pulsations									✓					✓				
Electrically excited vibrations																		
Vibration transmission																		
Oil-Seal-induced vibr.													✓✓					
NAME OF PROBLEM																		
Sub-harmonic resonance																		
Harmonic resonance																		
Friction induced whirl	✓	✓	✓	✓									✓✓					
Critical speed																		
Resonant vibration																		
Oil whirl					✓													
Resonant whirl																		
Dry whirl	✓	✓	✓															
Clearance induced vibrations	✓	✓	✓	✓														
Torsional resonance																		
Transient torsional	✓✓	✓✓																

✓ LIKELY TO OCCUR   ✓✓ FREQUENT CAUSES OF DIFFICULTY

(Sawyer's Turbomachinery Maintenance Handbook 1980 Edition)

CONDITIONS LIKELY TO BE RESPONSIBLE FOR DIFFICULTIES → ← INSTALLATION →

Exhaust was overheated	Excessive vacuum	Not operated at design speed	Over loaded	Offdesign p & t	Surging	Shaft currents	Incorrect leakoff pressure	Fluctuat. leakoff pressure	Hollow rotor filling w. fluid (Or boroscope hole)	Syncronized out of phase	Had short circuit	Phase fault	Resonant	Settling or shrinking	Unevenly heated (hot lines too close)	Not separated from building	Grout swelling or shrinking rust or deterioration under soleplates	Cross-Beams Key-Bars, or horizontal stiffness insufficient
		√	√	√	√				√	√	√	√						
				LOOK FOR LOST BLADES														
√	√√	√	√√	√√	√						√	√	√				√	√
		DUE TO EXCESSIVE BLADE LOAD																
√				√		√		√		√	√	√					√	√
√√				√						√√	√√	√		√	√		√	√
√					√√	√	√	√	√	√	√		√	√√	√√	√	√√	√√
				√√	√								√	√	√	√	√	
√√			√√	√					√√	√√	√		√√	√√	√	√√	√√	
			√	√√										√√	√√			√√
√		√	√	√	√√				√	√	√		√	√√	√√		√√	√
	√	√	√						√				√√	√	√	√√	√√	√√
																	√√	√√
	√	√	√	√√	√√	√√	√	√										
√		√	√√	√√	√			√		√	√							
				√						√	√							
√√			√√	√						√√	√√		√				√√	√√
				√						√√	√√	√						
	√	√√	√√	√√						√√	√√	√	√	√	√		√√	√√
√	√√	√√	√√	√√		√√	√√						√√				√√	√√
																	√	√
													√√				√√	√√
																	√	√
		√	√		√	√				√	√	√	√√		√√			
													√√			√√	√√	
				√√√		√												
													√√		√√	√√	√√	√√
													√√		√√	√√	√√	√√
																	√√	√√
													√√			√√	√√	√√
																	√√	√√
													√√		√√	√√	√√	√√
													√			√	√√	√√
		√√	√	√	√					√√	√√	√√			√√		√	√
		√	√	√	√					√								

© 1968 John S. Sohre, Turbomachinery Consultant
Revised June 1980. One Lakeview Circle, Ware, MA 01082 USA

POSSIBLE CAUSES OF DIFFICULTY, CONTINUED

These charts are reproduced with the permission of Turbomachinery International Publications, Division of Business Journals, Inc., 22 South Smith Street, Norwalk, Connecticut, U.S.A. 06855, and may not be reproduced without its prior written permission.

CHART NO. 4 — INSTALLATION →

CAUSES OF VIBRATION	FOUNDAT. CONT'D. Soleplates loose	Rigidity Insufficient	Excessive forces & moments	Expansion joints not properly installed	Piping not properly supported	Not properly sloped & drained	Resonant	Not taking off at top of headers	Water accumulates over valves	Casing drains run to common sewer or common header or into water	Traps not working	Drain pots under-size	Drain lines under-size	Pipe expansion restricted by contact with foundation or other pipes	Branch lines restricting expansion	Dead ends not drained
Unbalance																
Permanent bow or lost rotor parts (vanes)						√√		√√	√√	√	√	√	√	√	√	√
Temporary Rotor bow						√√		√√	√√	√√	√√	√√	√√	√	√	√√
Casing distortion		√√	√√	√	√√	√			√	√		√√	√	√√	√√	√√
Foundation distortion		√√	√	√	√									√	√	
Seal rub	√	√√	√√	√√	√√	√√		√√	√√	√√	√√	√√	√√	√√	√√	√√
Rotor rub, axial		√	√	√	√	√√		√√	√√	√		√	√√	√		√√
Misalignment	√	√√	√√	√√	√√									√√	√√	
Piping forces		√√	+	√√	√√									√√	√√	
Journal & bearing eccentricity																
Bearing damage	√	√√	√	√	√	√√		√√	√√	√√	√	√	√	√	√	√
Bearg. & Support excited vibration (oil whirls, etc.)	√√	√√	√	√		√								√√	√	
Unequal bearing stiffness, horizontal-vertical	√	√														
Thrust brg. damage						√√		√√		√		√√	√√	√√		√√
Insufficient tightness in assy. of:																
Rotor (shrink-fits)						√√		√√	√√	√√	√√	√√	√√			√√
Brg. liner														√	√	
Brg. case			√	√	√									√	√	
Casing support			√√	√√	√√									√√	√	*
Gear inaccuracy or damage																
Coupling inaccuracy or damage		√	√√													
Aerodynamic excitation				√√		√√	√√			√√	√√	√√	√√			√√
Rotor & brg. system critical	√	√√														
Coupling critical																
Overhang critical																
Structural resonance of:																
Casing				√	√√		√√							√√	√√	
Supports	√√			√√	√√	√√	√√							√√	√√	
Foundation	√√	√	√	√√	√√	√√	√√							√√	√	
Pressure pulsations				√√			√									
Electrically excited vibrations						√√								√		
Vibration transmission		√		√√	√√	√√								√√	√	
Oil-Seal-induced vibr.																
NAME OF PROBLEM																
Sub-harmonic resonance	√√	√√		√	√	√								√	√	
Harmonic resonance		√		√	√	√								√	√	
Friction induced whirl		√				√√		√√	√√	√√	√√	√√	√√			
Critical speed		√	√	√	√											
Resonant vibration	√√	√√		√√	√√	√√								√√		
Oil whirl																
Resonant whirl	√√	√√		√√	√√	√√								√√		
Dry whirl		√														
Clearance induced vibrations	√√		√√	√	√√	√								√	√	
Torsional resonance																
Transient torsional																

(Sawyer's Turbomachinery Maintenance Handbook 1980 Edition)

		ELECTRICAL		COMMENTS
rcuit hronized hase ault	Reverse current relay failed	Synchronous motor starting pulsations excessive for system	Starting cycle improperly timed	
✓		CHECK FOR TORSION CRACKS		Long, high-speed rotors often require field-balancing at full speed to make adjustments for rotor deflection and final support conditions. Make corrections at balancing ring or coupling.
✓		✓✓	✓	Bent rotors can sometimes be straightened by "hot-spot" procedure, but this should only be regarded as a temporary solution, because bow will come back in time, and rotor failures have resulted from this practice. If buckets, vanes, or disks are lost or cracked, check for corrosion fatigue, stress-corrosion, resonance and off-design operation.
✓	✓	✓	✓	Straighten bow slowly, running on turning gear or at low speed. If rubbing occurs, trip unit immediately and keep rotor turning 90 by shaft-wrench every 5 min. until rub clears. Then resume slow run. This may take 24 hours.
✓	✓			Often requires complete re-work or new case, but sometimes a mild distortion corrects itself with time (requires periodic internal and external re-alignment). Usually caused by excessive piping forces, thermal shock, unsuitable casing design, wrong material, welding, improper stress-relief.
✓				Caused by poor mat under foundation, or thermal stress (hot-spots), or unequal shrinkage. Usually requires extensive and costly repairs. Structural-steel baseplates warp from thermal strain and lack of stress relief.
✓	✓	✓	✓	Slight rubs may clear, but trip unit immediately if a high-speed rub gets worse. Turn until clear.
	✓	✓	✓	Unless thrust bearing has failed this is caused by rapid changes of load and temperature. Machine should be opened and inspected.
✓	✓			Caused by excessive pipe strain and/or inadequate mounting and foundation, but sometimes also by local heat from pipes or sun on base and foundation. Some compressors and turbines have no provision to control thermal expansion (keys, flexplates, sliding feet).
				Most trouble is caused by poor pipe supports (should use spring hangers), improperly used expansion joints, and poor pipe line-up at casing connections. Foundation settling can cause severe strain.
				Bearings may get distorted from heat. Make hot-check, if possible, checking contact. Check bearing case for excessive heat and distortion. Provide for thermal expansion and install heat shields.
✓	✓	✓	✓	Watch for brown discoloration which often precedes recurring failures. This indicates very high local oil-film temperatures. Check rotor for vibration. Check bearing design and hot clearances, possible dilution of oil with process fluid (gasoline), gas (chlorine). Check viscosity and contamination. Mount pressure gage on bearing cap.
				Check clearances and roundness of journal, as well as contact and tight bearing fit in case. Watch out for vibration transmission from other sources and check frequency. May require tilt-shoe bearings. Check especially for piping or foundation resonance at whirl frequency.
				Can excite resonances and criticals and combinations thereof at 2x running frequency. Usually difficult to field-balance because as horizontal vibration gets better, vertical gets worse and vice versa. It may be necessary to increase horizontal bearing support stiffness (or mass) if the problem is severe.
				May result from slugging the machine with fluid, solids built up on rotor, or off-design operation, especially surging.
				Note: Looseness of bolting and insufficient interference fit of wheels, coupling hubs (f), and bearing assemblies is the most common cause of problems with turbomachinery.
✓	✓	✓	✓	The frequency at rotor/support critical is characteristic. Disks and sleeves may have lost their interference fit by rapid temperature change. Parts usually are not loose at standstill. Usually requires rotor disassembly.
✓	✓	✓	✓	Often confused with oil whirl because characteristics are essentially the same. Before suspecting any whirl make sure everything in bearing assembly is absolutely tight, with interference fit. Do not use silicone-rubber (RTV) to seal horizontal joint of bearing case!
				Make sure to check attachment-bolts and split-bolts with torque-wrench!
				Usually involves sliding pedestals and casing feet. Check for friction, proper clearance, and piping strains. Check all bolting using a torque wrench.
				To get frequencies, tape microphone to gear case and record noise on magnetic tapk, play back through vibrograph. Strong axial vibration indicates pitch-line runout, bent shaft, gear wheel cracking.
			✓	Loose coupling sleeves are notorious troublemakers! Especially in conjunction with long, heavy spacers. Check tooth fit by placing indicators on top, then lift with hand or jack and note looseness. Should not be more than 1-2 mils at standstill, at most. Use hollow coupling spacers. Make sure coupling hubs are tightly mounted (1 mil/inch).
				Check stage pressures and pressure fluctuations by installing pressure gages, transducers, and thermometers in all accessible openings (drains, pressure-balancing lines). Measure pressure drop across balance-line, and especially balance-flow temperature. High temperature = stage in surge or "stonewalling". Check Molweight.
				Try field balancing; more viscous oil (colder); larger, longer bearings with minimum clearance and tight fit; stiffen bearing supports and other structures between bearing and ground. Basically a design problem. May require additional stabilizing bearings or solid coupling. Difficult to correct in field. Sometimes adding mass at bearing can help considerably, especially at speeds exceeding 8,000 RPM.
				These are criticals of the spacer-teeth-overhang sub-system. Often encountered with long spacers. Make sure of tight fitting teeth with slight interference at standstill, and make spacer as light and stiff as possible (tubular). Consider solid coupling if problem is severe. Check coupling balance!
				Can be exceedingly troublesome. Overhangs shift the nodal point of the rotor deflection line (free-free mode) toward the bearing, robbing the bearing of its damping capability. This can make criticals so rough that it is impossible to pass through the critical. Shorten overhang or put in an outboard bearing for stabilization. use lighter coupling and spacer (aluminum, titanium).
				Note: Resonances are very common with structural-steel baseplates, and with improperly supported piping. Oil piping resonance is very dangerous, especially in the vicinity of hot parts and steam piping.
				So called "case-drumming". Can be very persistent but is sometimes harmless. Danger is that parts may come loose and fall into the machine. Also, rotor/casing interaction may be involved. Diaphragm drumming is serious, it can cause catastrophic failure.
				Local drumming is usually harmless, but major resonances, resulting in vibration of entire case as a unit are potentially dangerous because of possible rubs and component failures, as well as possible excitation of other vibrations.
				As above, but with the added complications of settling, cracking, warping and misalignment. Also may get into piping troubles and possible case warpage. Foundation resonance is serious and greatly reduces unit reliability.
				Can excite other vibrations, possibly with serious consequences. Eliminate such vibrations by using restraints, flexible pipe supports, sway braces, shock absorbers, etc., plus isolation of foundation from piping, building, basement and operating floor (2). Unrestrained expansion joints are especially dangerous during compressor surge.
✓		✓	✓	Mostly at 2 x line frequency (7,200 CPM), coming from motor and generator fields. Turn fields off to verify source. Usually harmless, but if foundation or other components (rotor) are resonant, the vibrations may be severe. Shaft failures are likely if torsional critical coincides with line-frequency or 2 x line-frequency, and electrical fault or out-of-phase synchronization occurs.
				Can excite serious vibrations or cause bearing failures. Isolate piping and foundation and use shock absorbers and sway braces.
				Most likely caused by damage to seal faces (shaft-currents, dirt, nicks, surface roughness) and/or poor face lubrication. Also poor face contact. Lap seals with very fine compound. Use baked-on or bonded solid-film lubricant.
		BASIC PROBLEM MECHANISMS LISTED FOR IDENTIFICATION		
				Vibration at exactly ½, ¼, ⅛ of exciting frequency. Can only be excited in non-linear systems, therefore, look for such things as looseness and aerodynamic or hydrodynamic excitations. It may involve rotor "shuttling", then check seal system, thrust clearances, couplings, and rotor-stator clearance effects.
				Vibration at 2x, 3x, 4x, exciting frequency. Fairly common and troublesome. Treatment is the same as for direct resonance: Change frequency, add damping, reduce excitation.
				Can be very serious. If intermittent, look into temperature variations. Usually rotor must be rebuilt, but should try to increase stator damping first; larger bearings (tilt-shoe), increased stator mass and stiffness, better foundation. This problem is usually caused by mal-operation such as quick temperature changes and fluid slugging. Use membrane-type coupling.
				Basically a design problem but often aggravated by poor balancing and poor foundation. Usually corrects itself with good operation; seal oil temperature, use larger and tighter bearings.
		✓		Add mass or change stiffness to shift frequency. Add damping. Reduce excitation. Improve system isolation. Reducing mass or stiffness can leave the amplitude the same even if resonant frequency shifts. Check "mobility".
				Use tilt-shoe bearings. CHECK FOR LOOSE BEARINGS FIRST!
				As above, but with additional excitation of rotor, stator, foundation, piping; or external excitation. Find resonant members and sources of excitation. Tilt shoe bearings are best. CHECK FOR LOOSE BEARINGS!
				The "squeal" of a bearing or seal. May be ultrasonic and very destructive. Check for rotor vanes hitting stator, etc., especially if clearances are smaller than oil film thickness plus rotor deflection while passing through critical speed.
		✓✓		Very destructive and hard to identify. Symptoms: Gear noise, wear on back side of teeth, strong electrical noise or vibration, loose coupling bolts, fretting corrosion under coupling hubs. Wear on both sides of coupling teeth, torsional fatigue cracks in keyway ends. Best solution: Install properly tuned torsional vibration dampers.
		✓✓		As above but encountered only during start and shutdown due to very strong torsional pulsations. Occurs with: reciprocating machinery, synchronous motors (slip frequency excitation if torsional critical is below 2x line frequency). Check for torsional cracks.

1968 John S. Sohre, Turbomachinery Consultant. Revised June 1980.
One Lakeview Circle
Ware, MA 01082 USA

INDEX

data acquisition and analysis
  calibration 350
  operating conditions 348
  recommended method 346
decibel
  conversion to voltage ratio 45
  definition 44
demodulation
  as a method of analysis 120, 201
dial indicator 266, 269
  precautions making measurements 271
direct tape recording 98
displaying measurements
  steady state 108–120
  transient 123–128
distortion of data due to instrumentation
  characteristics 53
dynamic cascade spectra
  see cascade spectra
dynamic characteristics of machinery
  bladed 139
  centrifugal 139
  gearing 146
dynamic force
  defined 8
  variation with frequency 9, 25
dynamic range required for analysis with
  different transducers 103

E

electric motors
  failed rotor bars produce a gear
    failure 313
  monitoring systems 227
  problem analysis 202
  sum and difference frequencies 134
electrostatic discharge
  recognition 132, 188
envelope detection 120
  as a means of rolling element bearing
    analysis 136

F

filters
  definition 46
  equations for 54

limitations on sweep 51
rolloff characteristics 49
tracking filter defined 47
use in machinery analysis 52
use in monitoring 210, 213, 214, 218,
  222, 224–227
flash angle 240
flexible shaft machines defined 23, 239
frequency (of a sine wave)
  defined 6
  measured on an oscilloscope 6, 112
  measured with an analyzer 109
frequency domain analysis 82
frequency modulation tape
  recording 98
frequency spectrum plot 116
  use for assessing condition 117

G

gas turbine
  monitoring systems 221
  vibration characteristics 145
gearing
  AGMA vibration limits 164
  dynamic characteristics and common
    problems 193–202
  monitoring systems 222
  vibration characteristics 146
gear mesh frequency
  definition 146
  isolated for monitoring 225
  variation in amplitude 147, 148, 201

H

harmonics
  as a symptom of looseness 186
  generation of 132, 148, 190
hunting tooth frequency 149, 202

I

imbalance
  case histories 296, 297, 299, 300, 304,
    310
  causes 179–181, 237
  effects of bowed rotor 180
  vibration characteristics 179

instability
  case histories 294
  causes 172
  described 172
  induced by misalignment 178, 184
  vibration characteristics 173–178
integration, electronic
  accomplished with filters 55
  need for 57
  potential for problems when double
    integrating to very low
    frequencies 56

L

lag angle 239, 243, 246
leakage (spurious frequencies) 94
lissajou
  see orbit
locked coupling 184–186
  indication of in thrust bearing
    temperature 76
  on gears 227
looseness 186, 296, 315

M

machinery vibration
  characteristics 132–151
magnetic tape recorders 97
  calibration 351
  recording procedure 350
  tape log 348
  use in predictive analysis 337, 339, 346,
    348
mass, defined 9
mechanical impedance
  defined 18
  effect on the ratio between shaft and
    casing vibration 163
  importance in machinery analysis 19
misalignment
  as a cause of instability 178
  case histories 308, 310
  described 182–186
  tolerances as a function of spacer
    length 182
  vibration characteristics 182

mobile instrumentation trailer or van
  mounted 337, 339
modal plotting with a tracking
  analyzer 110, 317
monitoring
  predictive analysis on machinery
    equipped with continuous monitoring
    systems 334
  reasons for and selection
    criteria 205–208
monitoring/measuring systems
  addition capabilities 232–236
  axial compressors 214
  centrifugal compressors 210
  centrifugal pumps 208
  electrical machinery 227
  fans 212
  gas turbines 221
  gears 222
  installation 229–232
  steam turbines 215

N

noncontact displacement transducers
  attacked by ammonia 155
  cable routing 34, 229
  effects by changes in conductivity,
    permeability, temperature, and
    pressure 29
  linear range 27, 29
  mounting and installation 32, 230
  principle of operation 26, 29
  restrictions on component
    replacement 29
  runout and shaft imperfections, effects
    of 30
nonsynchronous spectral components
  transmitted from auxiliaries 314
Nyquist (polar) response plot
  see polar plot

O

octave, defined 48
operating variables, need for in a
  comprehensive monitoring system 234
orbital display 113